TABLE OF CONTENTS
(See Pages IV, V, VI, VII for Alphab...

1

2

3

4

5

6

7

8

9

10

11

12

13

14

I

COMMON SPECIFICATIONS FOR

1. Spark plug gap: .030   All Models

2. Condenser capacity: .18 to .24 MFD. All Models

3. Contact point gap: .020   All Models

	BASIC MODEL SERIES	IDLE SPEED	ARMATURE TWO LEG AIR GAP	ARMATURE THREE LEG AIR GAP	VALVE CLEARANCE INTAKE	VALVE CLEARANCE EXHAUST	VALVE GUIDE REJECT GAGE	TORQUE FLYWHEEL NUT FT. LBS.	TORQUE CYLINDER HEAD IN. LBS.	TORQUE CONN. ROD IN. LBS.
A L U M I N U M	6B, 60000	1750	.006 .010	.012 .016	.005 .007	.009 .011	19122	55	140	100
	8B, 80000, 81000, 82000	1750	.006 .010	.012 .016	.005 .007	.009 .011	19122	55	140	100
	92000, 94000	1750	.006 .010		.005 .007	.009 .011	19122	55	140	100
	100000	1750	.010 .014	.012 .016	.005 .007	.009 .011	19122	60	140	100
	110000	1750	.006 .010		.005 .007	.009 .011	19122	55	140	100
	130000	1750	.010 .014		.005 .007	.009 .011	19122	60	140	100
	140000	1750	.010 .014	.016 .019	.005 .007	.009 .011	19151	65	165	165
	170000, 171700●	1750 **	.010 .014		.005 .007	.009 .011	19151	65	165	165
	190000, 191700●	1750 **	.010 .014		.005 .007	.009 .011	19151	65	165	165
	220000, 250000	1750 **	.010 .014		.005 .007	.009 .011	19151	65	165	190
C A S T I R O N	5, 6, N	1750		.012 .016	.007 .009	.014 .016	19122	55	140	100
	8	1750		.012 .016	.007 .009	.014 .016	19122	55	140	100
	9	1200			.007 .009	.014 .016	19151	60	140	140
	14	1200			.007 .009	.014 .016	19151	65	165	190
	19, 190000, 200000●	1200 **	.010 .014	.022 .026	.007 .009	.014 .016	19151	115	190	190
	23, 230000	1200 **	.010 .014	.022 .026	.007 .009	.017 .019	19151	145	190	190
	243000	1200 **	.010 .014		.007 .009	.017 .019	19151	145	190	190
	300000	1200 **	.010 .014		.007 .009	.017 .019	19151	145	190	190
	320000	1200 **	.010 .014		.007 .009	.017 .019	19151	145	190	190

COMMONLY USED TOOLS FOR SERVICING

19051	Spark Tester, all models
19061	Carburetor jet screwdriver, all models
19062	Carburetor jet screwdriver, all models
19063	Valve spring compressor, all models
† 19161	Starter clutch wrench, use with ½" drive torque wrench
19203	Flywheel Puller, 170000 thru 320000 Aluminum Models & Cast Iron Models

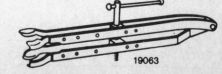

ALL POPULAR ENGINE MODELS

4. Top governed speed: See Briggs & Stratton Service Bulletin No. 467 or Engine Replacement Data

5. Crankshaft End Play: .002-.008   All Models

CRANKSHAFT REJECT SIZE			MAIN BEARING REJECT GAGE	CYLINDER BORE STD. ▲
MAG. JOURNAL	CRANKPIN	P.T.O. JOURNAL		
.8726	.8697	.8726	19166	2.375* / 2.374
.8726	.9963	.8726	19166	2.375 / 2.374
.8726	.9963	.8726	19166	2.5625 / 2.5615
.8726	.9963	.9976	19166 Mag. 19178 PTO	2.500 / 2.499
.8726	.9963	.8726	19166	2.7812 / 2.7802
.8726	.9963	.9976	19166 Mag. 19178 PTO	2.5625 / 2.5615
.9975	1.090	1.1790	19178	2.750 / 2.749
.9975 / 1.1790•	1.090	1.1790	19178	3.000 / 2.999
.9975 / 1.1790•	1.122	1.1790	19178	3.000 / 2.999
1.3760	1.2470	1.3760		3.4375 / 3.4365
.8726	.7433	.8726	19166	2.000 / 1.999
.8726	.7433	.8726	19166	2.250 / 2.249
.9832	.8726	.9832	19117	2.250 / 2.249
1.1790	.9964	1.1790	19117	2.625 / 2.624
1.1800	.9964 / 1.1219•	1.1790	19117	3.000 / 2.999
1.3769	1.1844	1.3759	19117	3.000 / 2.999
Ball	1.3094	Ball	Ball	3.0625 / 3.0615
Ball	1.3094	Ball	Ball	3.4375 / 3.4365
Ball	1.3094	Ball	Ball	3.5625 / 3.5615

INITIAL CARBURETOR ADJUSTMENT ALL MODELS — TURNS OPEN FROM SEAT

CARBURETOR TYPE	NEEDLE VALVE	IDLE VALVE
Pulsa-Jet / Vacu-Jet	1½	
Two Piece Flo-Jet	1½	1
One Piece Flo-Jet	2½	1½
One Piece Flo-Jet (6, 7, 8, 10 & 11 H.P Vertical Crankshaft)	1½	1¼
One Piece Flo-Jet (11 H.P. Horizontal Crankshaft)	1½	1

CYLINDER RESIZING

▲ Resize if .003 or more wear or .0015 out of round on C.I. cylinder engines, .0025 out of round on aluminum alloy engines.

Resize to .010, .020 or .030 over Standard.

*Model 6B series and early Models 60000 and 61000 series engines have cylinder bore of 2.3125 – 2.3115.

RING GAP REJECT SIZES

MODEL	COMP. RINGS	OIL RING
Alum. Cylinder Models	.035"	.045"
C.I. Cylinder Models	.030"	.035"

**GOVERNED IDLE

For Adjustment Procedures, see Service & Repair Instructions 270962, Section 5, for Single Cylinder Models and Repair Instructions MS-7000 or 271172, Section 5, for Twin Cylinder Models.

■ With Valve Springs Installed.

• Synchro-Balance.

BRIGGS & STRATTON ENGINES

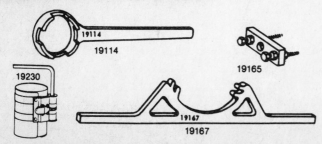

19114

19230

19165

19167

Flywheel puller, all models thru 130000 — 19069
Piston ring compressor, all models — 19230
Starter clutch wrench, all rewind starter models — 19114
Flywheel Puller, 140000, 170000, 190000 & 250000 Models — 19165
Flywheel holder, all models 6B thru 130000 — 19167

See Section 13 for Complete List of Tools

INDEX

INDEX (Continued)

INDEX OF TABLES

Section 1
GENERAL INFORMATION

Briggs & Stratton engines are of the same basic 4 stroke cycle design used in automobiles, aircraft trucks and tractors. As the name indicates, there are four strokes to one complete power cycle:

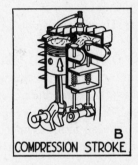
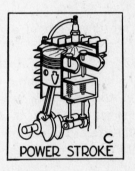
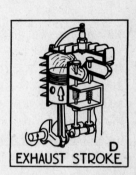

Fig. 1 — The 4-Stroke Cycle

a. INTAKE STROKE: The piston goes down, creating a vacuum in the cylinder which draws gas through open intake valve into the space above piston.

b. COMPRESSION STROKE: The piston comes up with both valves closed, highly compressing the gas into the space left between the top of the piston and cylinder head.

c. POWER STROKE: At this point the magneto sends high tension current to the spark plug, firing or exploding the compressed gas and driving the piston down.

d. EXHAUST STROKE: Exhaust valve opens and the upward stroke of the piston forces out all of the burnt gases, thus completing the power cycle.

CAUTION

Exhaust gases contain carbon monoxide which is odorless and a deadly poison. Proper care must be taken to provide efficient ventilation when running an engine indoors.

Fill the crankcase and air cleaner with proper oil before starting engine. See that oil level is maintained.

Do not fill the gasoline tank while the engine is running. Avoid spilling gasoline on a hot engine — This may cause an explosion and serious injury.

USE CLEAN GASOLINE

We recommend "regular" grade gasoline for all Briggs & Stratton engines. However, the use of lead-free, or low lead, gasolines will result in reduced combustion deposits and normally will improve engine life. Therefore, lead-free, or low lead, gasoline may be used, where available.

We also recommend that gasoline be purchased in small quantities, not more than a 30-day supply. FRESH gasoline minimizes gum deposits, and also insures a fuel with volatility tailored for the season.

GENERAL INFORMATION

CORRECT LUBRICATION IS IMPORTANT

Any high quality detergent oil having the American Petroleum Institute classification ''For Service SC, SD, SE or MS'' can be used in Briggs & Stratton engines. Detergent oils keep the engine cleaner and retard the formation of gum and varnish deposits.

SUMMER	WINTER
(Above 40° F.)	(Under 40° F.)
Use SAE 30	Use SAE 5W-20 or SAE 5W-30
If not available,	If not available,
Use SAE 10W-30	Use SAE 10W or SAE 10W-30
or	
SAE 10W-40	Below 0° F,
	Use SAE 10W or SAE 10W-30
	Diluted 10% with Kerosene

The oil recommendations are the result of extensive testing.   No special additives should be used.

OIL SHOULD BE CHANGED AFTER EACH 25 HOURS OF ENGINE OPERATION. (More often under dirty operating conditions). In normal running of any engine, small particles of metal from the cylinder walls, pistons and bearings will gradually work into the oil. Dust particles from the air also get into the oil. If the oil is not changed regularly, these foreign particles cause increased friction and a grinding action which shorten the life of the engine. Fresh oil also assists in cooling, for old oil gradually becomes thick and loses its cooling effect as well as its lubricating qualities.

The air cleaner should be serviced every 25 hours of engine operation. Dirty operating conditions require more frequent servicing.

CLEAN COOLING SYSTEM

Grass particles, chaff or dirt may clog the air cooling system, expecially after prolonged service in cutting dry grasses. Continued operation with a clogged cooling system may cause severe overheating and possible engine damage. The figures below show the blower housing removed and area to be cleaned. This should be a regular maintenance Operation.

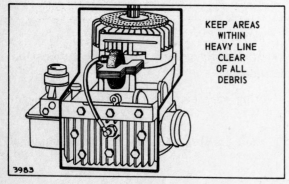

KEEP AREAS WITHIN HEAVY LINE CLEAR OF ALL DEBRIS

3983

Vertical Crankshaft

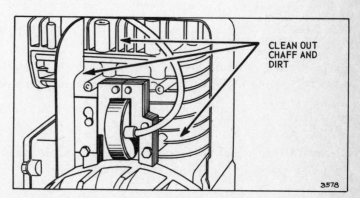

CLEAN OUT CHAFF AND DIRT

3578

Horizontal Crankshaft

TUNE-UP PROCEDURE

A "Tune-Up", see the steps listed below, would normally be performed on relatively new engines brought in for minor difficulties. By performing these steps you will either be sure that the engine is functioning properly or will know what major repairs should be made.

The steps are also covered in the Overhaul Procedure and will normally be performed as a part of the complete overhaul.

STEP NO.	
1.	Remove air cleaner, check for proper servicing.
2.	Check oil level and drain. (Clean fuel tank and lines if separate from carburetor).
3.	Remove blower housing, inspect rope and rewind assembly and starter clutch.
4.	Clean cooling fins and entire engine. Rock flywheel to check compression.
5.	Remove carburetor, disassemble and inspect for wear or damage. Wash in solvent, replace parts as necessary and assemble. Set initial adjustment.
6.	Inspect crossover tube or intake elbow for damaged gaskets.
7.	Check governor blade, linkage and spring for damage or wear, if mechanical also check adjustment.
8.	Remove flywheel, check for seal leakage, both flywheel and PTO sides. Check flywheel key.
9.	Remove breaker cover and check for proper sealing.

STEP NO.	
10.	Inspect breaker points and condenser. Replace or clean and adjust. Check plunger.
11.	Check coil, inspect all wires for breaks, damaged insulation. Be sure lead wires do not touch flywheel. Check stop switch and lead.
12.	Replace breaker cover, use sealer where wires enter.
13.	Install flywheel, time engine if necessary. Set air gap. Check for spark with #19051 tester.
14.	Remove cylinder head, check gasket, remove spark plug, and clean carbon, inspect valves for seating.
15.	Replace cylinder head, torque to specified torque, set spark plug gap or replace plug if necessary.
16.	Replace oil and fuel, check muffler for restrictions or damage.
17.	Adjust remote control linkage and cable if used, for correct operation.
18.	Service air cleaner, check gaskets and element for damage.
19.	Run and adjust mixture and top speed.

1

OVERHAUL PROCEDURE

The Overhaul Procedure which follows is intended to help you to become accustomed to a systematic method of repairing Briggs & Stratton engines. Naturally these steps could be rearranged in different order but efficiency is obtained when the repair operations are performed in the same sequence every time. The exact procedure will vary according to the engine model being repaired.

The Overhaul Procedure can also be used as an index. For information on how to perform most operations listed, refer to the page number or operation. Be careful to locate the instructions covering the specific model being repaired.

SECTION	PAGE NO.	DISASSEMBLY
8	1	Drain oil
3	1	Air cleaner and stud
		Fuel pipe and tank assembly
		Air cleaner elbow or pipe
		Carburetor and linkage
		Carburetor intake elbow
		Muffler
3	18 & 5	Check space between upper and lower carburetor body or carburetor to tank fit
3	18	Check throttle shaft and bushings for wear
		Disassemble carburetor
7	8 to 40	Electric starter (110 V) (12 V)
		Blower housing
6	1	Spin flywheel to check compression
2	1	Spark plug - adjust gap (.030") and clean and wash
		Fuel tank and bracket assembly or carburetor
2	3	Rope starter pulley
		Blower housing
2	6	Check air gap - armature to flywheel
5	1	Governor blade
8	3	Breather or valve cover
6	1	Cylinder head and shield
6	3	Check tappet clearance
6	2 & 3	Valve and springs
2	3	Rope starter pulley or recoil starter clutch
2	3 & 8	Flywheel
2	6	Breaker point cover
2	2 & 5	Check breaker point gap
2	4	Check breaker point plunger hole
2	4 & 7	Test condenser and remove if necessary

SECTION	PAGE NO.	DISASSEMBLY (Continued)
2	6	Test coil and remove if necessary
2	5	Breaker arm assembly and condenser
2	8 & 13	Breaker box
2	13	Breaker shaft
10	4 & 5	Check end play
10	1	Remove burrs from crankshaft extension
10	1	Crankcase cover, base or sump
10	7	Auxiliary drive
11	6	Damage seals
5	1 to 7	Mechanical governor parts
8	4	Inspect oil slinger
10	2	Cam gear
		Tappets
9	1	Connecting rod and piston
10	2	Crankshaft - inspect and check
2	12	Armature assembly and back plate
2	11 & 12	Rotor
2	6, 8, 12 & 13	Test coil or armature - check leads
11	3	Crankcase cover or sump
10	2	Crankshaft - inspect & check
10	2	Cam shaft and gear
10	2	Check automatic spark advance
		Tappets
11	1	Cylinder - check bore, main bearing, valve guides and seats, cylinder bore
9	1	Disassemble connecting rod and piston
9	2 & 3	Check piston, rings, connecting rod, piston pin

REPAIRS

SECTION	PAGE NO.	REPAIRS
		Clean parts
11	1 & 2	Resize cylinder bore to next oversize
6	3 & 4	Replace valve guide - intake or exhaust
6	2	Reface valves and seats and lap
6	4 to 6	Replace valve seat insert
11	3 to 5	Replace main bearings
11	6	Replace oil seal
2	4	Install breaker point plunger, bushing and plunger in cylinder (Internal breaker)
2	9 & 10	Install breaker point plunger bushing and plunger in cylinder (External breaker)
2	6 & 8	Replace armature and governor blade
2	12 & 13	Replace coil or armature or both
10	3	Replace automatic spark advance, weight and spring
3	17 & 18	Replace throttle shaft bushing
3	3 to 26	Repair carburetor
7	1, 2, 5 to 7	Replace rewind starter spring and rope
7	3	Starter clutch
11	3	Remove ball bearing and re-assemble to crankshaft

REASSEMBLE

SECTION	PAGE NO.	REASSEMBLE
10	3 & 4	Tappets, cam gear, camshaft
	5	Crankshaft and bearing support
	5	Crankshaft, bearing plate - adjust crankshaft end play
9	3 & 4	Piston, piston pin, connecting rod, rings
8	4	Oil Slinger
5	1 to 7	Mechanical governor
10	4	Sump or crankcase cover - adjust crankshaft end play
6	3	Adjust valve tappet clearance
6	2 & 3	Valves, springs, retainer

REASSEMBLE (Continued)

SECTION	PAGE NO.	REASSEMBLE (Continued)
2	6 & 8	Coil, armature, governor blade
2	5	Breaker points (Internal system)
2	5	Condenser (Internal system)
2	13	Breaker shaft - Magna-Matic
2	13	Primary wire - Magna-Matic
2	8, 9 & 12	Adjust Armature timing
2	7 & 14	Condenser
2	7 & 14	Adjust and clean breaker points (External)
2	6 & 8	Breaker point cover
2	12	Coil and armature assembly
2	11 & 2	Adjust rotor timing
2	7 & 14	Breaker box cover
2	3	Flywheel and starter pulley or clutch
7	8 to 40	Electric starter (110 V) (12 V)
2	6, 8 & 9	Adjust air gap - armature to flywheel
2	1	Check spark
8	3 & 4	Breather or valve cover
6	1	Cylinder head and shield
2	1	Spark plug
		Muffler
		Intake elbow or carburetor and tank
4	1 to 12	Carburetor and linkage and governor controls
5	1	Check air vane governor
5	2 to 7	Check and adjust mechanical governor
		Blower housing
		Fuel filter parts, tank & line
		Air cleaner elbow or pipe
8	1	Fill crankcase with oil
		Start engine (fill with gas)
2	1	Check spark
6	1	Retighten cylinder head screws
3	7 to 27	Adjust carburetor
5	2, 3 & 6	Set governor to obtain correct engine speed (Remote controls)
3	1	Clean, fill, assembly air cleaner
		Spray engine and apply decals

CHECK - UP

Most complaints concerning engine operation can be classified as one or a combination of the following:

1. Will not start
2. Hard starting
3. Kicks back when starting
4. Lack of power
5. Vibration
6. Erratic operation
7. Overheating
8. High oil consumption

When the cause of malfunction is not readily apparent, perform a check of the Compression, Ignition and Carburetion Systems. This check-up, performed in a systematic manner, can usually be done in a matter of minutes. It is the quickest and surest method of determining the cause of failure. This check-up will point up possible cause of future failures, which can be corrected at the time. The basic check-up procedure is the same for all engine models, while any variation, by model will be shown under the subject heading.

NOTE: What appears to be an engine malfunction may be a fault of the powered equipment rather than the engine. If equipment is suspect, see Equipment, affecting engine operation.

Check Compression

Spin flywheel in reverse rotation (counterclockwise) to obtain accurate compression check. The flywheel should rebound sharply, indicating satisfactory compression.

If compression is poor, look for —

1. Loose spark plug
2. Loose cylinder head bolts
3. Blown head gasket
4. Burnt valves and/or seats
5. Insufficient tappet clearance
6. Warped cylinder head
7. Warped valve stems
8. Worn bore and/or rings
9. Broken connecting rod

Check Ignition

Remove the spark plug. Spin the flywheel rapidly with one end of the ignition cable clipped to the 19051 tester and with the other end of the tester grounded on the cylinder head. If spark jumps the .166'' tester gap, you may assume the ignition system is functioning satisfactorily. Try a new spark plug.

If spark does not occur look for —
1. Incorrect armature air gap
2. Worn bearings and/or shaft on flywheel side
3. Sheared flywheel key
4. Incorrect breaker point gap
5. Dirty or burned breaker points
6. Breaker plunger stuck or worn
7. Shorted ground wire (when so equipped)
8. Shorted stop switch (when so equipped)
9. Condenser failure
10. Armature failure
11. Improperly operating interlock system

NOTE: If engine runs but misses during operation, a quick check to determine if ignition is or is not at fault can be made by inserting the 19051 tester between the ignition cable and the spark plug. A spark miss will be readily apparent. While conducting this test on Magna-Matic equipped engines, Models 9, 14, 19 and 23, set the tester gap at .060''.

Check Carburetion

Before making a carburetion check, be sure the fuel tank has an ample supply of fresh, clean gasoline. On gravity feed (Flo-Jet) models, see that the shut-off valve is open and fuel flows freely through the fuel line. On all models, inspect and adjust the needle valves. Check to see that the choke closes completely. If engine will not start, remove and inspect the spark plug. If plug is wet, look for —

1. Overchoking
2. Excessively rich fuel mixture
3. Water in fuel
4. Inlet valve stuck open (Flo-Jet carburetor)

If plug is dry, look for —

1. Leaking carburetor mounting gaskets
2. Gummy or dirty screen or check valve (Pulsa-Jet and Vacu-Jet carburetors)
3. Inlet valve stuck shut (Flo-Jet carburetors)
4. Inoperative pump (Pulsa-Jet carburetors)

A simple check to determine if the fuel is getting to the combustion chamber through the carburetor is to remove the spark plug and pour a small quantity of gasoline through the spark plug hole. Replace the plug. If the engine fires a few times and then quits, look for the same condition as for a dry plug.

Equipment - Effecting Engine Operation

Frequently, what appears to be a problem with engine operations, such as hard starting, vibration, etc., may be the fault of the equipment powered rather than the engine itself. Since many varied types of equipment are powered by Briggs and Stratton engines, it is not possible to list all of the various conditions that may exist. Listed are the most common effects of equipment problems, and what to look for as the most common cause.

Hard Starting, Kickback, or Will Not Start

1. Loose blade — Blade must be tight to shaft or adaptor.
2. Loose belt — a loose belt like a loose blade can cause a back-lash effect, which will counteract engine cranking effort.
3. Starting under load — See if the unit is disengaged when engine is started; or if engaged, does not have a heavy starting load.
4. Check remote Choke-A-Matic control assembly for proper adjustment.
5. Check interlock system for shorted wires, loose or corroded connections, or defective modules or switches.

Vibration

1. Cutter blade bent or out of balance — Remove and balance
2. Crankshaft bent — Replace
3. Worn blade coupling — Replace if coupling allows blade to shift, causing unbalance.
4. Mounting bolts loose — Tighten
5. Mounting deck or plate cracked — Repair or replace.

Power Loss

1. Bind or drag in unit — If possible, disengage engine and operate unit manually to feel for any binding action.
2. Grass cuttings build-up under deck.
3. No lubrication in transmission or gear box.
4. Excessive drive belt tension may cause seizure.

Noise

1. Cutter blade coupling or pulley — an oversize or worn coupling can result in knocking, usually under acceleration. Check for fit, or tightness.
2. No lubricant in transmission or gear box.

BRIGGS & STRATTON NUMERICAL MODEL NUMBER SYSTEM

This handy chart explains the unique Briggs & Stratton numerical model designation system. It is possible to determine most of the important mechanical features of the engine by merely knowing the model number. Here is how it works:

A. The first one or two digits indicate the CUBIC INCH DISPLACEMENT.

B. The first digit after the displacement indicates BASIC DESIGN SERIES, relating to cylinder construction, ignition, general configuration, etc.

C. The second digit after the displacement indicates POSITION OF CRANKSHAFT AND TYPE OF CARBURETOR.

D. The third digit after the displacement indicates TYPE OF BEARINGS and whether or not the engine is equipped with REDUCTION GEAR or AUXILIARY DRIVE.

E. The last digit indicates the TYPE OF STARTER

CUBIC INCH DISPLACEMENT	FIRST DIGIT AFTER DISPLACEMENT BASIC DESIGN SERIES	SECOND DIGIT AFTER DISPLACEMENT CRANKSHAFT, CARBURETOR GOVERNOR	THIRD DIGIT AFTER DISPLACEMENT BEARINGS, REDUCTION GEARS & AUXILIARY DRIVES	FOURTH DIGIT AFTER DISPLACEMENT TYPE OF STARTER
6	0	0 -	0 - Plain Bearing	0 - Without Starter
8	1	1 - Horizontal Vacu-Jet	1 - Flange Mounting Plain Bearing	1 - Rope Starter
9	2	2 - Horizontal Pulsa-Jet	2 - Ball Bearing	2 - Rewind Starter
10	3			
11	4	3 - Horizontal Flo-Jet (Pneumatic Governor)	3 - Flange Mounting Ball Bearing	3 - Electric - 110 Volt, Gear Drive
13	5	4 - Horizontal Flo-Jet (Mechanical Governor)	4 -	4 - Elec. Starter-Generator - 12 Volt, Belt Drive
14	6			
17	7	5 - Vertical Vacu-Jet	5 - Gear Reduction (6 to 1)	5 - Electric Starter Only - 12 Volt, Gear Drive
19	8			
20	9	6 -	6 - Gear Reduction (6 to 1) Reverse Rotation	6 - Alternator Only *
23				
24		7 - Vertical Flo-Jet	7 -	7 - Electric Starter, 12 Volt Gear Drive, with Alternator
25				
30		8 -	8 - Auxiliary Drive Perpendicular to Crankshaft	8 - Vertical-pull Starter
32				
		9 - Vertical Pulsa-Jet	9 - Auxiliary Drive Parallel to Crankshaft	* Digit 6 formerly used for "Wind-Up" Starter on 60000, 80000 and 92000 Series

EXAMPLES

To identify Model 100202:

10	0	2	0	2
10 Cubic Inch	Design Series 0	Horizontal Shaft - Pulsa-Jet Carburetor	Plain Bearing	Rewind Starter

Similarly, a Model 92998 is described as follows:

9	2	9	9	8
9 Cubic Inch	Design Series 2	Vertical Shaft - Pulsa-Jet Carburetor	Auxiliary Drive Parallel to Crankshaft	Vertical Pull Starter

Repair Instructions IV (Form 4750)

Section 2
IGNITION

Three basic types of ignition systems are used —

1. MAGNETRON™ ignition, a self-contained transistor module (no moving parts) and ignition armature.

2. A flywheel type, having either an internal or external breaker system. Fig. 4 and Fig. 25.

3. The Magna-Matic system, having the armature and rotor behind the flywheel, and an external breaker system. Fig. 44.

Check Ignition

Remove the spark plug. Spin the flywheel rapidly with one end of the ignition cable clipped to the 19051 tester and with the other end of the tester grounded on the cylinder head. If spark jumps the .166″ (4.2 mm) tester gap, you may assume the ignition system is functioning satisfactorily. Fig. 1.

NOTE: Flywheel must rotate at 350 RPM, minimum with MAGNETRON™ ignition.

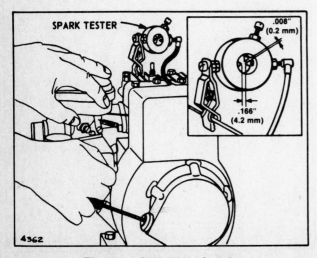

Fig. 1 — Checking Spark

NOTE: If engine runs but misses during operation, a quick check to determine if ignition is or is not at fault can be made by inserting the 19051 tester between the ignition cable and the spark plug. A spark miss will be readily apparent. While conducting this test on Magna-Matic equipped engines, Models 9, 14, 19 and 23, set the tester gap at .060″ (1.5 mm).

SPARK PLUG

The plugs recommended for Briggs & Stratton engines are as follows:

1-1/2″ Plug	2″ Plug	Manufacturer's Part Number
CJ-8	J-8	Champion
RCJ-8	RJ-8	Champion Resistor
235	295	Autolite
245	306	Autolite Resistor
WS9E	—	Robert Bosch
3/4″	13/16″	Plug wrench (deep socket)

Spark Plug Cleaning

Clean spark plug with a pen knife or wire brush and solvent and set gap at .030″ (0.75 mm) for all models. If electrodes are burned away, or the porcelain is cracked, replace with a new plug. DO NOT USE ABRASIVE CLEANING MACHINES. Fig. 2.

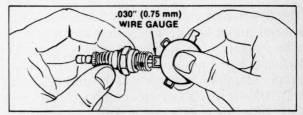

Fig. 2 — Adjusting Spark Plug Gap

Coil and Condenser Testing
All Models

Use an approved tester to test coils and condensers. Specifications are supplied by the tester manufacturer or refer to MS-7862, Testing Briggs & Stratton Ignition Coils.

IGNITION
General

TABLE NO. 1
SPECIFICATIONS FOR ALL POPULAR ENGINE MODELS

1. Spark plug gap: .030″ (0.75 mm)
2. Condenser capacity: .18 to .24 M.F.D.
3. Contact point gap: .020″ (0.50 mm)

| | ARMATURE | | | | | FLYWHEEL NUT TORQUE | | |
| | TWO LEG AIR GAP | | THREE LEG AIR GAP | | | | | |
BASIC MODEL SERIES	Inches	Milli-Meter	Inches	Milli-Meter	FLYWHEEL PULLER PART NO.	Foot Pounds†	Kilo-gram meter†	Newton meter†
ALUMINUM CYLINDER								
6B, 60000, 8B	.006 .010	0.15 0.25	.012 .016	0.30 0.41	19069	55†	7.6†	74.6†
80000, 82000, 92000, 93000, 94000, 95000, 110000	.006 .010	0.15 0.25	.012 .016	0.30 0.41	19069	55	† 7.6†	74.6†
100000, 130000	.010 .014	0.25 0.36	.012 .016	0.30 0.41	None	60†	8.3†	81.4†
140000, 170000, 190000, 220000, 250000	.010 .014	0.25 0.36	.016 .019	0.41 0.48	19165 or 19203*	65	† 9.0†	88.1†
CAST IRON CYLINDER								
5, 6, N, 8			.012 .016	0.30 0.41	None	55†	7.6†	74.6†
9					19068 or 19203	60	8.3	81.4
14					19068 or 19203	65	9.0	88.1
19, 190000, 200000	.010 .014	0.25 0.36	.022 .026	0.56 0.66	19068 or 19203	115†	15.9†	155.9†
23, 230000	.010 .014	0.25 0.36	.022 .026	0.56 0.66	19068 or 19203	115†	15.9†	155.9†
240000, 300000, 320000	.010 .014	0.25 0.36			19068 or 19203	145†	20.0†	196.6†

*Use on Model 250000 built after 1975.
†For rewind starter engines, use 19161 clutch wrench.

IGNITION MAGNETRON™

The flywheel is located on the crankshaft with a special metal key. It is held in place by a Belleville washer and nut or starter clutch. The flywheel key must be in good condition to assure proper location of the flywheel for ignition timing. DO NOT use a steel key under any circumstances. Use only the soft metal key, as originally supplied.

The keyway in both flywheel and crankshaft should not be distorted. Flywheels used are made of aluminum, zinc or cast iron.

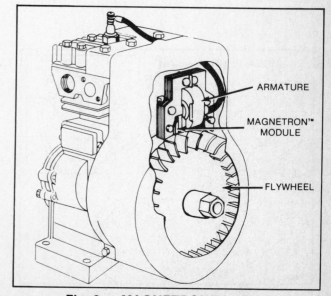

Fig. 3 — MAGNETRON™ Ignition

IGNITION
Flywheel Type — Internal Breaker

The flywheel is located on the crankshaft with a soft metal key. It is held in place by a nut or starter clutch. The flywheel key must be in good condition to insure proper location of the flywheel for ignition timing. DO NOT use a steel key under any circumstances. Use only the soft metal key, as originally supplied.

The keyway in both flywheel and crankshaft should not be distorted. Flywheels used are made of aluminum, zinc or cast iron.

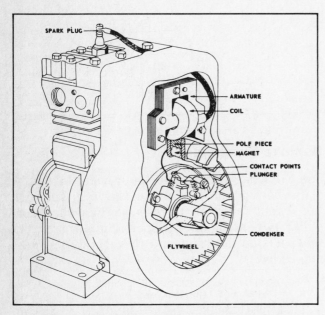

Fig. 4 — Flywheel Ignition Internal Breaker

REMOVING ARMATURE AND MAGNETRON™ IGNITION

The flywheel does not need to be removed to service MAGNETRON™ except to check keyways and flywheel key.

Remove armature screws and lift off armature. Use breaker point condenser P/N 294628 or 3/16″ pin punch to release stop switch wire from MAGNETRON™ module. Fig. 5. Stop switch wire is soldered to module and armature primary wires. Unsolder to disconnect.

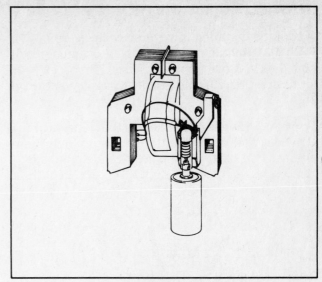

Fig. 5 — MAGNETRON™ Module

REMOVING MAGNETRON™ MODULE

Unsolder armature ground wire from module wire, Fig. 6. Remove tape and move module ground wire to clear armature coil and laminations. Push module retainer away from laminations and push module off laminations, Fig. 7.

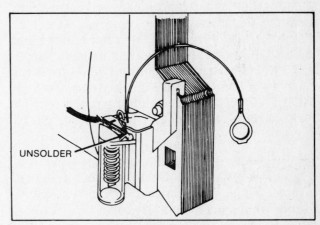

Fig. 6 —

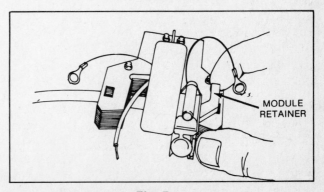

Fig. 7 —

IGNITION MAGNETRON™

INSTALLING MAGNETRON™ MODULE

Module is installed in reverse order of removal. Note that module retainer must be on back side of coil laminations, Fig. 8. Use Permatex™ or similar sealant to hold ground wires in place, Fig. 8.

Ignition timing is controlled by the location of the flywheel and crankshaft keyways on aluminum engines. On cast iron engines, refer to page 9.

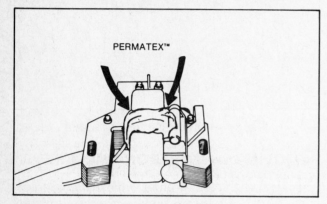

Fig. 8 —

Remove Flywheel Nut or Starter Clutch

On flywheels of 6-3/4″ (171 mm) diameter or less, use flywheel holder 19167, to keep flywheel from turning. On rope starter engines, the 1/2″ diameter thread flywheel nut is left handed and the 5/8″ diameter thread is right handed. Fig. 9. Starter clutch used on rewind and wind-up starter has a right hand thread. Fig. 10. Remove clutch using P/N 19114 starter clutch wrench or P/N 19244 or 19161 1/2″ square drive starter clutch wrench.

For flywheels or larger diameter place a block of wood under flywheel fin to prevent flywheel turning while loosening nut or starter clutch. Clamp engine base securely. Fig. 11.

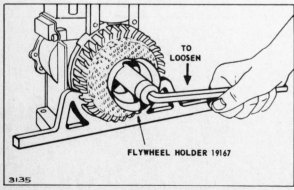

Fig. 9 — Loosen Flywheel, Rope Starter (1/2″ Dia. Threads)

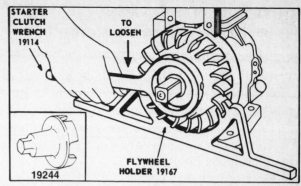

Fig. 10 — Loosening Flywheel Rewind Starter and Wind-Up Starter Engines

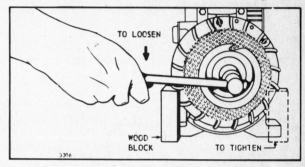

Fig. 11 — Loosening Large Flywheels

Remove Flywheel

Some flywheels have two holes provided for use of a flywheel puller. Use puller shown in Table 1. Leave nut loose on threads of crankshaft for puller to bear against, Fig. 12. Small cast iron flywheels do not require a flywheel puller. See note below.

Fig. 12 — Removing Flywheel

NOTE: To remove small cast iron flywheels without puller holes, support the flywheel with a gloved hand, exerting an upward pull. Using a rawhide hammer, strike the outside rim of the flywheel with a sharp blow. Several blows may be required on an extremely tight flywheel.

NOTE: Care is required not to damage the flywheel fins, magnets or ring gear.

Removing Breaker Cover

Care should be taken when removing breaker cover, to avoid damaging cover. If cover is bent or damaged it should be replaced to insure a proper dust seal.

Breaker Points

Breaker point gap on all models is .020" (0.5 mm). Breaker points should be checked for contact and for signs of burning or pitting. Points set too wide will advance spark timing and may cause kick back when starting. Points gapped too close retard spark timing and decrease engine power.

Remove Breaker Points

Breaker point assemblies of style shown in Fig. 13 are removed by removing condenser and armature wires from breaker points clip. Loosen adjusting lock screw and remove breaker point assembly.

Breaker point assemblies of style shown in Fig. 14 are removed by loosening the screw holding the post. The condenser on these models also includes the breaker point. The condenser is removed by loosening the screw holding the condenser clamp.

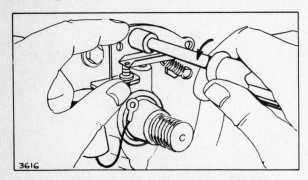

Fig. 13 — Breaker Point Assemblies

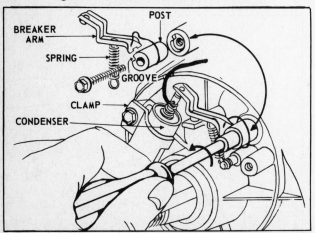

Fig. 14 — Breaker Point Assemblies

Check Breaker Point Plunger Hole

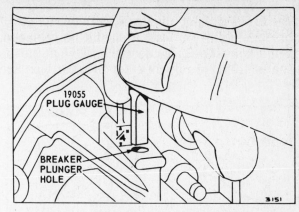

Fig. 15 — Checking Breaker Plunger Hole

If the breaker point plunger hole becomes worn excessively, oil will leak past the plunger and may get on the points, causing burning. To check, loosen breaker point mounting screw and move breaker points out of the way. Remove plunger. If the flat end of the 19055 plug gauge will enter the plunger hole for a distance of 1/4" (6.35 mm) or more, the hold should be rebushed. Fig. 15.

Install Breaker Point Plunger Bushing

To install the bushing, it is necessary that the breaker points, armature, crankshaft and starter be removed. Use reamer 19056, to ream out the old plunger hole. See Fig. 16. This should be done by hand. The reamer should be in alignment with the plunger hole. Drive the bushing 23513, with driver 19057 until the upper end of the bushing is flush with the top of the boss. Fig. 16. Finish ream the bushing with reamer 19058. All reaming chips or dirt must be removed.

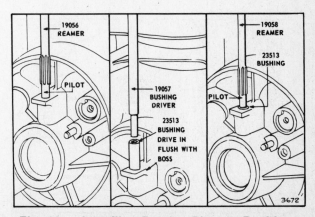

Fig. 16 — Installing Breaker Plunger Bushing

IGNITION
Flywheel Type — Internal Breaker

Breaker Point Plunger

If the breaker point plunger is worn to a length of .870" (22.1 mm) or less, it should be replaced. Plungers must be inserted with groove at the top when installed or oil will enter breaker box. See Fig. 17.

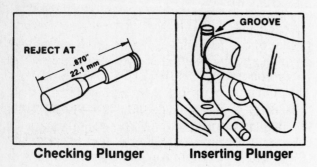

Checking Plunger   **Inserting Plunger**

Fig. 17

Install Breaker Points

Insert breaker plunger into the plunger hole in cylinder. Breaker points as shown in Fig. 14 are installed by placing the mounting post of the breaker arm into the recess in the cylinder so that the groove in the post fits the notch in the recess. Tighten the mounting screw securely. Use a 1/4" spinner wrench if available. Slip the open loop of breaker arm spring through the two holes in the arm, then hook closed loop of spring over the small post protruding from the cylinder. Push flat end of the breaker arm into the groove in the mounting post. This places tension on the spring and pulls arms against the plunger. If condenser post is threaded, attach the coil primary wire (and ground wire if furnished) with the lockwasher and nut. If primary wire is fastened to condenser with spring fastener, compress spring. Fig. 18, and slip primary wire (and ground wire where furnished) into hole in condenser post. Release spring. Lay the condenser in place and tighten the condenser clamp securely.

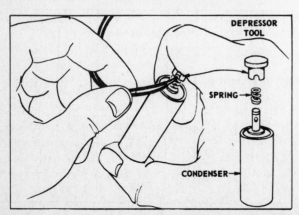

Fig. 18 — Assembling Condenser and Ignition Wires

When installing breaker point assemblies, as shown in Fig. 13, be sure the small boss on the magneto plate enters the hole in the point bracket. Mount points to magneto plate or cylinder with lock screw. Fasten the armature lead wire to the breaker points with the clip and screw. If these lead wires do not have terminals, the bare end of the wires can be inserted into the clip and screw tightened to make a good connection. Do not let the ends of the wire touch the point bracket or magneto plate or ignition will be grounded.

Adjusting Breaker Point Gap

Turn crankshaft until points open to widest gap. When adjusting breaker point assemblies as shown in Fig. 19, move condenser forward or backward with screw driver until a gap of .020" (0.5 mm) is obtained. Breaker points assemblies as shown in Fig. 20, are adjusted by loosening lock screw and moving contact point bracket up or down. Gap is .020" (0.5 mm).

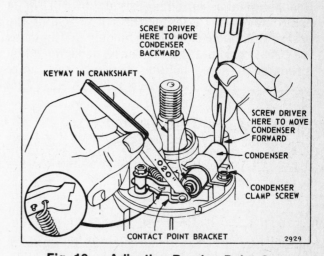

Fig. 19 — Adjusting Breaker Point Gap

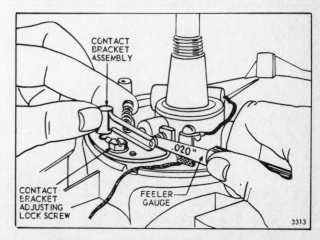

Fig. 20 — Adjusting Breaker Point Gap

NOTE: Always clean breaker points after adjustment. Open the points and insert a piece of lintless paper. Draw the paper through the points. Open points when removing paper so it will not tear, leaving paper between the points.

Breaker Point Cover

The breaker point cover, Fig. 21, protects the points from dirt. The opening for the primary and/or ground wire should be sealed with No. 2 Permatex™ or similar sealer to prevent dirt from entering the breaker box. Cover should not be distorted so as to lose its seal around the outer edge. Replace if damaged.

NOTE: Engines used for winter applications use vented breaker covers. See Engine Parts List.

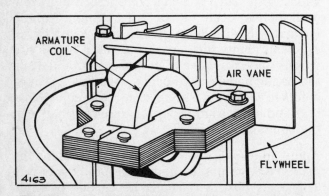

Fig. 21 — Breaker Point Cover

Install Armature

Install governor blade and armature, Fig. 22. The mounting holes in the armature laminations are slotted. Push armature up as far as possible and tighten one mounting screw to hold armature in place.

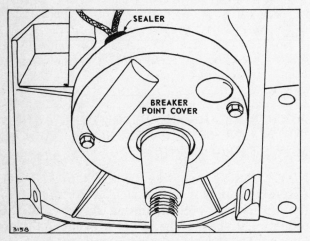

Fig. 22 — Install Armature and Governor Blade

Adjust Armature Air Gap

Three styles of armatures have been used (Fig. 23, Illus. 1, 2 and 3). Set air gap between the flywheel and armature as shown in Table 1. With armature up as far as possible, and one screw tightened, slip the proper gauge between armature and flywheel. Fig. 24. Turn flywheel until magnets are directly below the armature. Loosen the one mounting screw and the magnets should pull the armature down firmly against the thickness gauge. Then tighten the mounting screws.

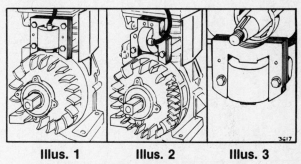

Illus. 1   Illus. 2   Illus. 3

Fig. 23 — Armature Style Variations

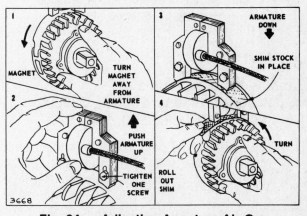

Fig. 24 — Adjusting Armature Air Gap

FLYWHEEL KEY

Inspect key for partial shearing. If sheared, replace. Check flywheel and crankshaft keyways for damage. If damaged, replace with new parts.

Install Flywheel, Nut and/or Starter Clutch

Remove all oil or grease, clean flywheel hole and tapered end of crankshaft before assembling flywheel to shaft. Insert zinc key into keyway. Slip spring washer over crankshaft with hollow side toward flywheel. To tighten flywheel nut or starter clutch, reverse removal operation. See "Remove Flywheel Nut or Starter Clutch." Torque to specifications listed in Table No. 1.

IGNITION
Flywheel Type — External Breaker
MODEL SERIES 193000, 200000, 230000, 243000, 300000, 320000, 19D, 23D

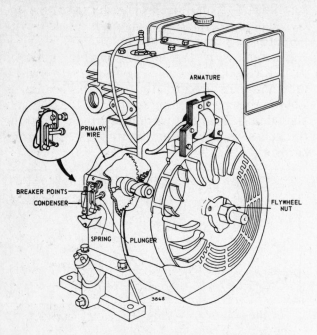

Fig. 25 — Flywheel Ignition External Breaker Models 193000, 200000, 233000, 243000, 300000, 320000

Replace Breaker Points — Model Series 193000, 200000, 230000, 243000, 300000, 320000, 19D, 23D

Turn crankshaft until points open to widest gap. This makes it easier to assemble and adjust points later if crankshaft is not removed. Remove condenser and upper and lower mounting screws. Loosen lock nut and back off breaker point screw. Fig. 26. Reverse process to install.

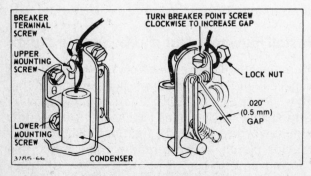

Fig. 26 — Breaker Points

To avoid the possibility of oil leaking past the breaker point plunger or moisture entering the crankcase between plunger and bushing, a plunger seal is now installed on engine models using this ignition system. Fig. 27. These parts may be added to engines in the field if contaminated points are experienced.

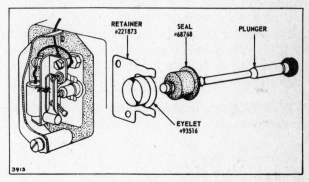

Fig. 27 — Seal Assembly

EXTREME CARE SHOULD BE TAKEN WHEN INSTALLING SEAL ON PLUNGER, OR SEAL MAY BE FRACTURED.

NOTE: Before mounting the breaker-condenser assembly, apply a sealer such as Permatex™ to the threads of both mounting screws and the adjustment screw. The sealer prevents oil from leaking into the breaker point area.

Mount the breaker point assembly, then tighten adjustment screw until the locknut has pushed the ferrule as far as possible toward the head of the adjustment screw. This secures the adjustment screw firmly to the breaker point.

Adjust and Clean Breaker Points

Turn the crankshaft until the points open to their widest gap. Turn breaker point adjusting screw until points open to .020" (0.5 mm). Tighten locknut, while holding adjustment screw, Fig. 26. To clean points turn crankshaft until points are closed. Insert a piece of lintless paper and draw the paper between the points. Open the breaker points to withdraw the paper (so the paper will not tear and allow a small portion to remain between the points).

Apply additional sealer at the point at which the primary wire passes under the breaker cover. This area must be re-sealed to prevent the entry of dust and moisture. See Fig. 28.

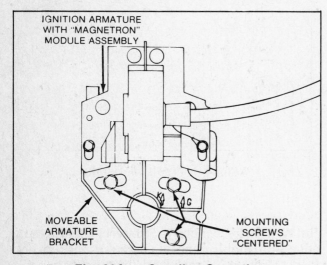

Fig. 28 — Sealing Breaker Cover

TIMING MAGNETRON™ IGNITION

1. Gasoline — Position armature bracket so mounting screws are centered in armature bracket and tighten screws, Fig. 29A.

2. Kerosene — Position armature bracket to the right, as far as it will go and tighten screws, Fig. 29B.

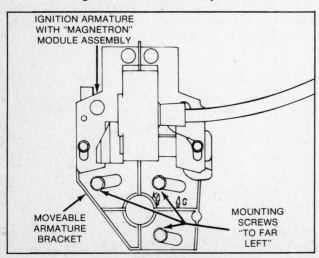

Fig. 29A — Gasoline Operation

Fig. 29B — Kerosene Operation

ADJUST ARMATURE TIMING WITH BREAKER POINTS
MODEL SERIES 193000, 200000, 230000, 243000, 300000, 320000

Remove Flywheel

Use puller 19203 or 19068, running puller screws into holes tapped into flywheel. Continue to tighten screws until flywheel loosens, Fig. 30.

NOTE: Use flywheel nut to protect crankshaft threads.

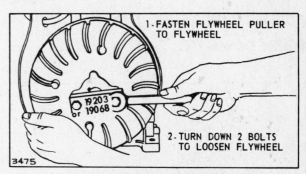

Fig. 30 — Removing Flywheel

Set point gap at .020″ (0.5 mm). Position flywheel on crankshaft taper. Slip key in place. Install flywheel nut finger tight. Rotate flywheel and crankshaft clockwise until breaker points are just opening. Use a timing light. When points just start to open, arrow on flywheel should line up with arrow on armature bracket, Fig. 31.

If arrows do not match, slip off flywheel without disturbing crankshaft position. Slightly loosen mounting screws holding armature bracket to cylinder, Fig. 31. Slip flywheel back on crankshaft. Insert flywheel key. Install flywheel nut finger tight. Move armature and bracket assembly to align arrows. Slip off flywheel, tighten armature bracket bolts. Install key and flywheel. Tighten flywheel nut to torque specifications listed in Table No. 1. Set armature air gap at .010″ – .014″ (0.25 – 0.36 mm), Fig. 32.

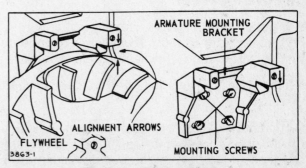

Fig. 31 — Timing Marks

IGNITION
Flywheel Type — External Breaker

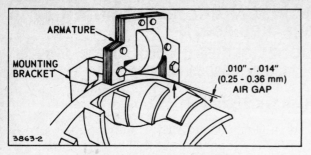

Fig. 32 — Armature Air Gap

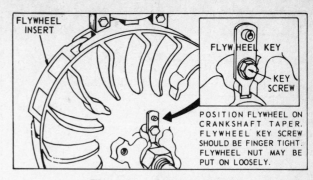

Fig. 34 — Flywheel Key

ADJUST ARMATURE TIMING
Model Series 19D, 23D

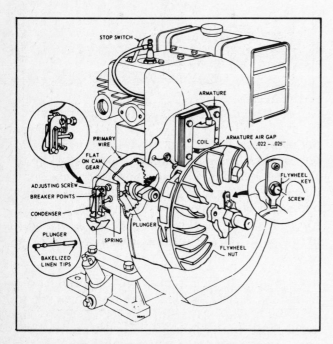

Fig. 33 — Model Series 19D, 23D

Remove Flywheel

Use puller 19203 or 19068, running puller screws into holes tapped into flywheel. Continue to tighten screws until flywheel loosens, Fig. 30.

NOTE: Use flywheel nut to protect crankshaft threads.

Set points at .020″ (0.51 mm) gap. Position flywheel on crankshaft taper. Flywheel key screw should be finger tight. Flywheel nut may be put on loosely, Fig. 33.

Rotate flywheel clockwise until breaker points are just opening (flywheel key drives crankshaft while doing this). Fig. 35. Use a timing light.

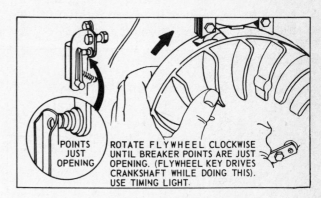

Fig. 35 — Flywheel Timing

Rotate flywheel slightly, counterclockwise, until edge of armature lines up with edge of flywheel insert, Fig. 36. (Crankshaft must not turn while doing this.) Tighten key screw. Tighten flywheel nut. See Table 1. Set armature air gap at .022″ – .026″ (0.56 – 0.66 mm).

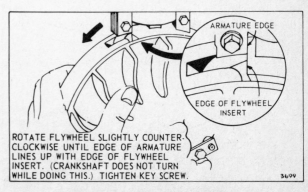

Fig. 36 — Flywheel Timing

REPLACING BREAKER PLUNGER AND BUSHING

Model Series 19D, 23D, 193000, 200000, 230000, 243000, 300000, 320000

Two styles of plunger bushing have been used. Removal and installation is as follows.

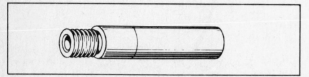

Fig. 37

Remove breaker box cover, condenser and breaker assembly, Fig. 38, Illus. 1.

Place a thick 3/8″ inside diameter washer, such as P/N 22238, over the end of bushing and screw on a 3/8-24 nut, as shown in Fig. 38, Illus. 2. Tighten the nut to pull the bushing. After the bushing has moved about 1/8″, remove the nut and put on a second thick washer, as shown in Fig. 38, Illus. 3. A total stack of 3/8″ of washers (2-22238) will be required to completely remove the bushing. Be sure the plunger does not fall out of the bushing as it is removed.

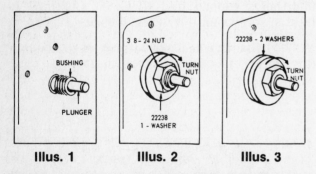

| Illus. 1 | Illus. 2 | Illus. 3 |

Fig. 38 — Removing Plunger and Threaded Bushing

Installing Threaded Bushing and Plunger

Place the new plunger in the bushing with the large end of the plunger opposite the threads on the bushing. Screw the 3/8-24 nut onto the threads to protect them. See Fig. 39.

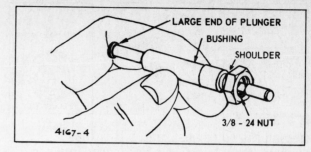

Fig. 39 — Plunger and Bushing

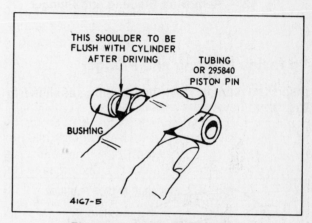

Fig. 40 — Inserting Bushing

Insert bushing into cylinder. Place a piece of tubing such as P/N 295840 piston pin against the nut, as shown in Fig. 40. Use a hammer to drive the bushing into the cylinder until the square shoulder on the bushing is flush with the face of the cylinder. Check to be sure plunger operates freely.

Alternate Design

Fig. 41 — To Remove Bushing and Plunger

Pull plunger outward as far as possible. Use a pliers to break plunger off as close to bushing as possible. See Illus. A, Fig. 42. Use a 1/4-20 tap or a 93029 self-threading screw to thread the hole in the bushing to a depth of approximately 1/2 to 5/8″ deep, as shown in Illus. B. Use 1/4-20 x 1/2″ hex head screw and two spacer washers as shown in Illus. C, to pull the bushing out of the cylinder. The bushing will be free when it has been extracted 5/16″. CAREFULLY remove the bushing and the remainder of the broken plunger. Do not allow the plunger or chips to drop into the crankcase.

IGNITION
Magna-Matic

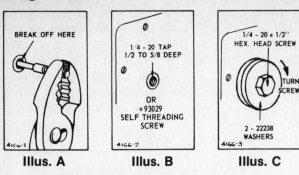

Illus. A **Illus. B** **Illus. C**

Fig. 42 — Removing Bushing and Plunger

To Install Bushing and Plunger

Insert the plunger in the new bushing as shown in Fig. 43.

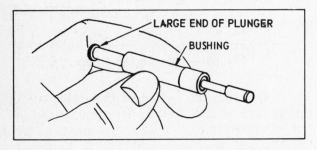

Fig. 43 — Inserting New Plunger in Bushing

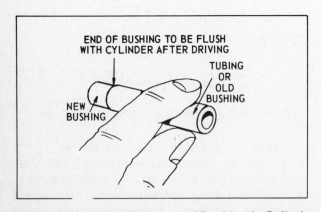

Fig. 44 — Inserting Plunger and Bushing in Cylinder

Insert plunger and bushing into the cylinder. Use a hammer and the old bushing to drive the new bushing into the cylinder until the new bushing is flush with the face of the cylinder. Check to be sure the plunger operates freely. Fig. 44.

MAGNA-MATIC SYSTEM

Engine Models 9-14-19-23-191000-231000

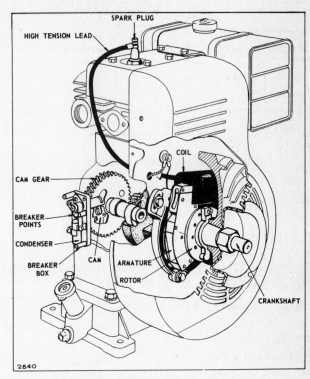

Fig. 45 — Magna-Matic System

Remove Flywheel

Use puller 19203 or 19068, running puller screws into holes tapped into flywheel. Continue to tighten screws until flywheel loosens. Fig. 46.

NOTE: Use flywheel nut to protect crankshaft threads.

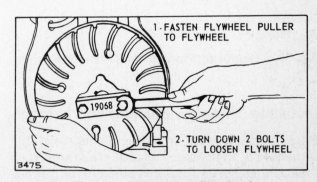

Fig. 46 — Removing Flywheel

Armature Air Gap

Armature air gap on engines equipped with Magna-Matic ignition is fixed and can change only if wear occurs on crankshaft journal and/or main bearing. Check for wear by inserting a feeler gauge 1/2" (12.7 mm) in width at points between the rotor and armature. Minimum feeler gauge thickness is .004" (0.1 mm). (Keep feeler gauge away from magnets on rotor or you will have a false reading.) Fig. 47.

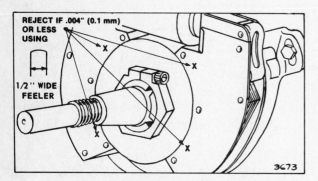

**Fig. 47 — Checking Armature Gap
Magna-Matic Ignition**

Remove Rotor

The rotor is held in place by means of a Woodruff key and a clamp on later engines, and a Woodruff key and set screw on older engines. Fig. 48. THE ROTOR CLAMP MUST ALWAYS REMAIN ON THE ROTOR (UNLESS THE ROTOR IS IN PLACE ON THE CRANKSHAFT AND WITHIN THE ARMATURE) OR A LOSS OF MAGNETISM WILL OCCUR.

Loosen the socket head screw in the rotor clamp, allowing the clamp to loosen. It may be necessary to use a puller to remove the rotor from the crankshaft. On older models, loosen the small lock screw, then the set screw.

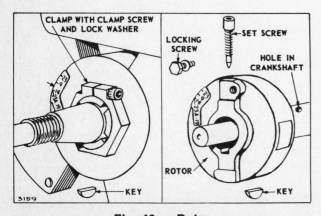

Fig. 48 — Rotor

Install Rotor

If rotor has a set screw, Fig. 48, Illus. 2, place the Woodruff key in keyway on crankshaft, then slide rotor onto crankshaft until the set screw hole in rotor and crankshaft are aligned. Be sure the key remains in place. Tighten the set screw securely, then tighten the lock screw to prevent set screw from loosening. The lock screw is self-threading and the hole does not require tapping.

If rotor has a clamp, Fig. 48, Illus. 1, place the Woodruff key in place in crankshaft, align keyways in rotor with Woodruff key. If necessary, use a short length of pipe and hammer to drive rotor onto shaft until .025" (0.64 mm) feeler gauge can be inserted between rotor and bearing support. Split in clamp must be between slots in rotor. Tighten clamp lock screws 60 to 70 inch pounds (.7 - .8 kg m or 6.8 - 8.0 newton m). Fig. 49.

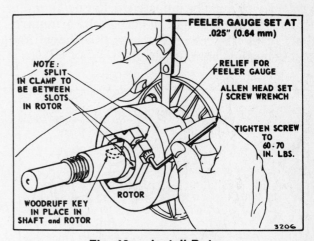

Fig. 49 — Install Rotor

Adjust Rotor Timing

The rotor and armature are correctly timed at the factory and require timing only if the armature has been removed from the engine, or if the cam gear or crankshaft has been replaced.

If necessary to adjust, proceed as follows: With the point gap set at .020" (0.5 mm) turn the crankshaft in normal direction of rotation until breaker points close and just start to open. Use a timing light or insert a piece of tissue paper between the breaker points to determine when points begin to open. With the three armature mounting screws slightly loose, rotate the armature until the arrow on armature lines up with the arrow on rotor as shown in Fig. 50. Align with corresponding number of engine model. On Models 9, align with 9, etc. Retighten armature mounting screws.

IGNITION
Magna-Matic

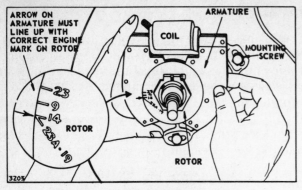

Fig. 50 — Adjusting Rotor Timing

Replace Coil or Armature or Both

Usually the coil and armature are not separated, but are left assembled for convenience. However, if one or both need replacement, proceed as follows: The coil primary wire and the coil ground wire must be unfastened. Pry out the clips that hold the coil and coil core to the armature. See Fig. 51. The coil core is a slip fit in the coil and can be pushed out of the coil.

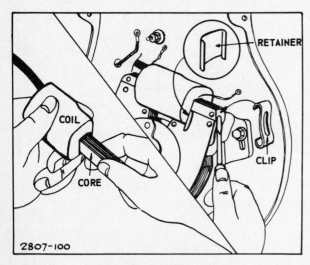

Fig. 51 — Replace Coil

To reassemble, push coil core into coil with rounded side toward the ignition cable. Place coil and core on armature with coil retainer between the coil and armature, with rounded side toward the coil. Hook the lower end of the clips into the armature; then press the upper end onto the coil core, Fig. 51.

Fasten the coil ground wire (bare double wires) to the armature support. (Replacing coil, Fig. 51). Now place the assembly against the cylinder around the rotor and bearing support. Insert the

three mounting screws together with washer and lockwasher into the three long oval holes in the armature. Tighten them enough to hold the armature in place but loose enough that the armature can be moved for adjustment of rotor timing. See Fig. 50. Attach primary wires from coil and breaker points to the terminal at the upper side of back plate. (This terminal is insulated from back plate.) Push the ignition cable through the louvered hole at left side of back plate.

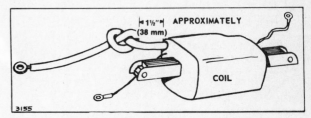

Fig. 52 — Shorten Cable — Model 9

NOTE: On Model 9 engines, knot the ignition cable before inserting it through the back plate. See Fig. 52. Be sure all wires clear flywheel.

Remove Breaker Points

Turn crankshaft until points open to widest gap. This makes it easier to assemble and adjust points later if crankshaft is not removed. With terminal screw removed, remove the spring screw. See Fig. 53. Loosen the breaker shaft nut until nut is flush with end of shaft. Tap nut to free breaker arm from tapered end of breaker shaft. Remove nut, lockwasher and breaker arm. Remove breaker plate screw, breaker plate, pivot, insulating plate and eccentric. Pry out breaker shaft oil seal with a sharp pointed tool.

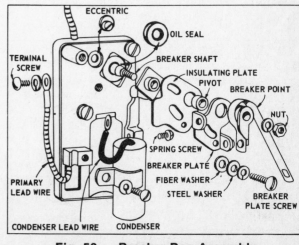

Fig. 53 — Breaker Box Assembly

Remove Breaker Box

Remove the two mounting screws, then remove the breaker box, turning it slightly to clear the arm at inner end of breaker shaft. See Fig. 54. Breaker points need not be removed to remove breaker box.

Install Breaker Points

Press in the new oil seal with the metal side out. Put new breaker plate on top of insulating plate, taking care that the detent in breaker plate engages hole in insulating plate. Fasten breaker plate screw only enough to put a light tension on the plate. See Fig. 55. Adjust eccentric so that left edge of insulating plate is parallel to edge of box and tighten screw. Fig. 56. This locates the breaker plate so that proper gap adjustments may be made. Turn breaker shaft clockwise as far as possible and hold in this position. Place new breaker point on shaft, then the lockwasher and tighen nut down on lockwasher. Replace spring screw and terminal screw.

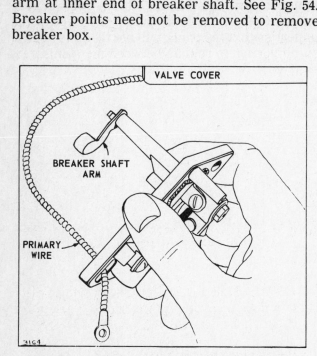

Fig. 54 — Removing Breaker Box Assembly

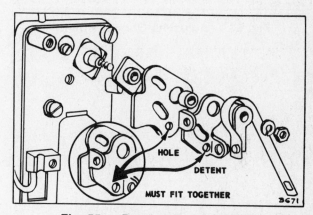

Fig. 55 — Breaker Box Assembly

Remove Breaker Shaft

The breaker shaft can be removed (after breaker points are removed) by turning the shaft one half turn to clear the retaining spur at the inside of the breaker box.

Install Breaker Shaft

Insert the breaker shaft with arm upward so arm will clear the retainer boss. Push the shaft all the way in, then turn arm downward.

Install Breaker Box

Pull the primary wire through the hole at lower left corner of breaker box. See that the primary wire rests in the groove at top end of box; then tighten the two mounting screws to hold box in place.

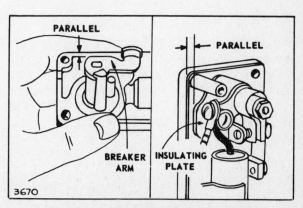

Fig. 56 — Insulating Plate Position

IGNITION
Magna-Matic

Adjust Breaker Points

To adjust breaker points, turn the crankshaft until the breaker points open to widest gap. Loosen the breaker plate screw slightly. Rotate the eccentric to obtain a point gap of .020″ (0.5 mm). Tighten the breaker plate screw. See Fig. 57.

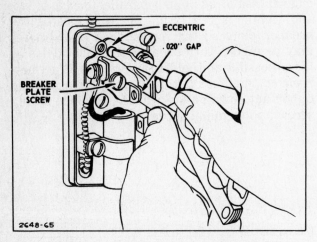

Fig. 57 — Adjusting Breaker Points

Clean Breaker Points

The points on all models should be cleaned by opening the points, inserting a piece of lintless paper and drawing the paper through between the points. Open the breaker points to withdraw the paper (so that the paper will not tear and allow a small portion to remain between the points.

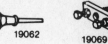

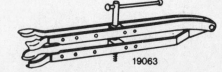

V

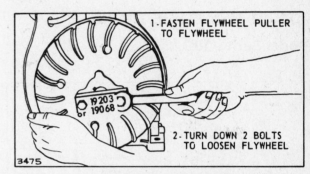

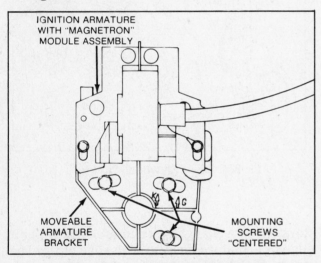

Section 3
CARBURETION

AIR CLEANERS

A properly serviced air cleaner protects the internal parts of the engine from dust particles in the air. If the air cleaner instructions are not carefully followed, the dirt and dust which should be collected in the cleaner, will be drawn into the engine and become a part of the oil film, which is very detrimental to engine life; dirt in the oil forms an abrasive mixture which wears the moving parts, instead of protecting them. No engine can stand up under the grinding action which takes place when this occurs. The air cleaner on every engine brought in for a check up or repair should be examined and serviced. If the cleaner shows signs of neglect, show it to the customer before cleaning, and instruct him on proper care to assure long engine life.

NOTE: Replace air cleaner gaskets and mounting gaskets that are worn or damaged, to prevent dirt and dust entering engine through improper sealing. Straighten or replace bent mounting studs.

Service Oil Foam Air Cleaner

Clean and re-oil air cleaner element every 25 hours or at three month intervals under normal conditions. The capacity of the "Oil Foam" air cleaner is adequate for a full season's use without cleaning in average homeowner lawn mower service. (Clean every few hours under extremely dusty conditions.) See Figures 1 and 2.

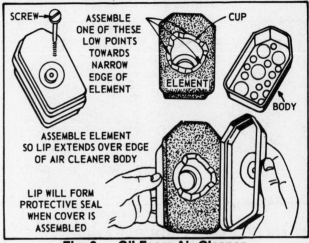

Fig. 2 — Oil Foam Air Cleaner

OIL FOAM AIR CLEANER (Figs. 1 and 2)

1. Remove screw or wing nut.

2. Remove air cleaner carefully to prevent dirt from entering carburetor.

3. Take air cleaner apart and clean.

   a. WASH foam element in kerosene or liquid detergent and water to remove dirt.

   b. Wrap foam in cloth and squeeze dry.

   c. Saturate foam with engine oil. Squeeze to remove excess oil.

4. Reassemble parts and fasten to carburetor securely with screw or wing nut.

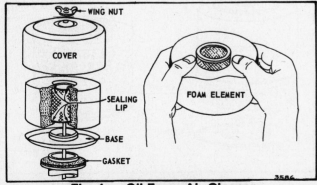

Fig. 1 — Oil Foam Air Cleaner

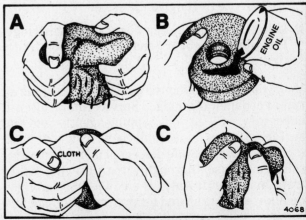

Fig. 3 — Cleaning Air Cleaner

CARBURETION
Air Cleaners

OIL FOAM AIR CLEANER VARIATIONS

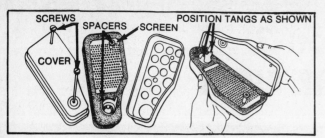

Standard Air Cleaner

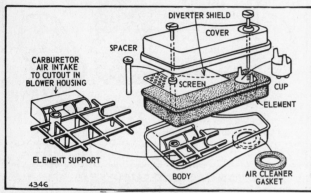

Ducted Air Cleaner

DUAL ELEMENT AIR CLEANER

Clean and re-oil foam pre-cleaner at three month intervals or every 25 hours, whichever occurs first.

NOTE: Service more often under dusty conditions.

1. Remove knob and cover.

2. Remove foam pre-cleaner by sliding it off of the paper cartridge.

3. a. Wash foam pre-cleaner in kerosene or liquid detergent and water.

   b. Wrap foam pre-cleaner in cloth and squeeze dry.

   c. Saturate foam pre-cleaner in engine oil. Squeeze to remove excess oil.

4. Install foam pre-cleaner over paper cartridge. Reassemble cover and screw knob down tight.

Yearly or every 100 hours, whichever occurs first, remove paper cartridge. Service more often if necessary. Clean by tapping gently on flat surface. If very dirty, replace cartridge, or wash in a low or non-sudsing detergent and warm water solution. Rinse thoroughly with flowing water from inside until water is clear. Cartridge must be allowed to stand and air dry thoroughly before using.

CAUTION: Petroleum solvents, such as kerosene, are not to be used to clean cartridge. They may cause deterioration of the cartridge. DO NOT OIL CARTRIDGE. DO NOT USE PRESSURIZED AIR TO CLEAN OR DRY CARTRIDGE.

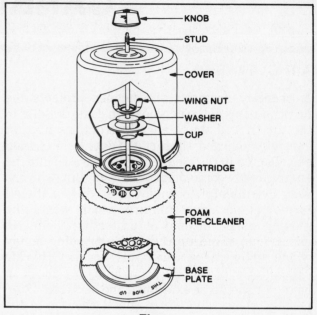

Fig. 4

CARTRIDGE TYPE

To clean — tap cartridge (top or bottom) on flat surface or wash in non-sudsing detergent and flush from inside until water is clear. After washing, air dry thoroughly before using. DO NOT OIL. Fig. 5.

CAUTION: Petroleum solvents, such as kerosene, are not to be used to clean cartridge. They may cause deterioration of the cartridge. DO NOT OIL CARTRIDGE. DO NOT USE PRESSURIZED AIR TO CLEAN OR DRY CARTRIDGE.

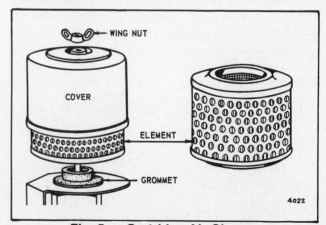

Fig. 5 — Cartridge Air Cleaner

CARTRIDGE AIR CLEANER — REVERSE AIR FLOW

1. Remove air cleaner stud, screw and gasket. Replace gasket if damaged.

2. Remove plate screw, washer and plate.

3. Remove cartridge and clean air cleaner body carefully to prevent dirt from entering carburetor. Brush dirt from body through holes into duct.

4. Clean cartridge by tapping gently on flat surface.

    a. If very dirty, replace cartridge or wash in a low or non-sudsing detergent and warm water solution.

    b. Rinse thoroughly from OUTSIDE IN until water is clear.

    c. Cartridge must be allowed to stand and air dry thoroughly before using.

5. Re-assemble air cleaner. Fig. 6.

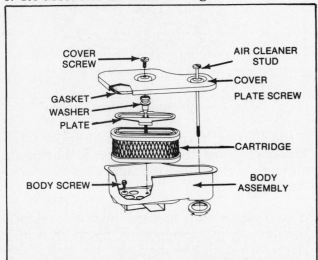

Fig. 6 — Cartridge Air Cleaner

CAUTION: Petroleum solvents, such as kerosene, are not to be used to clean cartridge. They may cause deterioration of the cartridge. DO NOT OIL CARTRIDGE. DO NOT USE PRESSURIZED AIR TO CLEAN OR DRY CARTRIDGE.

SERVICE OIL BATH AIR CLEANER

Pour out old oil from bowl. Wash element thoroughly in solvent and drain dry. Clean bowl and refill with same type of oil used in crankcase. See Fig. 7.

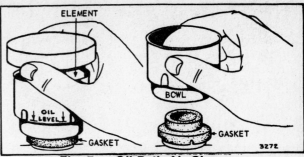

Fig. 7 — Oil Bath Air Cleaner

THREE BASIC CARBURETOR STYLES

There are three styles of carburetors used on Briggs & Stratton engines. Page 3 and 4, Fig. 8. Compare the carburetor to be repaired with the illustrations to determine style of carburetor and refer to that section for repair information.

Before removing any carburetor for repair, look for signs of air leakage, or mounting gaskets that are loose, have deteriorated, or are otherwise damaged.

Note position of governor springs, governor link, remote control or other attachments to facilitate re-assembly. Do not bend the links or stretch the spring. (Section 4 illustrates popular engine models.)

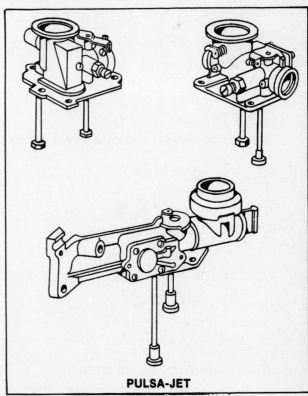

PULSA-JET

Fig. 8 — Style of Carburetors

3

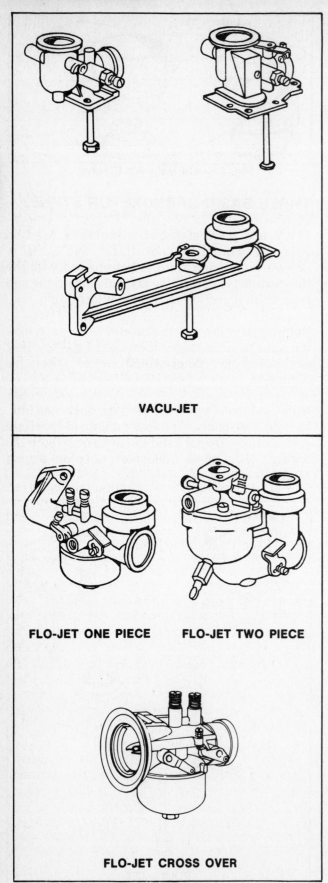

VACU-JET

FLO-JET ONE PIECE   **FLO-JET TWO PIECE**

FLO-JET CROSS OVER

Fig. 8 — Style of Carburetors (Cont'd.)

AUTOMATIC CHOKE
MODEL SERIES 92000, 94000, 110900, 111900

The automatic choke operates in conjunction with engine vacuum, similar to the Pulsa-Jet fuel pump.

A diaphragm under the carburetor is connected to the choke shaft by a link. See Fig. 9. A calibrated spring under the diaphragm holds the choke valve closed when the engine is not running.

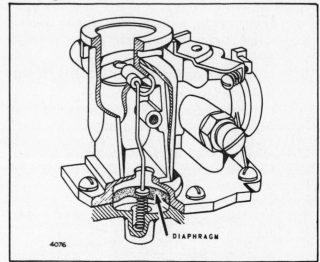

Fig. 9 — Automatic Choke System

Upon starting, vacuum created during the intake stroke is routed to the bottom of the diaphragm, through a calibrated passage, thereby opening the choke.

This system also has the ability to respond similar to an acceleration pump. As speed decreases during heavy loads, the choke valve partially closes enriching the mixture, thereby improving low speed performance and lugging power.

The automatic choke can easily be checked to determine if it is or is not functioning properly.

1. Remove the air cleaner and replace the stud. Observe the position of the choke valve; it should be fully closed.

2. Move the speed control to the stop position; the governor spring should be holding throttle in a closed position. Pull the starter rope rapidly. The choke valve should alternately open and close.

3. If the engine can be started, run for 2 or 3 minutes, at a normal operating speed. Check to be sure fuel tank is 1/2 full of fuel. Then, open the needle valve to be sure the mixture can be made too rich. Next close the needle valve to be sure the mixture can be made too lean. Adjust needle valve to midpoint between too rich and too lean.

Allow engine to run at idle speed for 3 to 5 minutes. Again, close needle valve; the mixture should become so lean the engine will stop. If the engine continues to run at idle with the needle valve closed, a fuel leak is occuring at one of the following areas: Check items 2D, 2H, 2I, 2J and 2K.

If the choke valve does not react as stated in Steps 1, 2 and 3, the carburetor will have to be disassembled to determine the problem. (See Repair Procedure below).

The following list is given to aid you in checking the performance of the Automatic Choke Carburetion System.

1. Engine Appears to be Under-Choked —

A. Carburetor adjusted too lean
B. Fuel pipe check valve inoperative (Vacu-Jet only)
C. Bent air cleaner stud
D. Sticking choke shaft due to dirt, etc.
E. Choke spring damaged or too short (See Repair Procedure)
F. Diaphragm not preloaded (See Repair Procedure)

2. Engine Appears to be Over-Choked —

A. Carburetor adjusted too rich
B. Bent air cleaner stud
C. Sticking choke shaft due to dirt, etc.
D. Ruptured diaphragm
E. Vacuum passage restricted
F. Choke spring distorted, stretched, etc.
G. Gasoline or oil in vacuum chamber
H. Leak between link and diaphragm
I. Diaphragm folded during assembly, causing vacuum leak
J. Machined surface on tank top not flat (See Repair Procedure)
K. Needle valve seat loose

REPAIR PROCEDURE

Inspect the automatic choke for freeness of operation. Any sticking problems should be corrected, as proper choke operation depends on freedom of the choke to travel as dictated by engine vacuum.

Repair procedures specific to the automatic choke are as follows:

Remove the carburetor and fuel tank assembly from the engine. The choke link cover may now be removed and the choke link disconnected from the choke shaft. Disassemble carburetor from tank top, using care to insure diaphragm is not damaged.

CHECKING DIAPHRAGM AND SPRING

The diaphragm is suitable for further use, provided it has not developed wear spots or punctures. (On Pulsa-Jet models check to insure fuel pump valves are not damaged.) Also check choke spring length. The Pulsa-Jet spring minimum length is 1-1/8" —maximum 1-7/32" and the Vacu-Jet spring minimum length is 15/16" — maximum 1". NOTE: On Model 110900 and 111900 choke spring minimum length is 1-5/16"; maximum 1-3/8". If spring length is shorter or longer than specified, replace diaphragm and spring.

CHECKING TANK TOP

The machined surface on the top of the fuel tank must be flat in order for the diaphragm to provide an adequate seal between the carburetor and tank. If the machined surface on the tank is not flat, it is possible for gasoline to enter the vacuum chamber by passing between the machined surface and diaphragm. Once fuel has entered the vacuum chamber, it can move through the vacuum passage and into the carburetor. The flatness of the machined surface on the tank top can be checked by straight edge and feeler gauge, as shown in Fig. 10. A .002" feeler gauge should not enter between the straight edge and machined surface, when checking at the shaded areas depicted in the drawing. Replace tank if gauge enters. NOTE: STRAIGHT EDGE MUST BE ACCURATE.

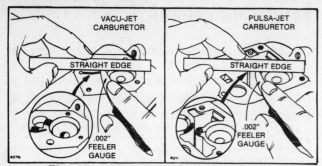

Fig. 10 — Checking Tank Top Flatness

Repair Kit #391413 may be used to repair Pulsa-Jet fuel tanks which are not flat. Install roll pin and teflon washer as shown in Fig. 11.

Fig. 11 — Installing Roll Pin and Teflon Washer

If needed, repair of the fuel metering and supply system may now be undertaken as shown on pages 9 and 10.

If a new diaphragm is being installed, assemble choke spring to diaphragm, as shown in Fig. 12. Be careful not to bend or distort the spring.

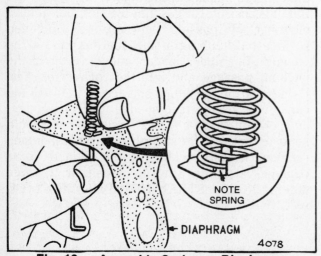

Fig. 12 — Assemble Spring to Diaphragm

Holding carburetor body upside down, place diaphragm on body while guiding choke link thru hole for link. On Pulsa-Jet carburetor, have pump spring and cap in fuel pump well, Fig. 13.

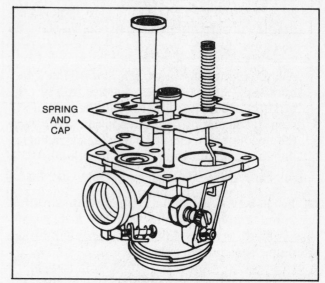

Fig. 13 — Locating Diaphragm on Carburetor

Lower tank down onto carburetor, while guiding choke spring into spring well, Fig. 14. Holding carburetor and body together, turn assembly right side up. Thread carburetor mounting screws into tank top about two (2) turns. DO NOT TIGHTEN.

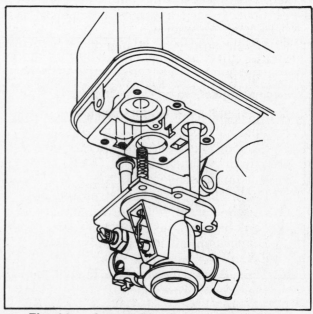

Fig. 14 — Assembling Tank to Carburetor

Close choke valve, insert choke link into choke shaft as shown. Fig. 15.

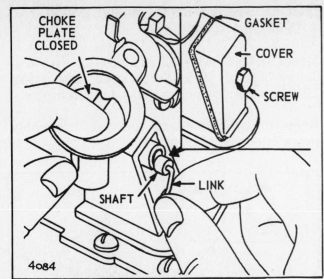

Fig. 15 — Inserting Choke Link

Move choke plate to an over center position as shown in Fig. 16. Tighten carburetor mounting screws in a staggered sequence. Please note — Opening the choke to an over center position places the diaphragm in a preloaded condition.

Move choke plate to a normal position. Choke plate should now fully close, Fig. 16.

If choke valve is not fully closed, check to be sure choke spring is properly assembled to diaphragm, and also properly inserted in its pocket in the tank top. Install choke link cover and gasket.

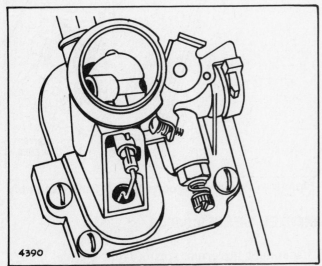

Fig. 16 — Pre-Loading Diaphragm

All carburetor adjustment should be made with the air cleaner on engine. Best adjustment is made with a fuel tank half full of gasoline.

To Adjust Carburetor:

1. Start engine and run long enough to warm it to operating temperature.

   NOTE: If engine is out of adjustment so that it will not start, close the needle valve by turning it clockwise. Then open needle valve 1-1/2 turns counterclockwise. Fig. 17.

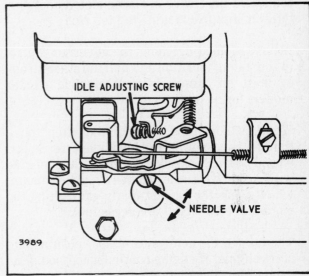

Fig. 17 — Adjusting Carburetor

2. Move speed control lever to run engine at normal operating speed.
   a. Turn needle valve in clockwise until engine starts to lose speed (lean mixture).
   b. Then slowly turn needle valve out counterclockwise past the point of smoothest operation until engine just begins to run unevenly (rich mixture).
   c. Turn needle back clockwise to midpoint (smoothest operation) between rich and lean mixture.
   d. Final adjustment of the needle valve should be at the midpoint between rich and lean.

3. Move engine to SLOW. Turn idle adjusting screw until a fast idle is obtained — 1750 R.P.M.

   If the engine idles at a speed lower than 1750 R.P.M., it may not accelerate properly. It is not practical to attempt to obtain acceleration from speeds below 1750 R.P.M., since the richer mixture which would be required, would be too rich for normal operating speeds.

CARBURETION
Pulsa-Jet, Vacu-Jet (Vertical Crankshaft)

4. To check adjustment move engine control from SLOW to FAST speed. Engine should accelerate smoothly. If engine tends to stall or die out, increase idle speed or re-adjust carburetor, usually to a slightly richer mixture.

NOTE: Flooding can occur if the engine is tipped at an angle for a prolonged period of time, if the engine is cranked repeatedly when the spark plug wire is disconnected or if carburetor mixture is adjusted too rich.

In case of flooding, move the governor control to the "Stop" position and pull the starter rope at least six times. (Crank electric starter models for at least 5 seconds.)

When the control is placed in the "Stop" position the governor spring holds the throttle in a closed (idle) position. Cranking the engine with a closed throttle creates a higher vacuum which opens the choke rapidly, permitting the engine to clear itself of excess fuel.

Then move the control to "Fast" position and start engine. If engine continues to flood, lean carburetor needle valve — 1/8 to 1/4 turn clockwise or see page 5.

If the engine on a mower with a high-inertia disc type cutter blade becomes hard starting when the engine is warm, a leaner carburetor mixture may be required.

A heavy, high-inertia disc type cutter blade rotates for a longer period of time, after the governor control is placed in the STOP position. During this "coasting" period, the engine continues to induct the fuel-air mixture, even when the choke is open. If the carburetor mixture is too rich, the warm engine may flood and become hard starting. If the original carburetor adjustment has not been changed, turn the needle valve clockwise (leaner) approximately 1/8 turn. If the original carburetor adjustment has been changed, follow previous adjustment procedure paragraph No. 2—A, B and C, then adjust 1/8 turn leaner.

Cleaning Fuel System

Gummy or dirty fuel tanks, lines and carburetors should be cleaned in a carburetor cleaner, such as Bendix. Do not soak diaphragms or nylon parts in cleaner.

MODEL SERIES 82000, 92000, 94000, 110900 and 111900 only

Model Series 82500, 92500 and 94500 have a Vacu-Jet carburetor. Model Series 82900, 92900, 94900, 110900 and 111900 have a Pulsa-Jet carburetor.

Remove carburetor and fuel tank assembly mounting bolts, Fig. 18.

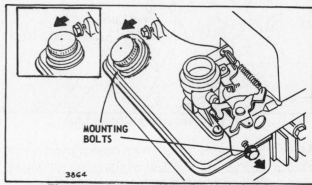

Fig. 18 — Removing Mounting Bolts

Slip carburetor and fuel tank assembly off end of fuel intake tube and turn assembly to free throttle link from throttle lever. This will leave governor link and governor spring connected to the governor blade and control lever, Fig. 19.

Fig. 19 — Remove Carburetor and Tank Assembly

MODEL SERIES 94000

Disconnect governor spring from control lever. Slide carburetor and fuel tank assembly off end of fuel intake tube and turn assembly to disconnect governor link from bell crank lever. This will leave governor spring and bell crank assembly on carburetor and fuel tank assembly, Fig. 20.

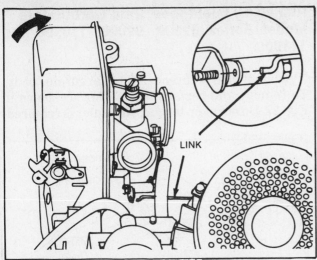

Fig. 20 — Removing Fuel Tank Assembly

Removing Carburetor, Model Series 82000 and 92000 Choke-A-Matic

Remove screws holding carburetor on tank body. Then lift carburetor straight up. Remove pump spring, spring cup and diaphragm.

Removing Carburetor, Model Series 92000, 94000, 110900 and 111900, Automatic Choke

Remove screws holding carburetor on tank body. On Model Series 110900 and 111900 a mounting screw is located under the choke valve. To gain access to the screw, open the choke valve completely. Use a #2 Phillips head screwdriver to remove the screw, Fig. 21. Then lift carburetor straight up. Remove pump spring, spring cup and diaphragm.

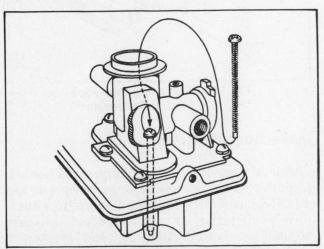

Fig. 21 — Screw Under Choke Valve

Carburetor Repair — Pulsa-Jet, Vacu-Jet

Zinc Carburetor Body

Remove and discard "O" ring. Remove and inspect needle valve, packing and seat. Metering holes in carburetor body should be cleaned with solvent and compressed air. Do not alter size of holes. See Fig. 22.

Always remove all nylon and rubber parts if carburetor is soaked in solvent.

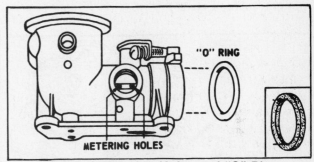

Fig. 22 — Metering Holes and "O" Ring

Minlon Carburetor Body

Remove and discard "O" ring. Remove needle and seat assembly by backing out mixture adjusting needle about 4 to 5 turns counterclockwise. Then pull needle and seat assembly out. Remove inner "O" ring. Metering holes in carburetor body should be cleaned with solvent and compressed air. CAUTION: Commercial carburetor cleaners will soften or dissolve Minlon bodies, if left in for long periods of time. DO NOT EXCEED 15 MINUTES. DO NOT ALTER SIZE OF METERING HOLES, Fig. 23.

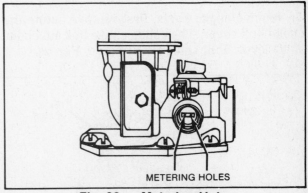

Fig. 23 — Metering Holes

Always remove all nylon and rubber parts if carburetor is cleaned in solvent.

CARBURETION
Pulsa-Jet, Vacu-Jet

Removing Nylon Choke and Shaft

Choke-A-Matic, Model Series 82000 and 92000

To remove choke parts, first disconnect choke return spring, Fig. 24. Then pull nylon choke shaft sideways to separate choke shaft from choke valve. If choke valve is heat-sealed to choke shaft, loosen by sliding sharp pointed tool along edge of choke shaft. Do not reseal parts on assembly. When replacing choke valve and shaft, install choke valve so poppet valve spring is visible when valve is in full choke position on carburetors using poppet valve, Fig. 25.

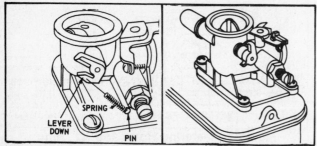

Fig. 24 — Choke Shaft and Valve — Choke-A-Matic

Fig. 25 — Poppet Valve

Automatic Choke, Model Series 92000, 94000, 110900 and 111900

To remove choke parts, first remove automatic choke link cover. Then slide choke link out choke shaft lever. Pull shaft out of valve, Fig. 26.

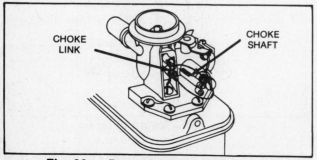

Fig. 26 — Removing Automatic Choke

Replacing Fuel Pipes, Zinc Carburetors Model Series 82000, 92000, 110900 and 111900

Nylon fuel pipe is threaded into carburetor body. To remove and replace, use socket as shown in Fig. 27. Do not over-torque. No sealer is required.

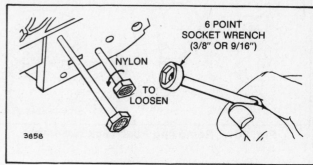

Fig. 27 — Replacing Nylon Fuel Pipes, Zinc Carburetor

Replacing Fuel Pipe, Minlon Carburetor Model Series 92500 and 94500

The fuel pipe on Minlon carburetors is of the snap-in design. The pipe may snap in and out with considerable force. Fig. 28.

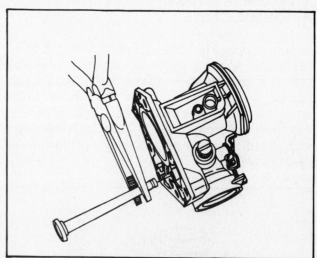

Fig. 28 — Replacing Fuel Pipe, Minlon Carburetor

Inspection and Repair

Check all parts for wear and replace as needed. Examine fuel pipe screens for gum deposits and dirt. Replace if dirty. Replace diaphragm if worn, torn, punctured or stiff. Inspect mixture adjustment needle, Fig. 29, and replace if damaged.

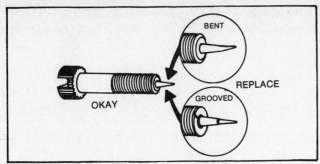

Fig. 29 — Mixture Needle

NOTE: On Vacu-Jet carburetors there is a check ball in the fuel pickup tube. To function properly, the screen must be clean and the check ball free. Replace pipe if screen is clogged or the check ball is not free to move.

Carburetor Assembly, Zinc and "Minlon"

When assembling carburetor, use new "O" rings, gaskets and/or diaphragms. Install choke plate and choke shaft. Choke shaft lever should be as shown in Fig. 30, Illus. I, II, III.

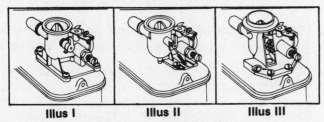

| Illus I | Illus II | Illus III |

Fig. 30 — Choke Lever

On zinc carburetors, install needle valve seat being sure not to cause burrs in slot. Then install needle valve assembly, Fig. 31 or Fig. 32.

NOTE: Some zinc carburetors use Minlon valve assembly, Fig. 32.

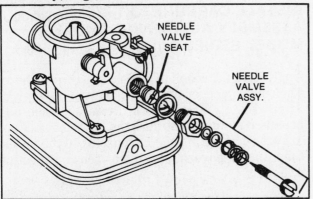

Fig. 31 — Needle Valve Assembly, Zinc Body

To install Minlon needle valve assembly, place "O" ring on shoulder of needle seat. Then turn needle in until large seal washer just touches needle seat, Fig. 32.

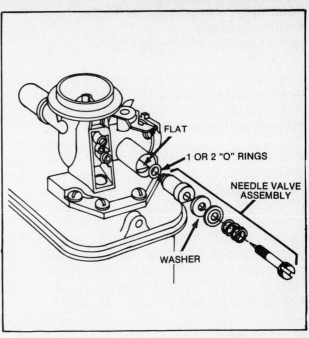

Fig. 32 — Needle Valve Assembly, Minlon Body

Install needle valve as an assembly being sure flat on valve seat lines up with flat in carburetor body, Fig. 33. Oil fill tube, part no. 280131 will help firmly seat valve assembly.

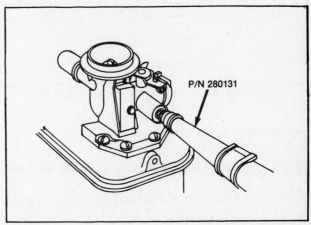

Fig. — 33 — Assembling Valve in Minlon Body

Place "O" ring in groove in throttle bore. Early "O" rings had a square cross section. Current "O" rings have a round cross section. Fig. 34.

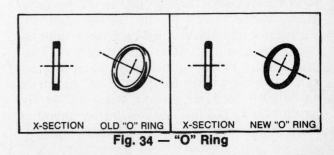

| X-SECTION | OLD "O" RING | X-SECTION | NEW "O" RING |

Fig. 34 — "O" Ring

CARBURETION
Pulsa-Jet, Vacu-Jet

Assembly, Carburetor to Tank, Choke-A-Matic, Model Series 82000, 92000

The gasket on Vacu-Jet carburetors acts as a seal between carburetor and tank top. The diaphragm on Pulsa-Jet carburetors also serves as a gasket between the carburetor and tank.

To assemble Vacu-Jet carburetor to tank, place gasket on tank and place carburetor on gasket. Install and tighten two (2) screws evenly to avoid distortion.

To assemble Pulsa-Jet carburetor to tank, first place diaphragm on tank. Then place spring cap and spring on diaphragm. Install carburetor and tighten four (4) screws evenly in staggered sequence to avoid distortion, Fig. 35.

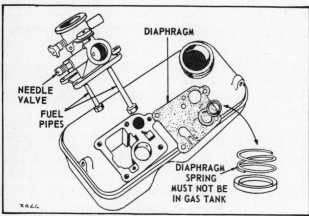

Fig. 35 — Exploded View – Carburetor and Tank Assembly

Assembly, Carburetor to Tank, Automatic Choke, Model Series 92000, 94000, 110900, 111900

Assemble carburetor to tank as outlined on pages 6 and 7 of this section.

Install Carburetor and Tank Assembly Choke-A-Matic, Model Series 82000, 92000

Put a light film of oil on "O" ring in throttle bore. With the governor link hooked to the governor blade, connect link to the throttle and slip carburetor into place. Align carburetor with the intake tube and breather tube grommet. Hold choke lever as shown in Fig. 36, so it does not catch on control plate. Be sure the "O" ring in the carburetor does not distort when fitting the carburetor to the intake tube. Install mounting bolts. Fig. 37 shows routings of ground wire.

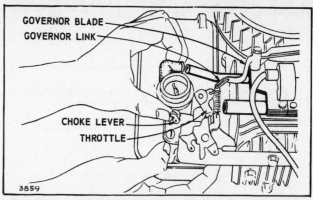

Fig. 36 — Install Carburetor and Tank Assembly

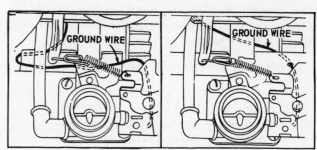

Fig. 37 — Ground Wire Leads

Install Carburetor and Tank Assembly Automatic Choke, Model Series 92000, 110900, 111900

Apply light film of oil to "O" ring in throttle bore. Then hook governor link to governor blade. Align the carburetor with the intake tube and breather tube grommet. Be sure the "O" ring does not distort when fitting the carburetor to the intake tube. Install governor spring as shown in Section 4, Page 7.

INSTALL CARBURETOR AND TANK ASSEMBLY AUTOMATIC CHOKE, MODEL SERIES 94000

Apply light film of oil to "O" ring in throttle bore. Then hook bell crank into governor lever rod. Align the carburetor with the intake tube and breather grommet. Be sure the "O" ring does not distort when fitting the carburetor to the intake tube. Install governor spring as shown in Section 4, page 8.

Carburetor Adjustment

NOTE: When making carburetor adjustments on Model Series 82000, 92000, 94000, 110900, 111900, air cleaner and stud must be installed on carburetor.

Model Series 82500, 92500 and 94500 engines should be adjusted with fuel tank half full of gasoline.

Initial Adjustment: Turn needle valve clockwise to close it. Then open 1½ turns. This initial adjustment will permit the engine to be started and warmed up before making final adjustment.

Final Adjustment: Place governor speed control lever in "FAST" position. Turn needle valve in until engine misses (clockwise — lean mixture) then turn it out past smooth operating point until engine runs unevenly (rich mixture). Now turn needle valve to the midpoint between rich and lean so the engine runs smoothly. Next, adjust idle RPM. Rotate throttle counterclockwise and hold against stop. Adjust idle speed adjusting screw to obtain 1750 RPM. Release throttle — engine should accelerate without hesitation or sputtering. If engine does not accelerate properly, the carburetor should be re-adjusted, usually to a slightly richer mixture.

Breather and Fuel Intake Tubes

Breather tube and fuel intake tube thread into the cylinder on Model Series 82000. Fuel intake tube is bolted to the cylinder on Model Series 92000, 94000, 110900 and 111900. See Fig. 38. Check for good fit or damaged gaskets to prevent air leaks or entry of dirt.

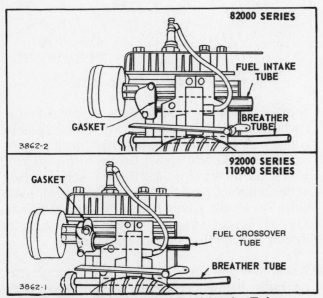

Fig. 38 — Breather and Fuel Intake Tubes

Choke-A-Matic Adjustment

The Choke-A-Matic feature was standard on Model Series 82000, 92500 (type nos. lower than 0600) 92900 (type nos. lower than 0500) engines. The remote control must be of the type in which the control wire moves out of the casing, when the control lever is moved from the stop position to the "Choke" or "Start" position. A minimum travel of 1-3/8" (34.9 mm) is required when the remote control is mounted, Fig. 39.

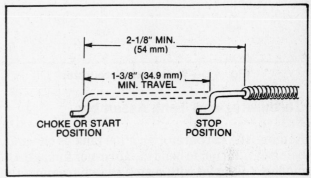

Fig. 39 — Remote Control

To install remote control assembly proceed as follows:

Remove the air cleaner and move the control lever to a position about midway between idle and fast. Then mount the remote control with the casing clamp as shown in Fig. 40.

Place control lever on equipment in fast (high speed) position. CONTROL MUST BE MOUNTED ON EQUIPMENT TO MAKE AN ACCURATE ADJUSTMENT. Lever "A" on carburetor should be just touching choke shaft at "B." Move casing "D" forward or backwards until correct position is obtained. Tighten screw "C." Recheck operation of controls after adjustment, Fig. 40.

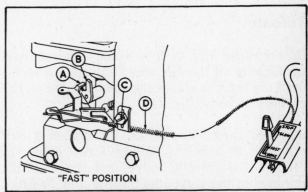

Fig. 40 — Choke-A-Matic Control (Typical)

CARBURETION
PULSA—JET

PULSA-JET CARBURETORS

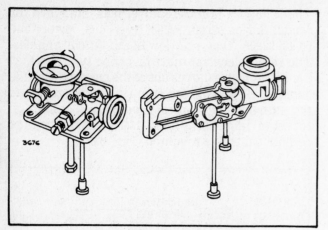

Fig. 41 — Pulsa-Jet Carburetor

Carburetor and Tank Assembly

Remove the carburetor and fuel tank as one unit, being careful not to bend the governor linkage. On models equipped with a stop switch, remove the ground wire. Fig. 42.

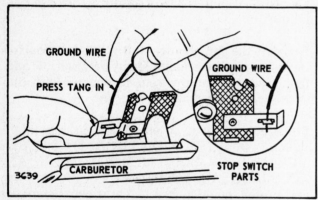

Fig. 42 — Removing Ground Wire

After removal of the carburetor from the fuel tank, inspect the tank for deposits of dirt and/or varnish.

Throttle

Cast throttles, Fig. 43, Illustration 1, are removed by backing off the idle speed adjustment screw until the throttle clears the retaining lug on the carburetor body, Fig. 44.

Stamped throttles, Fig. 43, Illustration 2, are removed by using a Phillips screw driver to remove the throttle valve and screw. After removal of the valve, the throttle may be lifted out, Fig. 45. Reverse procedure to install. Fig. 44.

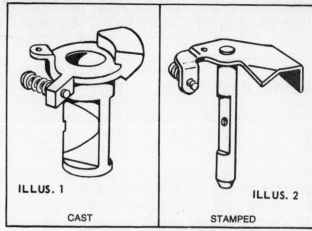

Fig. 43 — Throttle Types

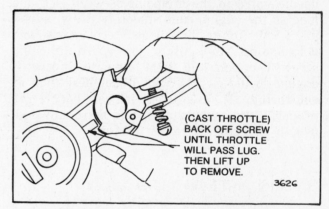

(CAST THROTTLE) BACK OFF SCREW UNTIL THROTTLE WILL PASS LUG. THEN LIFT UP TO REMOVE.

Fig. 44 — Removing Cast Throttle

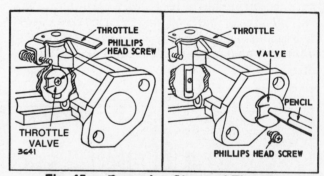

Fig. 45 — Removing Stamped Throttle

Some carburetor models have a spiral in the carburetor bore. To remove, fasten carburetor in a vise with smooth jaws about half an inch below top of jaws. Grasp spiral firmly with a pair of pliers, as shown, Fig. 46. Place a screw driver under ledge of pliers. Using edge of vise, push down on screw driver handle to pry out spiral, Fig. 46. Inspect gasket surface of carburetor. Repair if mounting surface is damaged.

When inserting spiral, top must be flush to 1/32" (.8 mm) below carburetor flange, and spiral parallel with fuel tank mounting surface, Fig. 46.

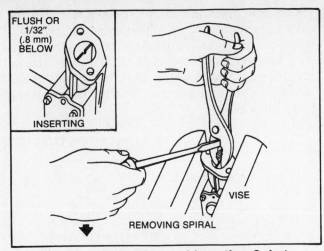

Fig. 46 — Removing and Inserting Spiral

Fuel Pipe

Check balls are not used in these fuel pipes. The screen housing or pipe must be replaced if the screen can not be satisfactorily cleaned. The long pipe supplies fuel from the tank to the pump. The short pipe supplies fuel from the tank cup to the carburetor. Fig. 47. Fuel pipes are nylon or brass. Nylon pipes are removed and replaced by using a 6 point socket, or open end wrench. Fig. 48. WHERE BRASS PIPES ARE USED, THE SCREEN HOUSING ONLY IS REPLACED. Fig. 49. Clamp the fuel pipe in a vise (do not overtighten). Drive off the brass housing with a screw driver. The new housing is installed by tapping it on the pipe with a soft hammer, Fig. 49.

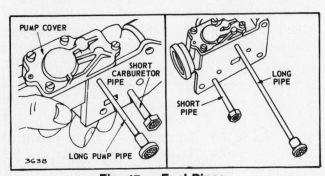

Fig. 47 — Fuel Pipes

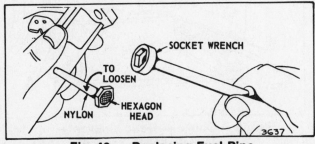

Fig. 48 — Replacing Fuel Pipe

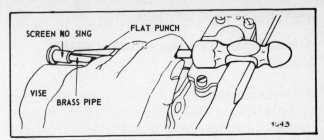

Fig. 49 — Replacing Screen Housing Assembly

Needle Valve and Seat

Remove needle valve to inspect. If carburetor is gummy or dirty, remove seat to allow better cleaning of metering holes. Fig. 50. Do not resize metering holes.

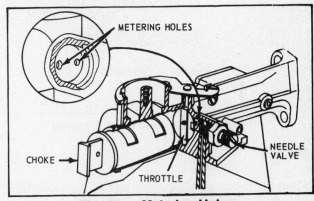

Fig. 50 — Metering Holes

Pump Disassembly and Repair

Remove fuel pump cover, diaphragm, spring and cup. Fig. 51. Inspect diaphragm for punctures, cracks and fatigue. Replace if damaged. Current style supersedes the previous style. When installing the pump cover, tighten the screws evenly in staggered sequence to insure a good seal. Inspect all sealing surfaces for nicks or damaged and repair or replace as required.

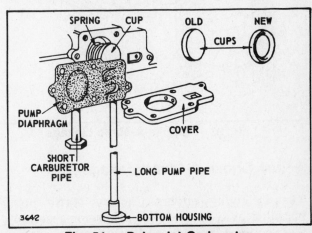

Fig. 51 — Pulsa-Jet Carburetor

CARBURETION
PULSA-JET

Choke-A-Matic Linkage

Disassembly (Except Model 100900, 130900)

To remove choke link, remove speed adjustment lever and stop switch insulator plate. Remove speed adjustment lever from choke link then pull out choke link through hole in choke slide. Fig. 52.

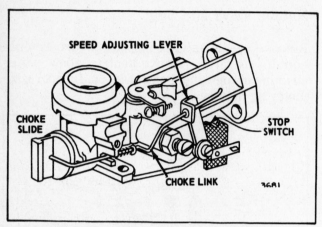

Fig. 52 — Choke-A-Matic Linkage

Repair

Replace worn or damaged parts. To assemble, slip washers and spring over choke link. Fig. 53. Hook choke link through hole in choke slide. Place other end of choke link through hole in speed adjustment lever and mount lever and stop switch insulator plate to carburetor.

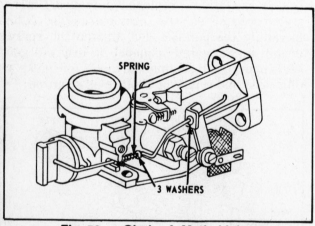

Fig. 53 — Choke-A-Matic Linkage

Adjust Choke-A-Matic Linkage

The following covers Choke-A-Matic parts installed as a part of the carburetor assembly. See Section 4 for Choke-A-Matic remote controls.

To check operation of Choke-A-Matic linkage, move speed adjustment lever to choke position. If choke slide does not fully close, replace link or use flat nose pliers to bend choke link. Fig. 54 (Do not overbend.) Speed adjustment lever must make good contact against stop switch when moved to stop position.

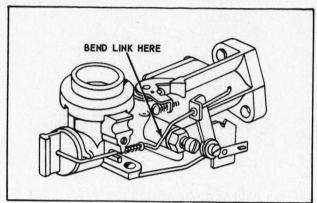

Fig. 54 — Adjust Choke Link

Choke-A-Matic Linkage Model 100900, 130900 and 131900

Manual or remote control for choke and stop is made by a lever on the control plate mounted to carburetor by two screws "A", Fig. 55. Lever for remote control has a loose fit, for manual control, a friction fit. To check lever action, move to left until it snaps into run detents. Lever "B" should just touch choke lever at "C."

If it does not, loosen screws "A" slightly and move control plate to right or left until lever just touches choke lever at "C." Tighten screws.

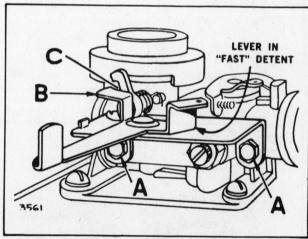

Fig. 55 — Choke-A-Matic Linkage — Model 100900, 130900, 131900

Choke-A-Matic Remote Controls

See Section 4 for illustrations by engine model.

Install Carburetor
Except Model 100900 and 130900

Install carburetor and tank as one assembly on engine. Hook throttle link into carburetor throttle and governor lever (for various illustrations, see Section 4). Raise carburetor into place, insert a new gasket and fasten with mounting screws. Install governor spring. Fig. 56. Install ground wire and remote control where used.

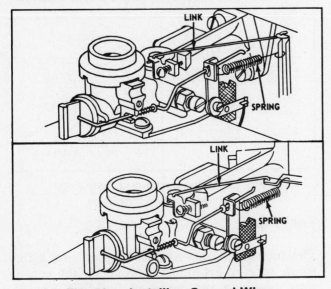

Fig. 56 — Installing Ground Wire

Install Carburetor
Model 100900, 130900, and 131900

Assemble carburetor to tank. Hold throttle link to throttle. Fig. 57. Slip carburetor over notch in cylinder shield and around intake tube. Oil the seal in carburetor body to prevent damage, when installing. Mount tank to cylinder. Hook up ground wire and governor spring.

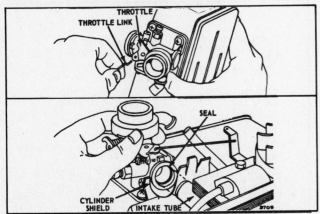

Fig. 57 — Install Carburetor — Model 100900 and 130900

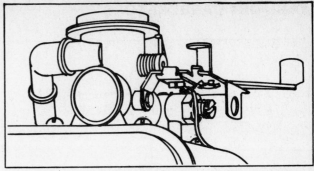

Fig. 57A — Install Carburetor — Model 131900

Carburetor Adjustment

Turn needle valve clockwise until it just closes.

CAUTION: Valve may be damaged by turning it in too far.

Now open needle valve 1½ turns counterclockwise, Fig. 58. This initial adjustment will permit the engine to be started and warmed up prior to final adjustment.

NOTE: All carburetor adjustments must be made with the air cleaner on engine. Best adjustments made with fuel tank 1/2 full.

Final Adjustment

Place governor speed control lever in "FAST" position. Turn needle valve in until engine misses (clockwise — lean mixture) then turn it out past smooth operating point until engine runs unevenly (rich mixture). Now turn needle valve to the midpoint between rich and lean so the engine runs smoothly. Next, adjust idle RPM. Rotate throttle counterclockwise and hold against stop. Adjust idle speed adjusting screw to obtain 1750 RPM. Release throttle — engine should accelerate without hesitation or sputtering. If engine does not accelerate properly, the carburetor should be re-adjusted, usually to a slightly richer mixture.

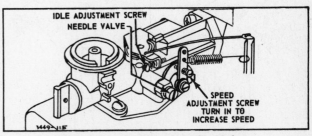

Fig. 58 — Setting Needle Valve

NOTE: When starting a Pulsa-Jet engine for the first time, fill fuel tank completely full. This eliminates priming the fuel pump, thus insuring a quick start.

CARBURETION
Vacu-Jet

VACU-JET CARBURETORS

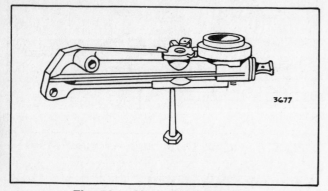

Fig. 59 — Vacu-Jet Carburetor

Carburetor and Tank Assembly

Remove the carburetor and fuel tank as one unit, being careful not to bend the governor linkage or spring. On models equipped with a stop switch, remove the ground wire. After removal of the carburetor from the fuel tank, inspect the tank for deposits of dirt and/or varnish and mounting surfaces. Tank should be cleaned in solvent.

Throttle

Cast throttles, Fig. 60, Illustration 1, are removed by backing off the idle speed adjusting screw until the throttle clears the retaining lug on the carburetor body. Fig. 61.

Stamped throttles, Fig. 60, Illustration 2, are removed by using a Phillips screw driver to remove the throttle valve screw. After removal of the valve, the throttle may be lifted out. Reverse procedure to install. Fig. 62.

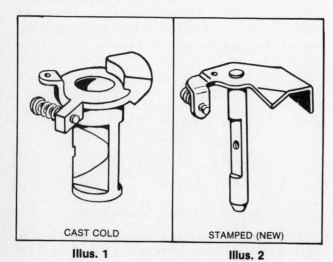

CAST COLD	STAMPED (NEW)
Illus. 1	**Illus. 2**

Fig. 60 — Throttle Types

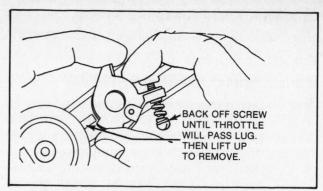

Fig. 61 — Removing Old Style Throttles

BACK OFF SCREW UNTIL THROTTLE WILL PASS LUG. THEN LIFT UP TO REMOVE.

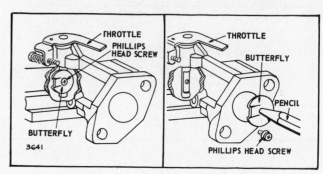

THROTTLE
PHILLIPS HEAD SCREW
BUTTERFLY
3641

THROTTLE
BUTTERFLY
PENCIL
PHILLIPS HEAD SCREW

Fig. 62 — Removing and Installing New Style Throttles

Fuel Pipe

The fuel pipe contains a check ball and a fine mesh screen. To function properly, the screen must be clean and the check ball free. Fig. 63. Replace pipe if screen and ball cannot be satisfactorily cleaned in carburetor cleaner. DO NOT LEAVE CARBURETOR IN CLEANER MORE THAN 1/2 HOUR WITHOUT REMOVING NYLON PARTS. Nylon fuel pipes, Fig. 64, Illustration 1, are remove and replaced with a 9/16" 6 point socket. Fig. 63. Brass fuel pipes, Illus. II, are removed by clamping the pipe in a vise and prying out as shown in Fig. 65.

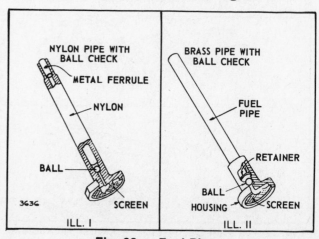

NYLON PIPE WITH BALL CHECK
METAL FERRULE
NYLON
BALL
3636
SCREEN
ILL. I

BRASS PIPE WITH BALL CHECK
FUEL PIPE
RETAINER
BALL HOUSING
SCREEN
ILL. II

Fig. 63 — Fuel Pipes

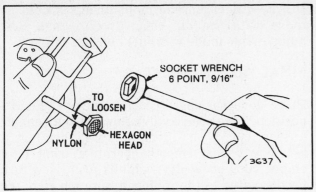

Fig. 64 — Replacing Nylon Fuel Pipe

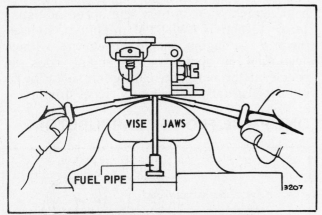

Fig. 65 — Removing Brass Fuel Pipe

To install brass fuel pipes, remove the throttle, if necessary, and place the carburetor and pipe in a vise. Press the pipe into the caburetor until it projects 2-9/32" (57.9 mm) to 2-5/16" (58.7 mm) from carburetor gasket surface. Fig. 66.

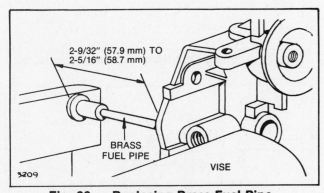

Fig. 66 — Replacing Brass Fuel Pipe

Needle Valve and Seat

Remove needle valve assembly to inspect. If carburetor is gummy or dirty, remove seat to allow better cleaning of metering holes. CAUTION: Do not change metering hole sizes. Fig. 67.

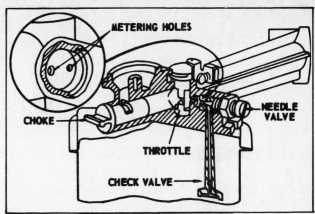

Fig. 67 — Metering Holes

Choke-A-Matic Linkage

Disassemble

To remove choke link, remove speed adjustment lever and stop switch insulator plate. Work link out through hole in choke slide. Fig. 68.

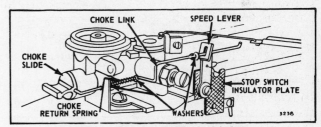

Fig. 68 — Choke-A-Matic Linkage

Repair

Replace worn or damaged parts. To assemble carburetor using choke slide, Fig. 68, place choke return spring and three washers on choke link. Push choke link through hole in carburetor body, turning link to line up with hole in choke slide. Speed adjustment lever screw and stop switch insulator plate should be installed as one assembly after placing choke link through end of speed adjustment lever.

Adjust Choke-A-Matic Linkage

The following covers Choke-A-Matic parts installed on and as a part of the carburetor assembly. See Section 4 for Choke-A-Matic remote controls. To check operation of Choke-A-Matic linkage, move speed adjustment lever to CHOKE position. If choke slide does not FULLY close, bend choke link. Fig. 69. Speed adjustment lever must make good contact against stop switch.

CARBURETION
Vacu-Jet and One Piece Flo-Jet

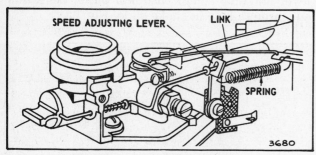

Fig. 69 — Adjust Choke Link

Install Carburetor

Install carburetor and fuel tank as an assembly. Hook throttle link into carburetor throttle and governor lever. (For various hook-ups, see Remote Control, Section 4.) Raise carburetor into place, insert a new gasket and fasten with mounting screws.

Install governor spring. Install ground wire and remote control where used. Fig. 70.

Fig. 70 — Install Carburetor

Choke-A-Matic Remote Controls

See Remote Controls, Section 4, for illustrations by engine model.

Carburetor Adjustment

The initial setting of the needle valve, Fig. 71, is made by turning the needle valve all the way in, then turning out 1½ turns. Final adjustment is made with the engine running.

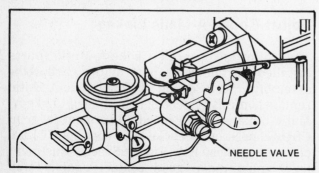

Fig. 71 — Carburetor Adjustment

NOTE: All carburetor adjustments should be made with the air cleaner on engine. Best adjustments made with fuel tank 1/2 full.

FINAL ADJUSTMENT

Place governor speed control lever in "FAST" position. Turn needle valve slowly in until engine misses (clockwise — lean mixture) then turn it out slowly past smooth operating point until engine runs unevenly (rich mixture). Now turn needle valve to the midpoint between rich and lean so the engine runs smoothly. Next, adjust idle RPM. Rotate throttle counterclockwise and hold against stop. Adjust idle speed adjusting screw to obtain 1750 RPM minimum. Release throttle — engine should accelerate without hesitation or sputtering. If engine does not accelerate properly, the carburetor should be readjusted, usually to a slightly richer mixture.

ONE PIECE FLO-JET CARBURETOR

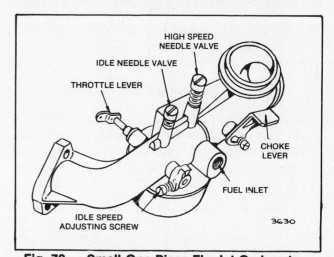

Fig. 72 — Small One Piece Flo-Jet Carburetor

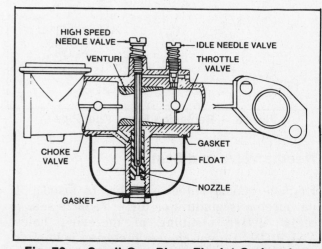

Fig. 73 — Small One Piece Flo-Jet Carburetor

The small one piece Flo-Jet carburetor is illustrated in Figs. 72 and 73 and was used on Model Series 60700, 61700, 80700, 81700, 140700, 141700, 144700 and 145700. These are float feed carburetors with high speed and idle needle valve adjustments.

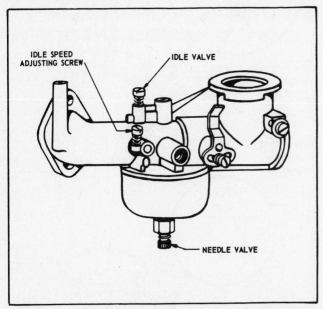

Fig. 74 — Large One Piece Flo-Jet Carburetor

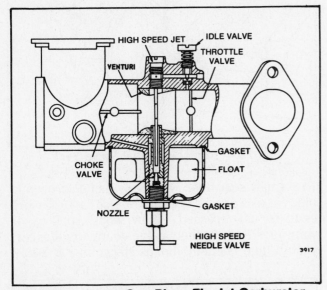

Fig. 75 — Large One Piece Flo-Jet Carburetor

The large one piece Flo-Jet carburetor is similar to the small one piece Flo-Jet. The main difference is that the high speed needle is below the float bowl. See Figs. 74 and 75.

Repair procedures for small and large Flo-Jet carburetors are similar except for location of adjusting needles.

Disassemble Carburetor, Small One-Piece Flo-Jet

Remove idle and high speed adjusting needles. Remove bowl nut and float bowl. Use screw driver to remove nozzle. Remove float pin to remove float and float needle. Use a large wide screw driver to remove float valve seat.

Disassemble Carburetor, Large One-Piece Flo-Jet

Remove idle mixture needle. Remove high speed needle valve assembly from float bowl and remove float bowl. Use a thick blade screw driver to remove nozzle, then remove jet from top of carburetor. Remove float pin to remove float and float needle.

Disassemble Continued, Small and Large One-Piece Flo-Jet

If necessary to remove choke shaft, venturi or throttle shaft, proceed in following sequence. Pry out welch plug. Remove choke valve. On carburetors with nylon choke shafts, remove choke valve as shown in Fig. 78. Venturi can now be removed, Fig. 77. (Choke-A-Matic large carburetors have a plate stop pin which must be pressed out to remove venturi.) To check for throttle shaft wear, refer to Two Piece Flo-Jet for procedure for checking.

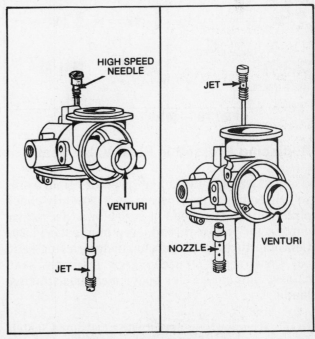

Fig. 76 — Repair Carburetor

CARBURETION
One Piece Flo-Jet

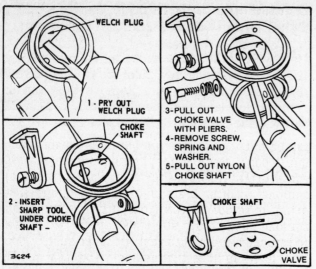

Fig. 77 — Nylon Choke Shaft

Inspection

Reject idle and high speed mixture needles if damaged, Fig. 78. Check float for leakage. If it contains fuel or is crushed, it must be replaced. Replace float needle, if worn. If carburetor leaks with new float needle on carburetors with pressed in float needle seat, refer to next paragraph.

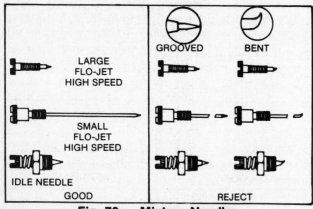

Fig. 78 — Mixture Needles

Replacing Pressed in Float Valve Seat

Use a #93029 self-threading screw or remove one self-threading screw from a #19069 flywheel puller and clamp head of screw in a vise. Turn carburetor body to thread screw into seat. Fig. 80. Continue turning carburetor body drawing seat out. Leave seat fastened to screw. Insert new seat #230996 into carburetor body. (Seat has starting lead.)

NOTE: If engine is equipped with a fuel pump, install #231019 seat.

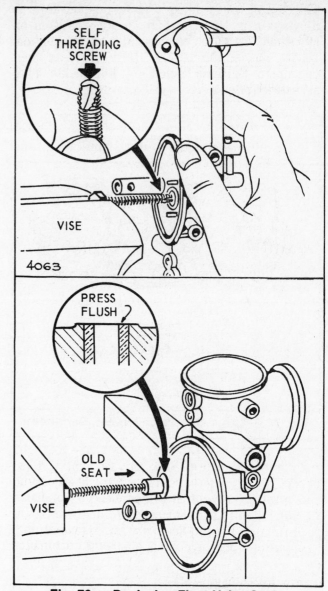

Fig. 79 — Replacing Float Valve Seat

Press new seat flush with body using screw and old seat as a driver. See Fig. 79. Use care to insure seat is not pressed below body surface or improper float to float valve contact will occur. Install float needle valve as shown in Fig. 80.

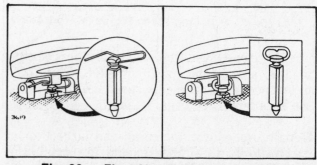

Fig. 80 — Float Needle Valve Variations

Checking Float Level

With body gasket in place on upper body and float valve and float installed, the float should be parallel to the body mounting surface. Fig. 81. If not, bend tang on float until they are parallel. DO NOT PRESS ON FLOAT. Fig. 81.

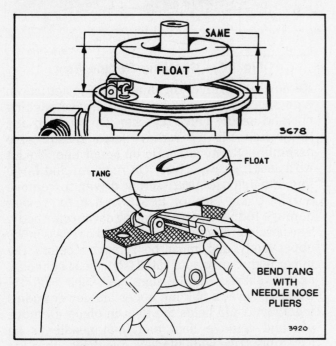

Fig. 81 — Checking Float Level

Repair Carburetor

Use new parts where necessary. Always use new gaskets. Carburetor repair kits are available. See illustrated parts list for particular model. If throttle shaft and/or venturi has been removed, install throttle and throttle shaft first. Then install venturi. Now install jet on small one piece or nozzle on large one piece Flo-Jet. The nozzle or jet holds the venturi in place, Fig. 76. Replace choke shaft and valve. Install new welch plug using sealer around edge of plug. Stake plug in two (2) places. Sealer is to prevent entry of dirt into engine. Install float bowl, idle and high speed adjustment needles.

Initial Adjustments

On small one piece Flo-Jets, turn in idle and high speed needles until they just bottom. Open high speed needle 2½ turns and idle needle 1½ turns on large one piece Flo-Jets, turn both idle and high speed needles in until they just bottom. Then turn both valves 1½ turns open.

These settings will allow the engine to start. Final adjustment should be made when engine is running and has warmed up. See carburetor adjustment. (Two piece Flo-Jet carburetor.)

Choke-A-Matic Remote Control Adjustment

On Choke-A-Matic carburetors, the remote control must be correctly adjusted in order to obtain proper operation of the choke and stop switch. See Section 4 for illustrations by engine model.

TWO-PIECE FLO-JET CARBURETOR

SMALL, MEDIUM AND LARGE FLO-JET

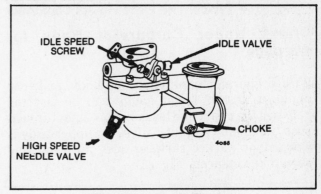

Fig. 82 — Small Flo-Jet

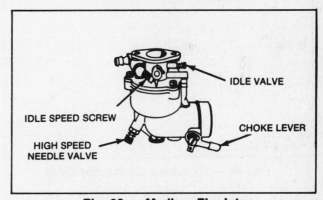

Fig. 83 — Medium Flo-Jet

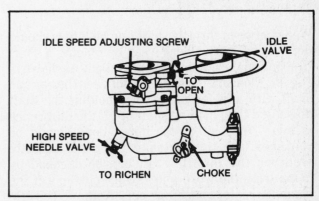

Fig. 84 — Large Flo-Jet

CARBURETION
Two Piece Flo-Jet

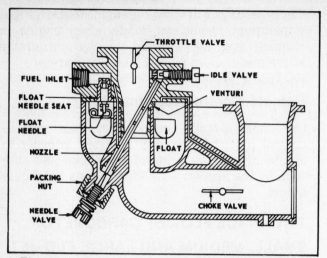

Fig. 85 — Typical Two Piece Flo-Jet Carburetor

Check Upper Carburetor Body for Warpage

With carburetor assembled and body gasket in place, if a .002" feeler gauge can be inserted between the upper and lower bodies at the air vent boss, just below the idle valve, the upper body is warped or gasket surfaces are damaged and should be replaced. Fig. 86.

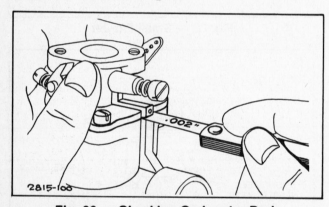

Fig. 86 — Checking Carburetor Body

Check Throttle Shaft and Bushings for Wear

Wear between throttle shaft and bushings should not exceed .010". Check wear by placing a short iron bar on the upper carburetor body as shown in Fig. 87. Measure the distance between the bar and shaft with a feeler gauge while holding the shaft down and then holding shaft up. If the difference is over .010", either the upper body should be rebushed, the throttle shaft replaced, or both. Wear on the throttle shaft can be checked by comparing the worn and unworn portions of the shaft. To replace bushings, see "Remove Throttle Shaft and Bushings."

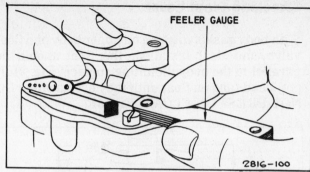

Fig. 87 — Checking Throttle Wear

Remove idle valve. On small line Flo-Jet loosen high speed valve packing nut. Remove packing nut and needle valve together. On medium and large line Flo-Jet remove high speed valve assembly. Remove nozzle on small line Flo-Jet with 19061 screw driver. On medium and large line Flo-Jet use 19062 screw driver to remove nozzle. Using 19061 or 19062 will help to prevent damage to the threads in lower carburetor body. The nozzle projects diagonally into a recess in the upper body and must be removed before the upper body can be separated from the lower body, or the nozzle will be damaged. See Fig. 85. Remove screws holding upper and lower bodies together. A pin holds the float in place. Remove pin and remove float and float needle as an assembly. Use wide blade screw driver that fits slot to remove float inlet seat. On carburetors with pressed in float seats, see "Replacing Pressed In Float Valve Seat." On small Flo-Jets the venturi is a separate part and can be slipped out of the lower body. Some carburetors have a welch plug. This should be removed, only if it is necessary, to remove the choke shaft or choke plate. Some carburetors have a nylon choke shaft. Remove as shown in Fig. 88.

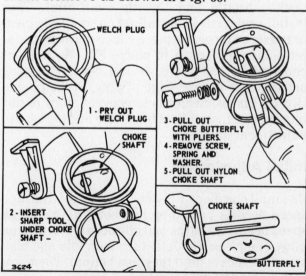

Fig. 88 — Nylon Choke Shaft

Remove Throttle Shaft and Bushings

Throttle shaft should be removed only when necessary to replace throttle shaft and/or bushings. To remove throttle shaft, use a thin punch to drive out the pin holding throttle stop to the shaft, remove the throttle valve, then pull out the shaft. Fig. 89.

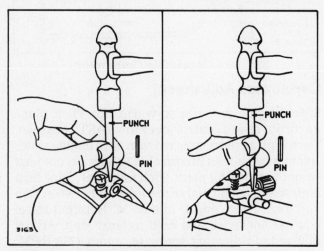

Fig. 89 — Remove Throttle Shaft and Bushings

Replace Throttle Shaft Bushings

Place a 1/4" x 20 tap or an E-Z out in a vise. Turn carburetor body so as to thread tap or E-Z out into bushings enough to pull bushings out of body, Fig. 90. Press new bushings into carburetor body with a vise. Insert throttle shaft to be sure it is free in the bushings. If not, run a size 7/32" drill through both bushings to act as a line reamer. Install throttle shaft, valve and stop.

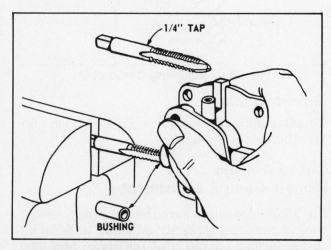

Fig. 90 — Replacing Throttle Shaft Bushings

Repair Carburetor

Use new parts when necessary. Always use new gaskets. Old gaskets take a set or harden and may leak. Carburetor repair kits are available, see illustrated parts list for part number for specific model. Tighten inlet seat with gasket securely in place, if used, Some float valves have a spring clip to connect the float valve to the float tang. Others are nylon with a stirrup which fits over the float tang. Older type float valves and earlier engines with fuel pumps have neither spring or stirrup.

A viton tip float valve is used on later models of the Flo-Jet carburetor. These needles are used with the inlet needle seat pressed into the upper carburetor body and does not need replacement unless damaged.

Replacing Pressed-In Float Valve Seat

Use a #93029 self-threading screw or remove one self-threading screw from a #19069 flywheel puller and clamp head of screw in a vise. Turn carburetor body to thread screw into seat. Fig. 91. Continue turning carburetor body drawing seat out. Leave seat fastened to screw. Insert new seat #230996 into carburetor body. (Seat has starting lead.)

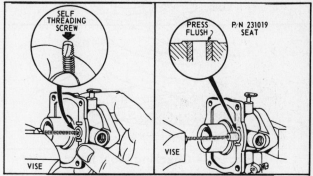

Fig. 91 — Replacing Float Valve Seat

NOTE: If engine or equipment is equipped with a fuel pump, install #231019 seat. Carburetors factory equipped with fuel pump seat have letter "P" stamped on flange, Fig. 92.

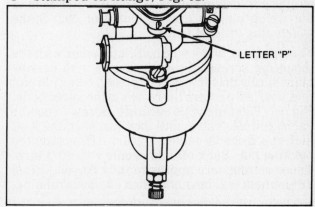

Fig. 92 — Flange

CARBURETION
Two Piece Flo-Jet

Press new seat flush with body using screw and old seat as a driver. See Fig. 91. Use care to insure seat is not pressed below body surface or improper float to float valve contact will occur. Install float valve as shown in Fig. 93.

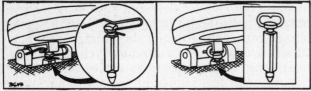

Fig. 93 — Float Valve Variations

Checking Float Level

With body gasket in place on upper body and float valve and float installed, the float should be parallel to the body mounting surface. If not, bend tang on float until they are parallel. DO NOT PRESS ON FLOAT TO ADJUST. Fig. 94A and 94B.

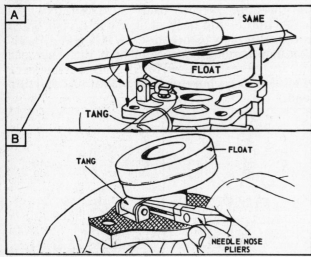

Fig. 94 — Checking Float Level

Assemble Carburetor

Assemble venturi and venturi gasket to lower body. Be sure holes in the venturi and venturi gasket are aligned. Most models do not have a removable venturi. Install choke parts and welch plug if previously removed. Use a sealer around the welch plug to prevent entry of dirt. Stake welch plug at least twice.

Fasten upper and lower bodies together with the mounting screws. Screw in nozzle with narrow blunt screw driver #19061 or #19062, being careful that nozzle tip enters the recess in the upper body. Fig. 95. Tighten nozzle securely. Screw in needle valve and idle valve until they just seat. Back off high speed needle valve 1-1/2 turns. Do not tighten packing nut. Back off idle needle valve 3/4 turn. These settings are approximately correct. Final adjustment will be made when engine is running.

NOTE: All carburetor adjustments must be made with the air cleaner installed.

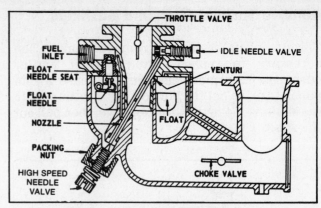

Fig. 95 — Assemble Carburetor

Carburetor Adjustment

Start engine and run to warm up. Then place governor speed control lever in "FAST" position. Turn high speed needle valve in until engine slows (clockwise — lean mixture). Then turn it out past smooth operating point (rich mixture). Now turn high speed needle valve to midpoint between rich and lean. Next, adjust idle RPM. Rotate throttle counterclockwise and hold against stop. Adjust idle speed adjusting screw to obtain 1750 RPM, aluminum engines; 1200 RPM, cast iron engines.

Holding throttle against idle stop, turn idle valve in (lean) and out (rich). Set at midpoint between rich and lean. Recheck idle RPM. Release throttle. If engine will not accelerate properly, the carburetor should be re-adjusted, usually to a slightly richer mixture.

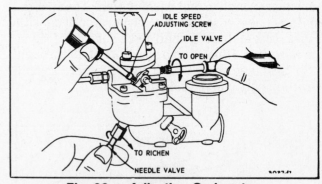

Fig. 96 — Adjusting Carburetor

Governed Idle

To adjust for governed idle, refer to Section 4 for specific model of engine.

Choke-A-Matic
Remote Control Adjustment

On Choke-A-Matic carburetors, the remote control must be correctly adjusted in order to obtain proper operation of the choke and stop switch. For adjustment, see Section 4.

Idling Device and Throttle Control
(Two Piece Flo-Jet)

A manual friction control may be used to limit throttle movement, to any pre-set position. It is commonly used for two purposes. 1. To return the throttle to a "no-load" position on a pump, generator, etc.; 2. For cold weather starting on governed idle engines. The throttle can easily be kept in a "near closed" position, while starting, which is most favorable for cold weather starts. Fig. 97.

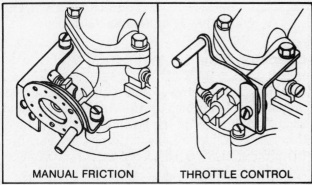

Fig. 97 — Idling Device and Throttle Control

Remote Throttle Control
(Two Piece Flo-Jet)

The remote throttle control opens the carburetor throttle until the full governed speed is obtained, at which point the governor takes over control of the throttle. At any point below the governed speed, the throttle is held in a fixed position and the engine speed will vary with the load. Fig. 98.

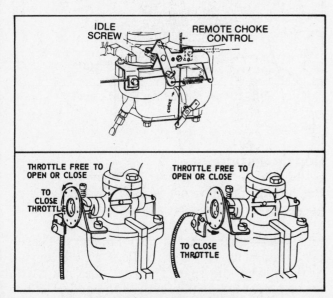

Fig. 98 — Remote Throttle Control

CROSS-OVER FLO-JET

The cross-over Flo-Jet carburetor is used on Model Series 253400 engines and is a float type carburetor with idle and high speed adjustment needles. This carburetor also has an integral fuel pump. All adjustments can be made from the top of the carburetor, Figs. 99 and 100.

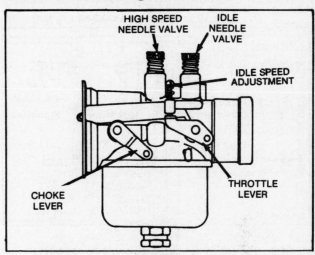

Fig. 99

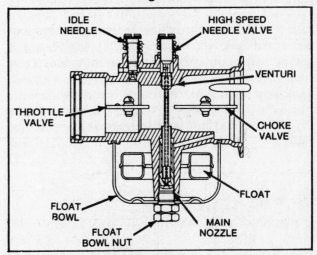

Fig. 100

Disassembly, Cross-Over Flo-Jet

Remove idle and high speed needle adjustment valves. Remove float bowl mounting screw, washer and float bowl. Using a large blunt screw driver, remove nozzle screw. Remove float hinge pin, float and float inlet needle. Use screw driver to remove two (2) screws from choke shaft. Then remove choke plate and choke shaft. Use screw driver to remove screw from throttle shaft. Then remove throttle plate and throttle shaft. Use screw driver to remove three (3) screws from fuel pump body. Remove fuel pump from carburetor taking care not to lose the pump valve springs.

CARBURETION
Cross-Over Flo-Jet

Inspection

Check idle and high speed needle valves for burrs, grooves or bent needle tips. Reject if damaged, Fig. 101. Check float for fuel in float, damage or leaks. If it contains fuel or is crushed it must be replaced. If carburetor leaks with new inlet needle valve, replace inlet needle seat. See next paragraph.

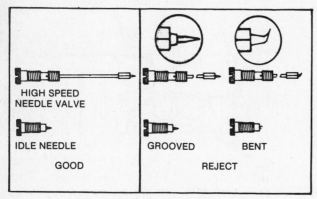

Fig. 101

Replacing Pressed-In Float Valve Seat

Use a #93029 self-threading screw or remove one self-threading screw from a #19069 flywheel puller and clamp head of screw in a vise. Turn carburetor body to thead screw into seat. Fig. 102. Continue turning carburetor body drawing seat out. Leave seat fastened to screw. Insert new seat #231019 into carburetor body. (Seat has starting lead.)

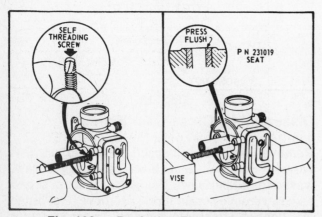

Fig. 102 — Replacing Float Valve Seat

Press new seat flush with body using screw and old seat as a driver. See Fig. 102. Use care to insure seat is not pressed below body surface or improper float to float needle valve contact will occur. Install float valve as shown in Fig. 103.

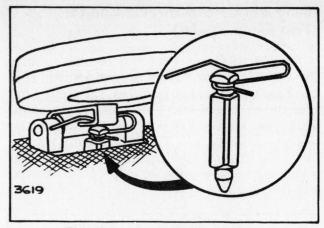

Fig. 103 — Float Needle Valve

Checking Float Level

With float needle valve, float and float hinge pin installed, hold carburetor upside down. The float should be parallel to the bowl mounting surface. If not, bend tang on float until they are parallel. DO NOT PRESS ON FLOAT TO ADJUST, Fig. 104.

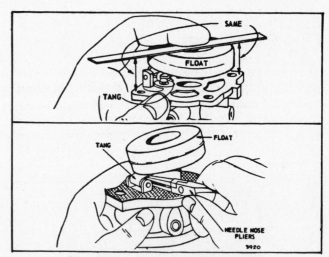

Fig. 104 — Checking Float Level

Repair Carburetor

Use new parts where necessary. Always use new gaskets. Old gaskets take a set or harden and may leak. Carburetor repair kits are available, see illustrated parts list for part numbers. These carburetors use a viton tip float needle and a pressed-in needle seat. The seat does not need replacement unless the seat is damaged or leaks with a new float needle.

Assemble Carburetor

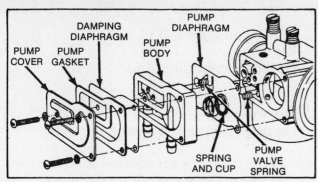

Fig. 105 — Assemble Fuel Pump

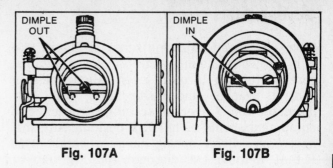

Fig. 107A   Fig. 107B

Install main nozzle using blunt screw driver to prevent damage to slot and metering hole. Place bowl on carburetor and install bowl nut and washer. Install one (1) pump valve spring on spring boss, Fig. 106, and then place diaphragm on carburetor. Put pump spring cup and pump spring on diaphragm, Fig. 105. Place a pump valve spring on spring boss in pump body, Fig. 106, and place pump body on carburetor. Place damping diaphragm, pump gasket and pump cover on pump body and install three (3) screws. A fuel pump repair kit is available, see illustrated parts list for part number.

Carburetor Adjustments

INITIAL ADJUSTMENT — Turn idle and needle valves clockwise until they just close, Fig. 108.

CAUTION: Valves may be damaged by turning them in too far.

Now open high speed needle valve 1½ turns counterclockwise and idle valve one turn. This initial adjustment will permit the engine to be started and warmed up prior to final adjustment.

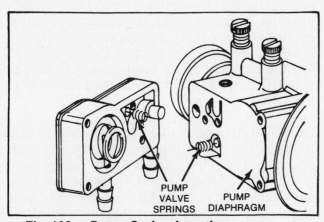

Fig. 106 — Pump Spring Location
(Valve Flap Bent Down for Clarity)

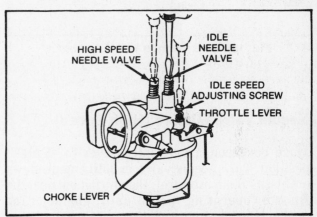

Fig. 108 — Carburetor Adjustment

NOTE: Carburetor adjustments should be made with the air cleaner on engine.

FINAL ADJUSTMENT PROCEDURE

Idle Valve Mixture

Place choke shaft in carburetor body and slide in choke valve with notch out and dimple down toward float bowl, Fig. 107A. Install two (2) screws using a screw driver. Slide in throttle shaft and then slide in throttle plate with two (2) dimples facing toward the idle valve. When valve is installed correctly, the dimples will be down and the number on the plate visible with the throttle in the closed or idle position, Fig. 107B. Install the idle and high speed needle valves.

Place governor speed control lever in "IDLE" position. Set idle speed adjusting screw to obtain 1750 R.P.M. minimum while holding throttle lever again screw. Turn idle valve in until R.P.M. slows or misses (clockwise — lean mixture), then turn it out past smooth idling point until engine runs unevenly (rich mixture). Now turn idle valve to the midpoint between rich and lean so the engine runs smoothly. Release throttle lever.

CARBURETION
L.P. Fuel

Governed Idle

Turn idle speed adjusting screw to obtain 1600 R.P.M. while holding throttle lever against screw. Release throttle lever. Align holes in control bracket and inside lever with 1/8″ diameter rod. Governor speed control lever of equipment should be in IDLE position. Adjust if necessary. Bend spring tang to obtain 1750 R.P.M. Remove 1/8″ diameter rod, Fig. 109.

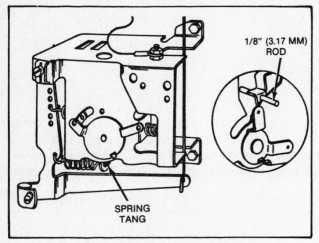

Fig. 109 — Governed Idle Adjustment

Needle Valve Mixture (High Speed)

Move governor speed control lever to "FAST" position. Turn needle valve in until engine slows or misses (lean mixture), then turn it out past the smooth operating point until engine runs unevenly (rich mixture). Now turn needle valve to the midpoint between rich and leans so the engine runs smoothly, Fig. 108.

Engine should accelerate smoothly. If engine does not accelerate properly, the carburetor should be re-adjusted usually to a slightly richer mixture.

L.P. GAS FUEL SYSTEM

The following information is provided to assist you in servicing LP gas fuel systems. This information applies only to Garretson Equipment Company systems installed by Briggs & Stratton. For parts information refer to MS-3915. Parts for the Garretson system must be obtained from a Garretson parts distributor. For information about LP conversion kits, contact:

Garretson Equipment Co., Inc.
Box 111
Mount Pleasant, Iowa 52641
or
Beam Products Manufacturing Co.
3040 Rosslyn Street
Los Angeles, California 90065

For LP fuel systems not covered in this section contact the manufacturer of the fuel system.

WARNING: LP gas fuel system should only be worked on in a very well ventilated area. Many state, county and city governments require that service be performed only outdoors. Before loosening any fuel line connections, have a fan blowing directly across the engine.

Checking and Adjusting Fuel System

Loosen fuel line at primary regulator. Open valve on cylinder for an instant, to be sure there is pressure in fuel cylinder. Escaping gas can be heard. Shut off valve at cylinder, Fig. 110, page 32.

Remove fuel line between primary and secondary regulator (fuel controller). Attach pressure gauge to outlet of primary regulator, leaving gauge connection loose enough to permit a slight leakage of gas. (This will permit adjustment of regulator under conditions of actual gas flow.) Remove cap or top of primary regulator, Fig. 110.

Open fuel cylinder valve. Turn pressure regulating screw in primary regulator, until a pressure of 1-1/2 pounds is obtained at pressure gauge. Shut off fuel cylinder valve. Re-assemble cap. Remove pressure gauge. Loosen secondary regulator bracket from carburetor. Pull secondary regulator away from carburetor so that short rubber fuel line is disconnected. Assemble fuel line between primary regulator and secondary regulator (fuel controller). Secondary regulator must remain mounted so the diaphragm is in a vertical plane, Fig. 110.

Open fuel cylinder valve. Apply soap suds to outlet at the center of secondary regulator to which rubber fuel line has been attached. If a bubble forms, it indicates that the valve is leaking or not locking off. If no bubble appears, press the primer button. A bubble should appear, indicating fuel is flowing into regulator. Put soap suds on the outlet again. Then slowly turn adjusting screw at bottom of secondary regulator counterclockwise until a bubble forms at the outlet. Then turn adjusting screw in (clockwise) slowly until soap bubbles on outlet no longer form. Hold adjusting screw at this point and tighten locknut. Press primer button to allow fuel to flow. Release and again put soap suds on outlet to make certain the fuel shuts off. Repeat several times. If bubble should form after primer button is released, the adjusting screw should be turned in until flow stops and soap bubble does not break or enlarge. Loosen fuel line between regulators. Re-assemble secondary regulator to carburetor with short rubber fuel line in place. Tighten fuel line, Fig. 110.

Adjusting Carburetor, L.P. Fuel System

See Fig. 110.

Loosen locknut on load needle screw and turn needle screw in until it seats. Do not force; open 2-1/2 turns. Turn idle needle in until it seats, then open one turn. If engine will not be required to idle, leave idle needle closed. Depress the primer button momentarily, then start engine, run engine to allow it to warm up before final adjustment. With engine running at normal operating speed, turn the load needle screw in slowly (clockwise) until engine starts to miss (lean mixture). Then turn load screw out slowly past the point of best operation until engine begins to run unevenly (rich mixture). Then turn load screw in just enough so engine will run smoothly. Hold load screw and tighten locknut. Hold throttle at idle position, then release throttle. Engine should accelerate quickly and smoothly.

If engine will be required to run at idle, turn the idle speed adjusting screw on throttle until engine runs at proper idle speed for engine model. See Check Chart. Hold throttle at this point and turn the idle slowly in or out until engine runs at maximum idle speed. Then re-adjust idle speed screw until proper idle speed is obtained. Allow throttle to open. Engine should accelerate quickly and smoothly. If not, re-adjust load screw, usually to a richer mixture. To stop engine, turn off fuel supply valve at fuel cylinder.

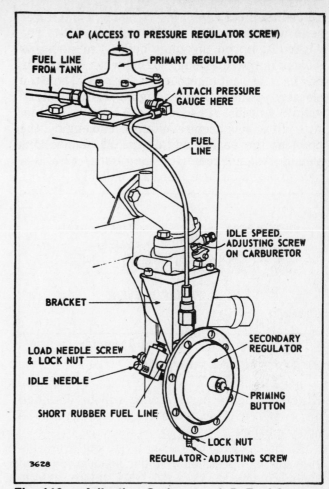

Fig. 110 — Adjusting Carburetor, L.P. Fuel System

Starting Engine

To start engine, do not use choke, but depress primer button momentarily, then start engine immediately. In cold weather, it may be necessary to partially close the carburetor choke valve to permit the engine to run smoothly until the engine warms up.

Cleaning L.P. Gas Filter (Optional)

Unscrew filter head from filter body. Remove element assembly from the head. Fig. 111. Wash the element in commercial solvent cleaner or gasoline. If the accumulated dirt is gummy, we suggest a short soaking period in solvent cleaner. The element should then be rinsed in clean gasoline and blown with compressed air.

ALWAYS USE REVERSE FLOW FROM THE INSIDE OUT. NEVER USE COMPRESSED AIR ON THE OUTSIDE SURFACE OF THE ELEMENT. NEVER DIP ELEMENT IN "BRIGHT DIP" OR OTHER ACID SOLUTION.

CARBURETION
Kerosene and Fuel Pumps

To re-assemble filter, insert element into filter head with the round washer entering first. The gasket is put on the filter body. The spring is located in the filter body so that when filter body and head are put together, the spring will hold the element against the head. Tighten body and head with 75 foot lbs. (10.4 Kg/m, 8.5 N/m) of torque. After filter has been re-assembled to engine, the point at the gasket and other line connections should be checked with soap suds, with fuel turned on, to be sure there are no leaks.

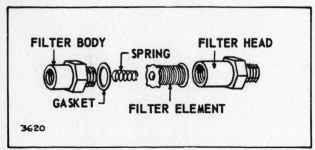

Fig. 111 — Element Assembly

KEROSENE OPERATION

Efficient engine performance will be obtained only when the following changes are accomplished:

1. A low compression cylinder head is required for models 23, 23A, 23C, 23D, 131400, 231000, 233000, and 243000. Other models may use two cylinder head gaskets.

2. A special spark plug — #291835 — must be used on models 23C, 23D, 233000, and 243000. Spark plug gap .030″ all models.

3. A reduced breaker gap .015 is used on models 23C, 23D, 233000 and 243000. The engine must be retimed using the reduced breaker gap. Follow timing procedure in Ignition Section.

Power loss will vary between 15% to 25% and fuel consumption will be approximately 15% less while running on kerosene.

Fig. 112 through Fig. 115 illustrates various types of Briggs & Stratton combination fuel systems used.

Due to the low volatility of kerosene, engines operated on kerosene-gasoline fuel systems can be started on kerosene only when the engine is at operating temperature. Cold engines must be started on gasoline, and switched over to kerosene operation only after warmed up.

After warm-up and while operating on kerosene, adjust carburetor needle valves to a point where engine runs smoothest, and accelerates without hesitation when throttle is quickly opened. When shutting down engine, the carburetor must be emptied of kerosene so the engine can be started on gasoline when cold. Refer to Flo-Jet Carburetor for adjustment of carburetor and adjust carburetor while running on kerosene.

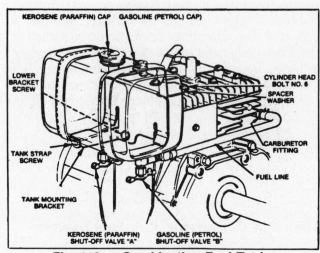

Fig. 112 — Combination Fuel Tank

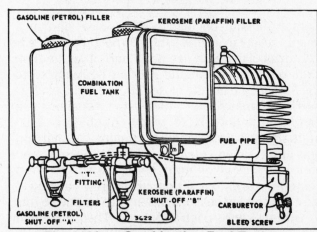

Fig. 113A — Combination Fuel Tank

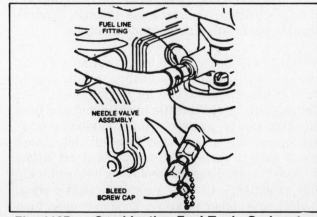

Fig. 113B — Combination Fuel Tank, Carburetor

Units equipped as per Fig. 114 and Fig. 115, close fuel filter valve and open bleed screw in needle valve to drain the carburetor. Close bleed screw. Remove wing plug to fill fuel line and carburetor with gasoline. Combination fuel tank units, Fig. 112 and Fig. 108, open gasoline shut-off valve "A," and close kerosene shut-off valve "B" two or three minutes before shutting off engine. This will stop the flow of kerosene to the carburetor, and will admit gasoline to the carburetor.

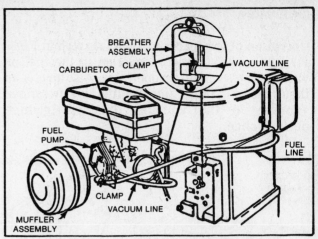

Fig. 116 — Pump on Carburetor, Breather Valve Vacuum

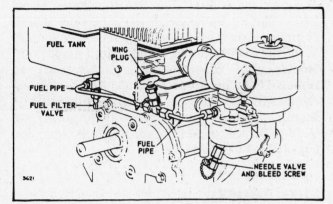

Fig. 114 — Kerosene Fuel System

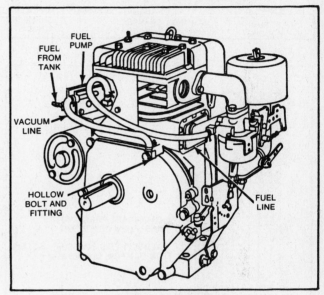

Fig. 117 — Pump on Bracket, Vacuum thru Hollow Bolt

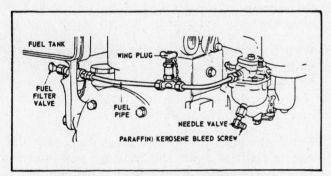

Fig. 115 — Kerosene Fuel System

Fuel Pumps
(Crankcase Vacuum Operated)

Some models are factory or field equipped with fuel pumps operated by crankcase vacuum. Fuel pumps may be mounted directly to the carburetor or on a mounting bracket, Fig. 116 or Fig. 117. Crankcase vacuum is obtained by a fitting on the dipstick tube, Fig. 118, a hollow bolt and fitting, Fig. 117, or from the crankcase breather valve, Fig. 116.

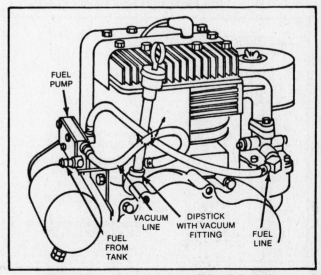

Fig. 118 — Vacuum from Dipstick Tube

CARBURETION
Fuel Pumps

Operation

Operation of the fuel pump is illustrated in Figs. 119, 120 and 121. Any restriction in the fuel or vacuum lines will affect operation. Also any leaks that cause air to get into the fuel line or reduce vacuum in the vacuum line will reduce performance.

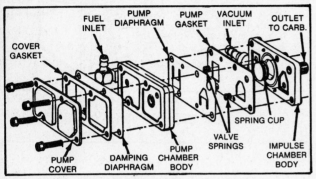

Fig. 119

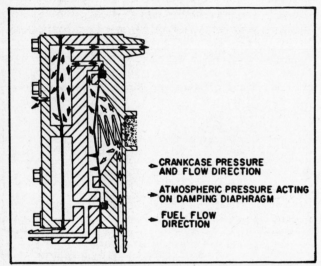

Fig. 120 — Fuel Flow with Crankcase Pressure

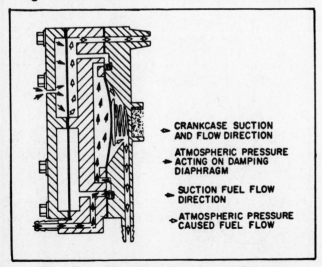

Fig. 121 — Fuel Flow Crankcase Vacuum

To service fuel pump, pump should be removed from carburetor or mounting bracket. When removing fuel supply line from tank to pump, be sure to plug fuel line or turn off fuel valve, if so equipped.

Disassemble fuel pump by removing four (4) 1/4″ head cap screws from pump cover. Separate pump cover, pumping chamber and impulse chamber. Discard old gaskets, diaphragms and springs. Clean pump parts in carburetor solvent or lacquer thinner.

A repair kit is available. See Illustrated Parts Lists. The kit includes all parts needed. Install chamber gasket using locator pins. Place springs in spring recesses and install pump diaphragm locator pins. Place pump chamber body on impulse body using locator pins. Place damping diaphragm and cover gasket on pump body. Install cover and four (4) screws. Torque screws to 10-15 in. lbs. (.12-.17 mkp, 1.13-1..69 Nm). See Fig. 119 for exploded view.

FUEL PUMPS, ECCENTRIC OPERATED
To Replace Pump Diaphragm

Remove pump from cylinder and then remove four screws to separate pump head from pump body.

With a narrow punch, drive lever pin out until pump lever is loose. Pin may then be driven in either direction, but need not be removed entirely. Remove old diaphragm, but leave diaphragm spring in pump body.

Place new diaphragm into pump body with the slot in shaft at right angles to the pump lever. Diaphragm spring should fit into the cup under the diaphragm. Without the lever spring, insert the pump lever into body holding the diaphragm down. Fit the hook at the end of lever into the slot in diaphragm shaft. Fig. 122.

Assemble Fuel Pump

Align holes in lever and body, then drive lever pin into place. Place lever spring into body with inner end of spring over the projection in pump body, then use a screw driver to force outer end of spring into body until it slips over the projection on lever. Fig. 122, Illus. 2. Place pump head on body and partially insert the four screws. Press pump lever down as far as possible and then tighten the four screws.

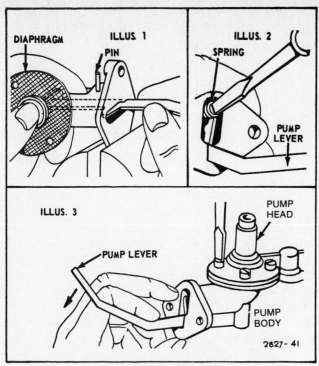

Fig. 122 — Fuel Pump

To Install Fuel Pump

Place a liberal supply of grease or gear lubricant on the portion of fuel pump lever that contacts the crankshaft. Fig. 123. Assemble fuel pump to cylinder using new gasket. Keep mounting face of fuel pump parallel to mounting face of cylinder while inserting lever of fuel pump. The lever must ride in the narrow groove which is located on the crankshaft between the gear and the counterweight. Revolve crankshaft to be sure that fuel pump is correctly installed. Assemble fuel pipe from outlet of carburetor. Fuel supply pipe should be connected to the inlet of the fuel pump.

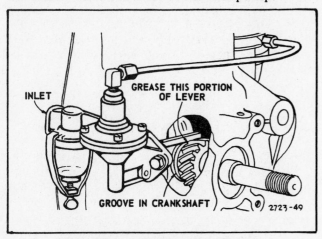

Fig. 123 — Installing Fuel Pump

AUTOMATIC CHOKE

Automatic Choke Adjust

Hold choke shaft so thermostat lever is free. At room temperature the screw in the thermostat collar should be in the center of the stops, if not, loosen stop screw and adjust.

Loosen set screw on lever of thermostat assembly. Slide lever to right or left on shaft to insure free movement of choke link in any position. Rotate thermostat shaft clockwise until stop screw strikes tube. Fig. 124. Hold in position and set lever on the thermostat shaft so that choke valve will be held open about 1/8″ from closed position. Then tighten set screw in lever.

Rotate thermostat shaft counterclockwise until stop screw strikes the opposite side of tube. Fig. 124. Then open choke valve manually until it stops against the top of the choke link opening. The choke valve should now be open approximately 1/8″ as before.

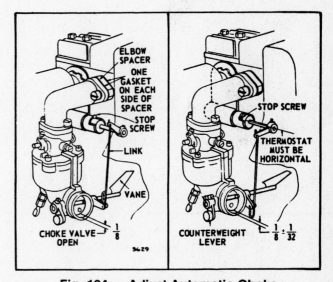

Fig. 124 — Adjust Automatic Choke

Check position of counterweight lever. With the choke valve in wide open position (horizontal) the counterweight lever should also be in a horizontal position with free end toward the right.

Operate the choke manually to be sure that all parts are free to move without binding or rubbing in any position.

3

Section 4
GOV. CONTROLS & CARB. LINKAGE

REMOTE CONTROLS

In general, there are three types of remote controls: Governor Control, Throttle Control, Choke-A-Matic Control. Fig. 1 to Fig. 6, show the operation of these control systems. See following pages for specific control assemblies and installation hook-up by engine model.

Remote Governor Control

The Remote Governor control regulates the engine speed by changing the governor spring tension, thus allowing the governor to control the carburetor throttle at all times and maintain any desired speed. Fig. 1.

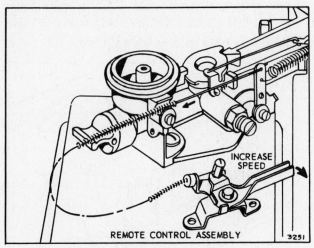

Fig. 1 – Remote Governor Control

Remote Throttle Control

The Remote Throttle control is used on an engine having a fixed no load governed speed setting such as 3600 or 4000 R.P.M.

This control enables an operator to control the speed of an engine, similar to an accelerator used on an automobile. However, when full governed speed is obtained, the governor prevents over speeding and possible damage to the engine. At any point below the governed speed, the throttle is held in a fixed position and the engine speed will vary with the load. See Fig. 2.

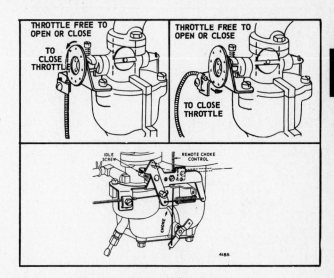

Fig. 2 – Remote Throttle Control

Choke-A-Matic Remote Control

On Choke-A-Matic carburetors, the remote control must be correctly adjusted in order to obtain proper operation of the choke and stop switch.

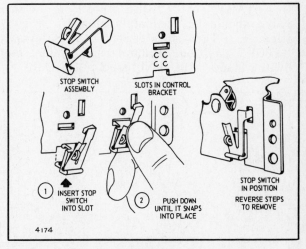

Fig. 3 – Typical Stop Switch Installation

NOTE: REMOTE CONTROL SYSTEM MUST BE MOUNTED ON POWERED EQUIPMENT IN NORMAL OPERATING POSITION BEFORE ADJUSTMENTS ARE MADE.

Fig. 4 illustrates typical remote control installations used with Choke-A-Matic carburetors. To adjust, move remote control lever to "FAST" position. Choke actuating lever "A" should just contact choke shaft "B" or link "B" as shown in Fig. 4. If not, loosen screw "C" slightly and move casing and wire "D" in or out to obtain this condition.

Travel of remote control wire must be a minimum of 1-3/8" in order to achieve full "CHOKE" and "STOP" position. Fig. 6.

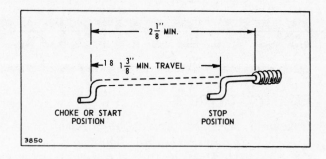

Fig. 6 — Control Wire Travel

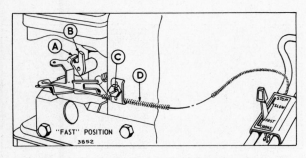

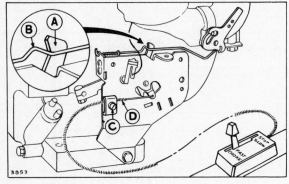

Fig. 4 — Choke-A-Matic Control (Typical)

Check operation by moving remote control lever to "START" or "CHOKE" position. Choke valve should be completely closed. Fig. 5. Illus. 1. Then move remote control lever to "STOP" position. Control must contact stop switch blade. Fig. 5. Illus. 2.

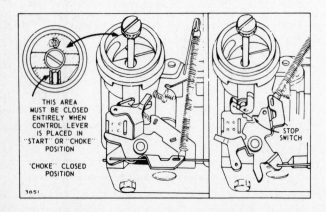

Illus. 1   Illus. 2

Fig. 5 — Choke and Stop Position

CHOKE-A-MATIC DIAL CONTROL ADJUSTMENTS

Dial Controls seldom require adjustment unless blower housing has been removed. To Adjust: Place dial control knob in "Start" position. Loosen control wire screw "A" — move lever "C" to full choke position. Allow a 1/8" gap between lever and bracket as shown.

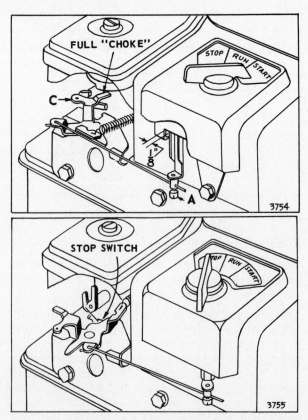

Fig. 7 — Choke-A-Matic Dial Control Adjustments

4

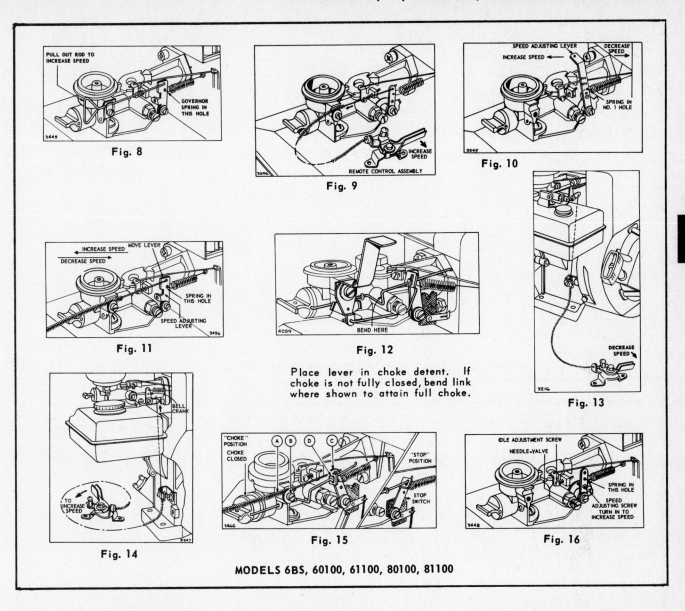

Fig. 8

Fig. 9

Fig. 10

Fig. 11

Fig. 12

Place lever in choke detent. If choke is not fully closed, bend link where shown to attain full choke.

Fig. 13

Fig. 14

Fig. 15

Fig. 16

MODELS 6BS, 60100, 61100, 80100, 81100

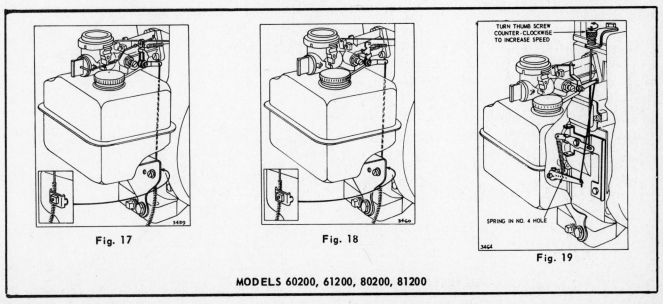

Fig. 17

Fig. 18

Fig. 19

MODELS 60200, 61200, 80200, 81200

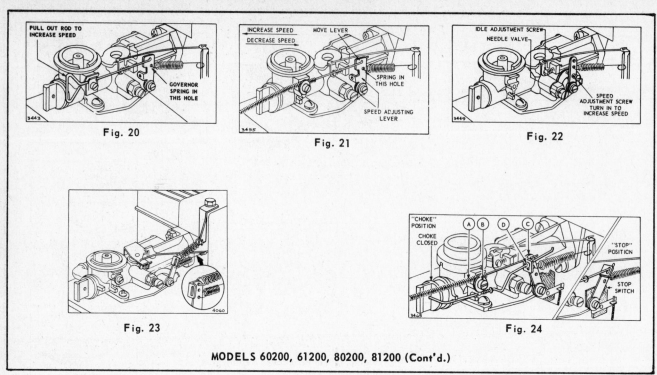

Fig. 20

Fig. 21

Fig. 22

Fig. 23

Fig. 24

MODELS 60200, 61200, 80200, 81200 (Cont'd.)

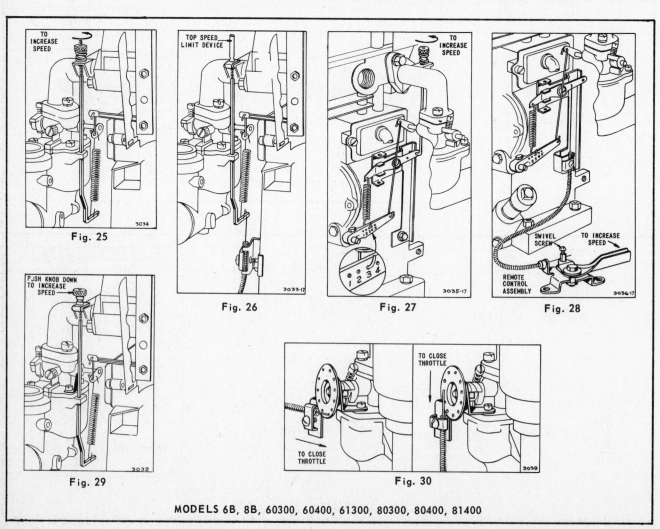

Fig. 25

Fig. 26

Fig. 27

Fig. 28

Fig. 29

Fig. 30

MODELS 6B, 8B, 60300, 60400, 61300, 80300, 80400, 81400

4

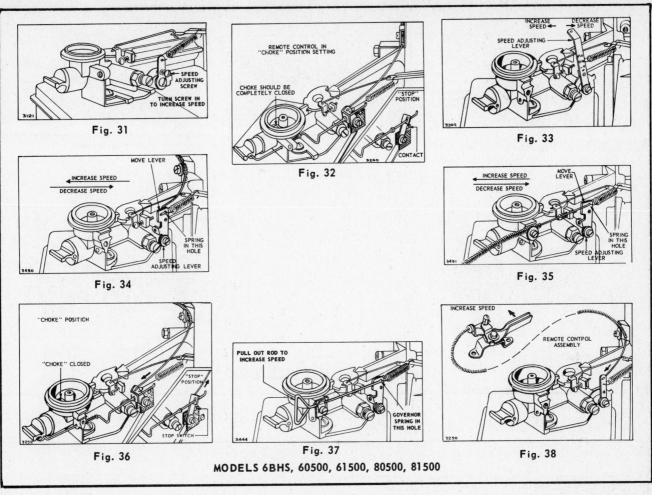

Fig. 31

Fig. 32

Fig. 33

Fig. 34

Fig. 35

Fig. 36

Fig. 37

Fig. 38

MODELS 6BHS, 60500, 61500, 80500, 81500

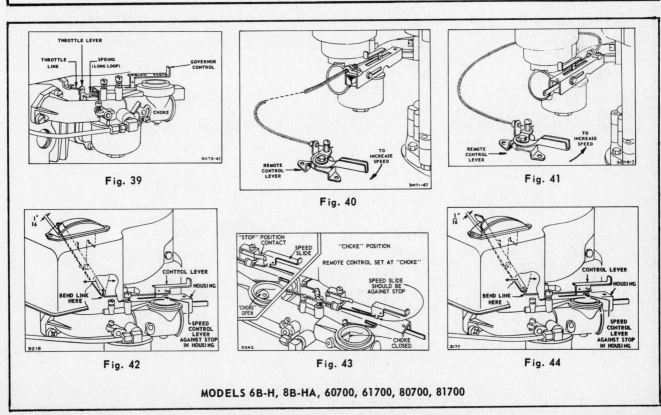

Fig. 39

Fig. 40

Fig. 41

Fig. 42

Fig. 43

Fig. 44

MODELS 6B-H, 8B-HA, 60700, 61700, 80700, 81700

4

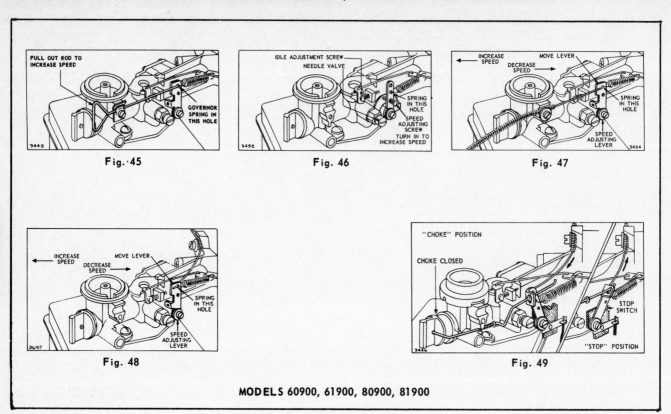

Fig. 45

Fig. 46

Fig. 47

Fig. 48

Fig. 49

MODELS 60900, 61900, 80900, 81900

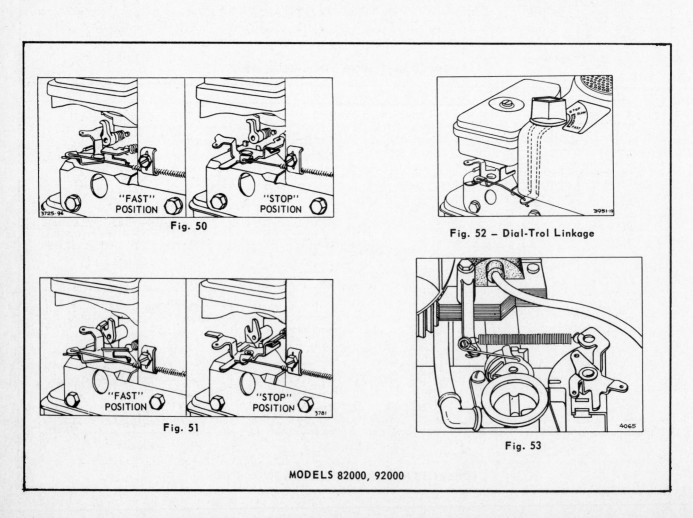

Fig. 50

Fig. 52 – Dial-Trol Linkage

Fig. 51

Fig. 53

MODELS 82000, 92000

REMOVAL AND INSTALLATION OF GOVERNOR SPRING ON MODEL SERIES 92500 AND 92900

The governor springs used on engine Model Series 92500 and 92900 are made with double end loops for a secure attachment and proper governor regulation. Springs with double end loops are easily removed and installed by following the procedure shown below. Do NOT use a needle-nosed pliers, or the end loops of the governor spring will be deformed. When the governor spring is correctly installed, the spring must be positioned as shown in Figure 54.

CORRECT POSITION OF SPRING

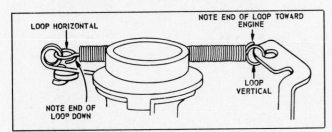

Fig. 54

REMOVING SPRING

① REMOVE SPRING FROM CONTROL LEVER

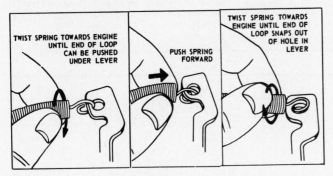

Fig. 55

② REMOVE SPRING FROM EYELET IN LINK

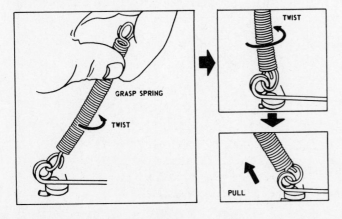

Fig. 56

INSTALLING SPRING

① ASSEMBLE SPRING TO LINK EYELET

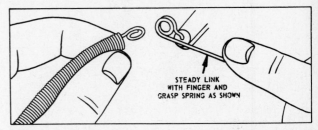

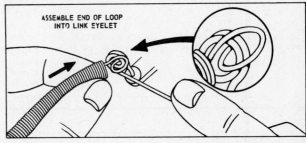

Fig. 57

② ASSEMBLE SPRING TO CONTROL LEVER

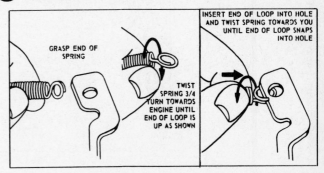

Fig. 58

4

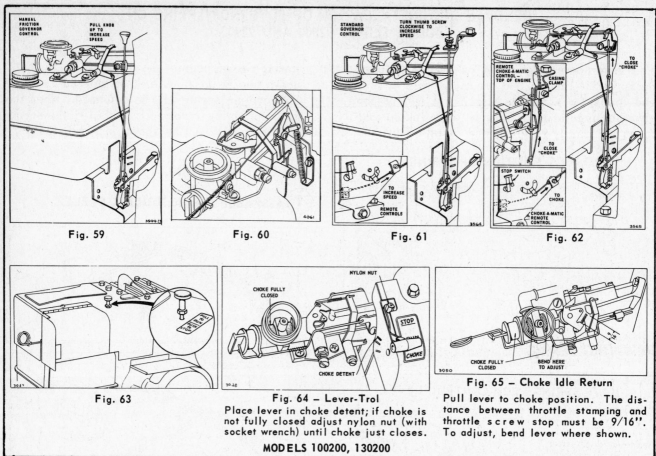

Fig. 59

Fig. 60

Fig. 61

Fig. 62

Fig. 63

Fig. 64 — Lever-Trol

Place lever in choke detent; if choke is not fully closed adjust nylon nut (with socket wrench) until choke just closes.

Fig. 65 — Choke Idle Return

Pull lever to choke position. The distance between throttle stamping and throttle screw stop must be 9/16". To adjust, bend lever where shown.

MODELS 100200, 130200

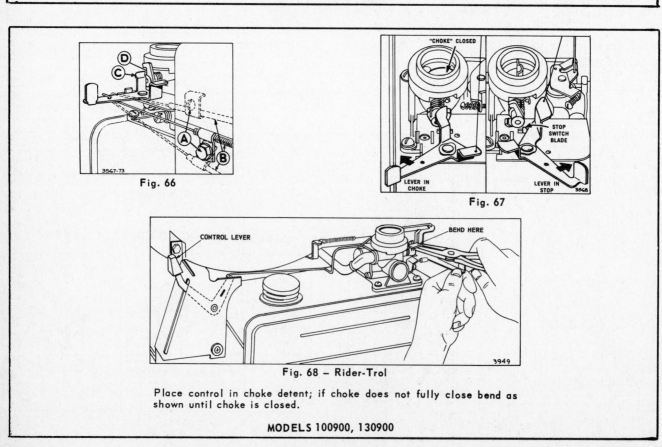

Fig. 66

Fig. 67

Fig. 68 — Rider-Trol

Place control in choke detent; if choke does not fully close bend as shown until choke is closed.

MODELS 100900, 130900

4

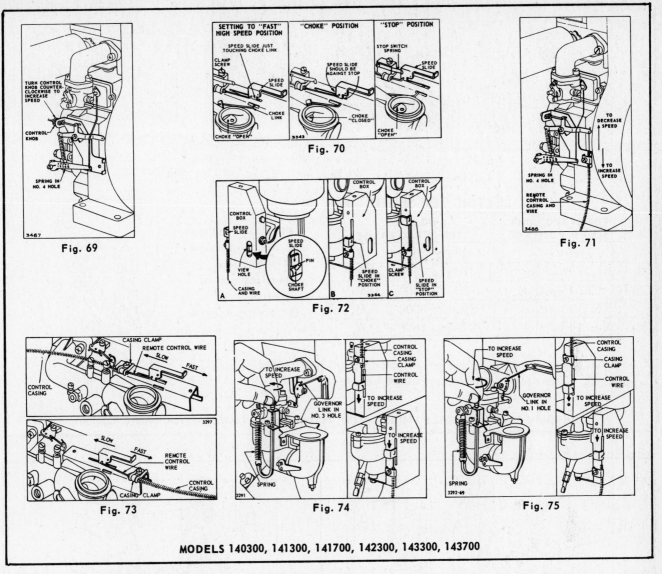

Fig. 69

Fig. 70

Fig. 71

Fig. 72

Fig. 73

Fig. 74

Fig. 75

MODELS 140300, 141300, 141700, 142300, 143300, 143700

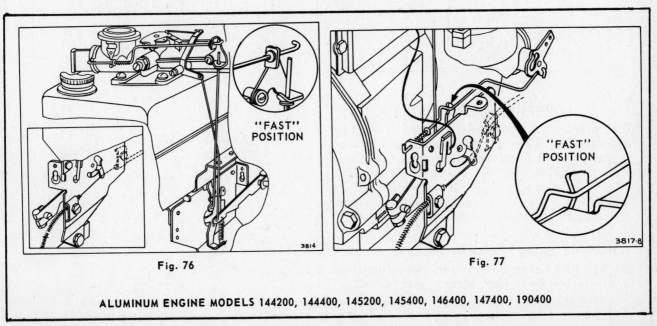

Fig. 76

Fig. 77

ALUMINUM ENGINE MODELS 144200, 144400, 145200, 145400, 146400, 147400, 190400

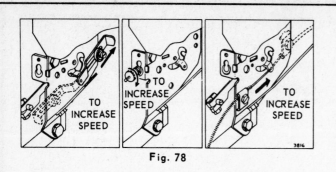

Fig. 78

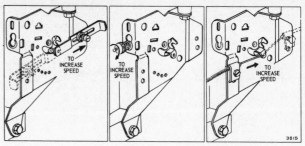

Fig. 79

SETTING TOP SPEED – FIG. 80

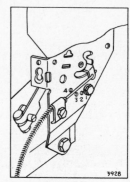

TOP SPEED LIMIT SCREW POSITION	NO LOAD TOP SPEED RANGE
None	4000 to 3800 R.P.M.
No. 1 Position	3700 to 3400 R.P.M.
No. 2 Position	3300 to 3000 R.P.M.
No. 3 Position	2900 to 2500 R.P.M.
No. 4 Position	2400 to 1800 R.P.M.

Always set desired no load top speed at power test by bending end of control lever at the spring anchor. See Section 5, Fig. 16

Fig. 80

Choke-A-Matic top speed range is 4000 to 3700 R.P.M. with standard spring. (Top speed limit screw cannot be used).

ALUMINUM ENGINE MODELS 144200, 144400, 145200, 145400, 146400, 147400, 190400 (Cont'd.)

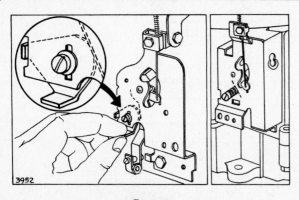

GOVERNED IDLE – FIG. 81

To adjust, first make final carburetor mixture adjustments. Then place remote control in idle position. Hold throttle shaft in closed position with fingers, adjust idle speed screw to 1550 RPM. Release throttle. Set remote control to 1750 RPM. Loosen governed idle stop and place against remote control lever. Tighten governed idle stop.

Adjustable Spring Loaded Screw Type

Follow above procedure, turn screw until it contacts remote control lever. See Fig. 81.

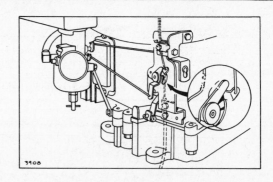

Fig. 82

Fig. 83

ALUMINUM ENGINE MODELS 144700, 145700, 146700, 147700, 170700, 171700, 190700, 191700

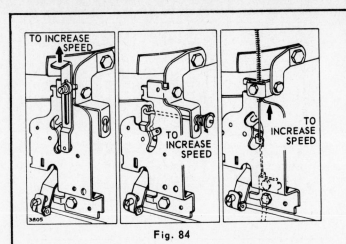

Fig. 84

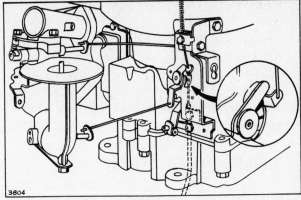

Fig. 85

SETTING TOP SPEED – FIG. 86

TOP SPEED LIMIT SCREW POSITION	NO LOAD TOP SPEED RANGE
None	4000 to 3500 R.P.M.
No. 1 Position	3400 to 2900 R.P.M.
No. 2 Position	2800 to 2400 R.P.M.

Always set desired no load top speed at power test by bending end of control lever at the spring anchor. See Section 5, Fig. 16

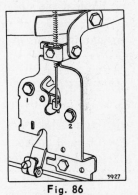

Fig. 86

Choke-A-Matic top speed range is 4000 to 3000 R.P.M. with standard spring. (Top speed limit screw cannot be used).
See Top Speed Limit Illustration, Section 5, Fig. 16

ALUMINUM ENGINE MODELS 144700, 145700, 146700, 147700, 170700, 171700, 190700, 191700 (Cont'd.)

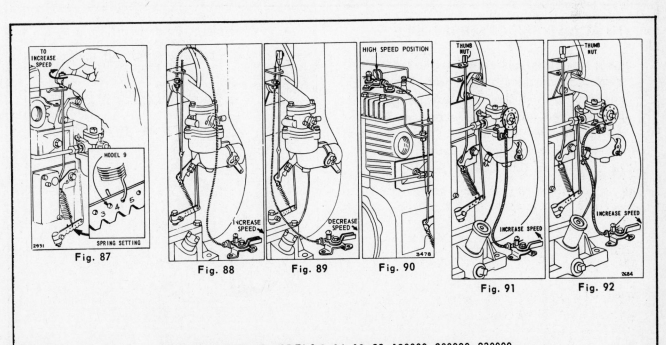

Fig. 87

Fig. 88

Fig. 89

Fig. 90

Fig. 91

Fig. 92

CAST IRON ENGINE MODELS 9, 14, 19, 23, 190000, 200000, 230000

4

REMOTE GOVERNOR CONTROL

Attach remote control casing and wire as shown in Figure 93 or Figure 94. Do not change the position of the small elastic stop nuts. They provide for a governed idle speed and protection against overspeeding.

THUMB NUT ADJUSTMENT

Remove thumb nut and upper elastic stop nut. Replace thumb nut and adjust to desired operating speed. See Figure 95. Do not change the position of the lower elastic stop nut. It provides protection against overspeeding.

GOVERNED IDLE

All engines in Model Series 243400, 300400, 320400 and some Model Series 23D and 233400 engines use two governor springs as shown in Figures 96 and 97. The shorter spring keeps the engine on governor, even at idle speed. If moderate loads are applied at idle, the engine will not stall.

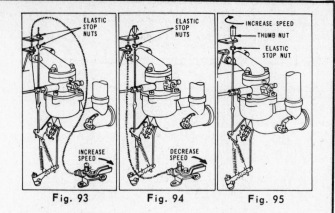

Fig. 93   Fig. 94   Fig. 95

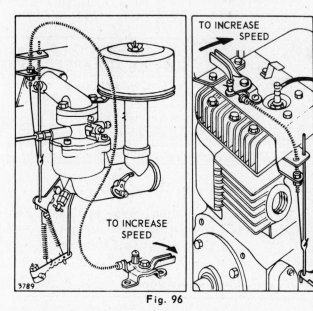

Fig. 96

TO ADJUST FOR GOVERNED IDLE

First make final carburetor mixture adjustments. Then place remote control in idle position. Hold throttle shaft in closed position and adjust idle screw to 1000 R.P.M. Release the throttle. With remote control in idle position, adjust upper elastic stop nut to 1200 R.P.M. See Fig. 97.

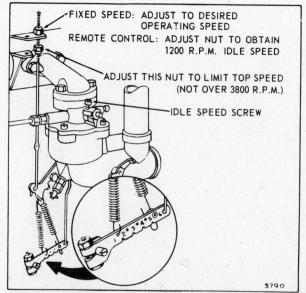

Fig. 97

Section 5
GOVERNORS

THE PURPOSE OF THE GOVERNOR IS TO MAINTAIN WITHIN CERTAIN LIMITS, A DESIRED ENGINE SPEED, EVEN THOUGH THE LOAD MAY VARY.

AIR VANE GOVERNOR

The governor spring tends to open the throttle. Air pressure against the air vane tends to close the throttle. The engine speed at which these two forces balance is called the governed speed. The governed speed can be varied by changing governor spring tension, Fig. 1, or changing governor spring, Fig. 2.

Checking

Worn linkage or damaged governor springs should be replaced to insure proper governor operation. If spring or linkage is changed, check and adjust TOP NO LOAD R.P.M., Fig. 1 or check TOP NO LOAD R.P.M., Fig. 2, with engine assembled.

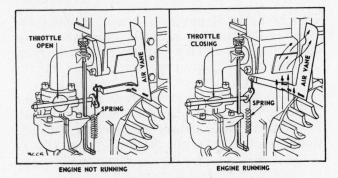

Fig. 1 — Air Vane Governor (Typical)

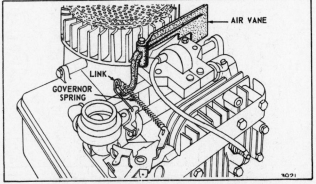

Fig. 2 — Air Vane Governor (Typical)

MECHANICAL GOVERNOR

The governor spring tends to pull the throttle open. The force of the counterweights, which are operated by centrifugal force, tends to close the throttle. The engine speed at which these two forces balance is called the governed speed. The governed speed can be varied by changing governor spring tension or governor spring. See Fig. 3.

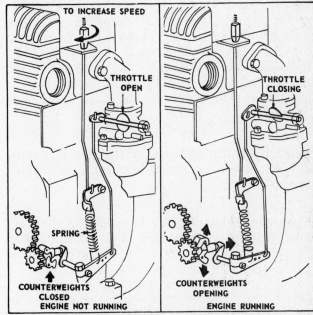

Fig. 3 — Mechanical Governor

GOVERNED SPEED LIMITS

To comply with specified top governed speed limits, Briggs & Stratton supplies manufacturers with engines using either calibrated governor springs or an adjustable top speed limit. Calibrated springs or an adjustable top speed limit will allow no more than a desired top governed speed when the engine is operated on a rigid test stand at our own Factory. However, the design of the cutter blade, deck, etc., can affect engine speeds. Therefore, the top governed speed should be checked with tachometer when the engine is operated on a completely assembled machine. If on a lawn mower, it should be operated on a hard surface to eliminate cutting load on the blade.

5

GOVERNOR
Speed Limits & Repair

If a Service Replacement Engine is used, check the top governed speed using a tachometer, with the engine operating on a completely assembled mower, to be sure the blade tip speed will not exceed 19,000 feet per minute. If necessary, change the governor spring or adjust the top speed limit device, so the engine will not exceed the recommended speed, based on blade length as shown. See page 6 for adjustment procedure for mechanical governor.

If a governor spring must be replaced, consult the appropriate Illustrated Parts List. Choose the proper governor spring by engine type number. AFTER A NEW GOVERNOR SPRING IS INSTALLED, CHECK ENGINE TOP GOVERNED SPEED WITH AN ACCURATE TACHOMETER.

Run engine at half throttle to allow the engine to reach normal operating temperature before measuring speed with a tachometer. To account for tolerances, which may be required by tachometer manufacturers, we suggest that the top governed speed of the engine be adjusted at least 200 R.P.M. lower than the maximum speeds shown.

Since blade tip speed is a function of engine R.P.M., lower tip speeds require lower engine speeds.

The chart below lists various lengths of rotary lawnmower cutter blades, and the maximum blade rotational speeds, which will produce blade tip speeds of 19,000 feet per minute.

BLADE LENGTH	MAXIMUM ROTATIONAL R.P.M.
18"	4032
19"	3820
20"	3629
21"	3456
22"	3299
23"	3155
24"	3024
25"	2903
26"	2791

NOTE: For correct no load R.P.M. by model and type, see engine sales manual, Note column.

MECHANICAL GOVERNOR
MODELS N, 6, 8 (CAST IRON)
Disassembly

Loosen the two mounting screws to remove governor housing. The cup can be pulled off the governor gear and the gear will slide off the shaft. See Fig. 4. To disassemble the governor crank, drive the roll pin out at the end of the governor lever; remove the governor crank bushing. Then pull governor crank out of the housing.

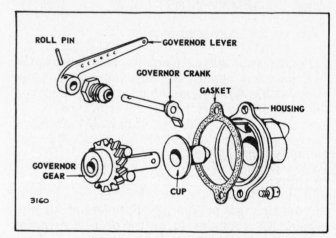

Fig. 4 — Governor Housing and Gear Assembly

Re-Assembly

To assemble the governor crank, bushing and lever to the housing, push the governor crank, lever end first, into the housing. Slip the bushing onto the shaft; then thread the bushing into the housing and tighten securely. Place the lever on the shaft with the governor crank in the position shown in Fig. 5. Place the governor gear on shaft in cylinder. Place gasket on governor housing; then assemble governor housing to the cylinder and tighten in place with two mounting screws.

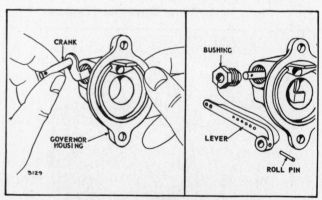

Fig. 5 — Install Crank and Lever

5

Adjustment

There is no adjustment between governor lever and governor crank on these models. However, governor action can be changed by inserting governor link or spring in different holes of governor and throttle levers. Fig. 6. In general, the closer to the pivot end of the lever, the smaller the difference between load and no load engine speed. The engine will begin to "hunt" if the spring is brought too close to the pivot point. The further from the pivot end, the less tendency to "hunt" but the greater the speed drop with increasing load. If the governed speed is lowered, the spring can usually be moved closer to the pivot. The standard setting is shown in Fig. 6.

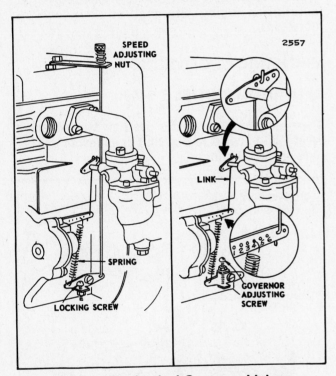

Fig. 6 — Mechanical Governor Linkage

MECHANICAL GOVERNOR

MODELS 6B, 8B, 60000, 80000, 140000 (ALUMINUM)

Disassembly

To service governor, remove crankcase cover. Loosen the screw on the governor lever and pull lever from governor crank. Loosen the two mounting screws to remove gear housing. See Fig. 7. As the housing is removed, the governor gear will slip off the shaft. There is a steel thrust washer on the shaft between the gear and the governor housing.

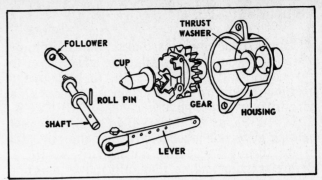

Fig. 7 — Mechanical Governor Parts

To remove governor lever shaft, remove roll pin and washer. Unscrew governor lever shaft by turning clockwise. Remove governor lever shaft. Fig. 7.

Re-Assembly

Push governor lever shaft into crankcase cover, with the threaded end in. Assemble the small washer on the inner end of the shaft, then screw the shaft into the governor crank follower by turning the shaft counterclockwise. Tighten securely. Turn the shaft until follower points down as illustrated, Fig. 8. Place the washer on the outside end of the shaft. Install roll pin. The leading end of the pin should just go through the shaft so the pin protrudes from only one side of the shaft.

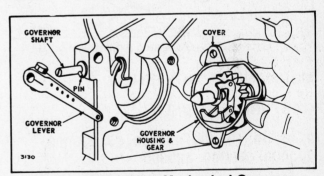

Fig. 8 — Assembling Mechanical Governor

Place the thrust washer and then the governor gear on the shaft in the gear housing. Hold crankcase cover in a vertical (normal) position and then assemble the housing with gear in position so that the point of the steel cup on the gear rests against the crank follower. Tighten housing in place with two mounting screws. See Fig. 8.

Assemble the governor lever to the lever shaft with lever pointing downward at about a 30° angle. Adjustment will be made later when carburetor linkage is assembled.

5

3

GOVERNORS
Repair & Adjustment
Adjustment

With crankcase cover, carburetor and all linkage installed, loosen screw holding governor lever to governor shaft. Place throttle in high speed position. Hold throttle in this position and with a screwdriver turn governor shaft COUNTER-CLOCKWISE as far as it will go. Tighten screw holding governor lever to governor shaft to 35-45 in. lbs. torque (.4-.52 mkp, 4.0-5.0 Nm). See fig. 9. Before starting engine, manually move governor linkage to check for any binding. Correct any binding in linkage or carburetor.

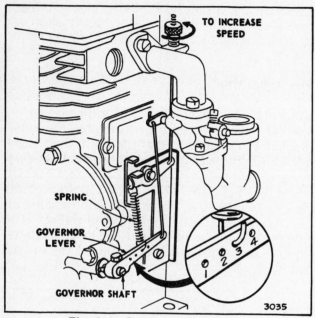

Fig. 9 — Governor Adjustment

MECHANICAL GOVERNOR

CAST IRON MODELS

9, 14, 19, 190000, 200000, 23, 230000, 240000, 300000, 320000

Disassembly

To service, remove engine base. Remove the cotter key and washer from outside end of governor shaft. Remove governor crank from inside the crankcase. Governor gear slides off the shaft.

Re-Assembly

Assemble the governor gear and cup assembly on shaft protruding on inside of cylinder. Then insert governor shaft assembly through bushing from inside of cylinder. Assemble governor lever to governor shaft loosely.

NOTE: Later models have a spacer between governor shaft assembly and bushing.

Adjustment

Loosen screw holding governor lever to governor shaft. Place throttle in high speed position. Hold throttle in this position and with a screwdriver turn governor shaft COUNTERCLOCKWISE as far as it will go. Tighten screw holding governor lever to governor shaft to 35-45 in. lbs. torque (.4-.52 mkp, 4.0-5.0 Nm). See Fig. 9. Before starting engine, manually move governor linkage to check for any binding.

NOTE: If governor bushing is replaced it should be finish reamed to .239-.2385 (6.07-6.05 mm) after installation using Stanisol or kerosene as lubricant.

MECHANICAL GOVERNOR

ALUMINUM MODELS 94000

The mechanical governor used on Model Series 94000 is illustrated in Fig. 10. The governor gear is part of the oil slinger.

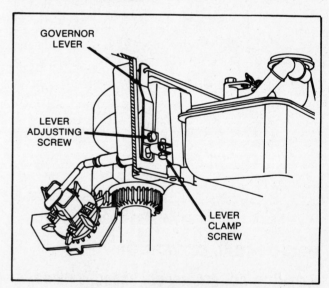

Fig. 10 — 94000 Governor

Disassembly

Before governor can be serviced, it is necessary to remove engine sump. To remove governor shaft, remove lever adjusting screw, Fig. 10 and loosen lever clamp screw, Fig. 10. Slide off clamp. Lift governor lever up to release slot in governor shaft and slide governor shaft out of bushing. If oil slinger and governor gear assembly interferes, remove.

Re-Assembly

Insert governor shaft into governor bushing from inside cylinder. Then slide governor lever on governor shaft and slide lever down onto shaft slot. Slide on lever clamp and start screw in adjusting slot on clamp. Torque lever clamp screw to 15 in. lbs. (.17 mkp, 1.7 Nm). Install oil slinger and governor gear assembly, sump gasket and oil sump. Place non-hardening sealant on screw "A," Fig. 11, and tighten all sump screws.

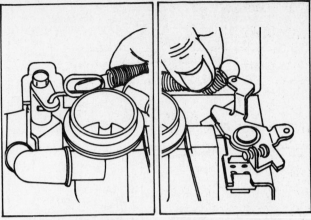

Fig. 12 — Installing Governor Spring   **Fig. 13 — Governor Spring Installed**

100000, 130000, 140000, 170000, 190000, 220000 and 250000 (Aluminum Cylinders)

Disassembly

The governor used on the horizontal shaft models is illustrated in Figs. 14 and 16. The governor used on the vertical shaft models is incorporated with the oil slinger. Figs. 15 and 16.

The only disassembly necessary is removing the governor assembly as one unit from the shaft on the crankcase cover on horizontal models. On vertical shaft models, it is removed as part of the oil slinger. Further disassembly is unnecessary.

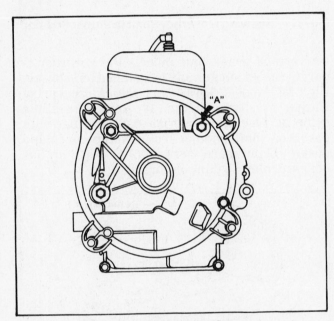

Fig. 11 — Sealant on Screw

Adjustment

Loosen lever adjusting screw, Fig. 10. While holding governor lever and governor clamp to the left (counterclockwise), tighten lever adjusting screw to 15 in. lbs. (.17 mkp, 1.7 Nm).

Replacement, Governor Shaft Bushing

When a new governor shaft bushing is pressed in, it should be pressed in until 1/16" (1.58 mm) extends out from crankcase. Finish ream with 19058 reamer using Stanisol or kerosene for lubricant.

Installation, Governor Spring

Hold governor spring as shown in Fig. 12 with open end of small loop down. Hook large loop in throttle link loop as shown in Fig. 12 and pull loop toward throttle lever until end of spring loop snaps on. Hook small loop in throttle control lever as shown in Fig. 13.

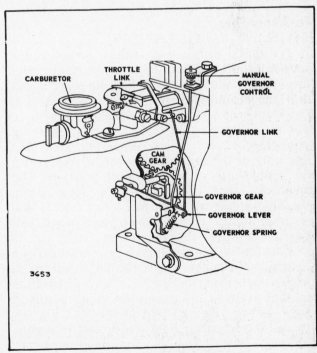

Fig. 14 — Horizontal Shaft

5

GOVERNORS
Repair & Adjustment

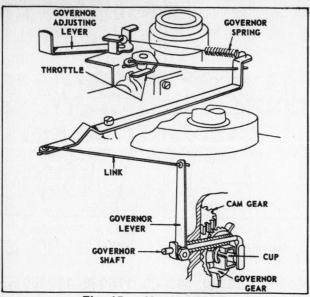

Fig. 15 — Vertical Shaft

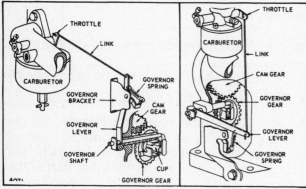

Fig. 16 — Large Aluminum Engines

Re-Assembly

On horizontal crankshaft models, the governor rides on a short stationary shaft and is retained by the governor shaft, with which it comes in contact after the crankcase cover is secured in place. Press governor cup against crankcase cover to seat retaining ring on shaft, prior to installing crankcase cover. It is suggested that the assembly of the crankcase cover be made with the crankshaft in a horizontal position. The governor shaft should hang straight down parallel to the cylinder axis. Fig. 17. If the governor shaft is clamped in an angular position, pointing toward the crankcase cover, it is possible for the end of the shaft to be jammed into the inside of the governor assembly, resulting in broken parts when the engine is started. After the crankcase cover and gasket are in place, install cover screws. Be sure that screw "A," Fig. 19, has nonhardening sealant on threads of screw. Complete installation of remaining governor linkages and carburetor and then adjust governor shaft and lever.

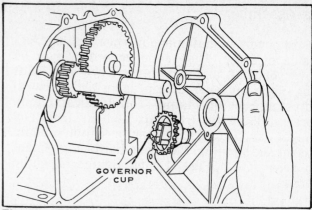

Fig. 17 — Showing Governor Shaft in Proper Position

On vertical crankshaft models the governor is part of the oil slinger and is installed as shown in Fig. 18. Models 100900 and 130900 use spring washer as shown in Fig. 18. Before installing sump be sure that governor cup is in line with governor shaft paddle. Install sump cover and gasket being sure screw "A," Fig. 19 has nonhardening sealant on threads.

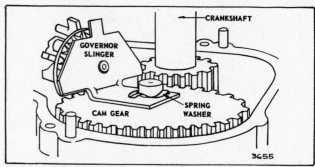

Fig. 18 — Shows Spring on Camshaft after Governor is Installed. Models 100900 and 130900 Only.

NOTE: On right angle auxiliary drive power take off models, screw "A" does not need sealant but the four screws holding the gear sump cover do need sealant. See insert, Fig. 19.

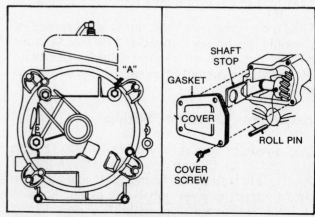

Fig. 19 — Sealant on Screw "A"

Complete installation of remaining governor linkages and carburetor and then adjust governor shaft and lever.

NOTE: If governor bushing is replaced it should be finished reamed to .2435-.2410 (6.18-6.12 mm) for 1/4″ (6.35 mm) or with 19058 reamer for 3/16″ (4.76 mm) governor shaft.

Adjustment

Loosen screw holding governor lever to governor shaft. Place throttle in high speed position. While holding throttle in this position and with a screwdriver turn governor shaft clockwise as far as it will go. Tighten screw holding governor lever to governor shaft to 35-45 in. lbs. (.4-.52 mkp or 4.0-5.0 Nm) torque. See Fig. 20.

Before starting engine, manually move governor linkage to check for any binding.

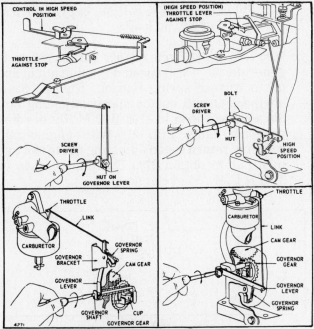
Fig. 20 — Adjust Governor

MECHANICAL GOVERNOR — ADJUSTING TOP NO LOAD SPEED ALUMINUM MODELS 100200, 130200, 170000, 190000, 220000, 250000 (Except 253400)

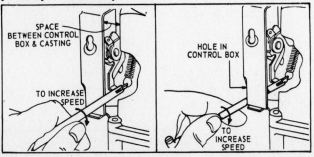

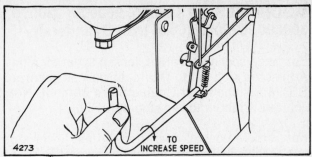
Fig. 21 — Setting Top No Load Speed

1. Set control lever to maximum speed position, with engine running. see Fig. 20.

2. Use tool 19229 to bend spring anchor tang to get desired top speed. See Fig. 21. To make own tool, see Fig. 22.

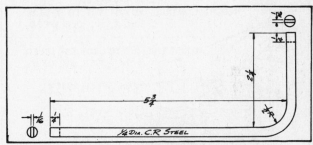
Fig. 22 — Tang Bending Tool

To adjust governed idle refer to Section 4, Governor Controls and Carburetor Linkages.

ADJUSTING MECHANICAL GOVERNOR

MODEL SERIES 253400

On Model Series 253400, governor adjustments are the same except top governed speed. To set top governed speed, turn screw "A" in to decrease or out to increase R.P.M. Refer to Engine Sales Manual, Note column for recommended governed R.P.M. See Fig. 23.

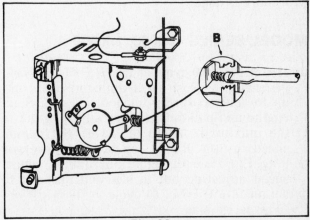
Fig. 23

GOVERNORS
Speed Setting

MODEL SERIES 190000, 200000, 230000, 300000, 320000 (Cast Iron Cylinders)

For fixed speed operation, loosen lower stop nut. Adjust top stop nut to obtain top no load governor R.P.M. as shown in Engine Sales Manual, Note column. Tighten lower stop nut. Fig. 24.

For remote control operation, adjust lower stop nut to obtain top no load governed R.P.M. as specified in the Engine Sales Manual, note column. Fig. 24.

To adjust governor idle refer to Section 4, Governor Controls and Carburetor Linkages.

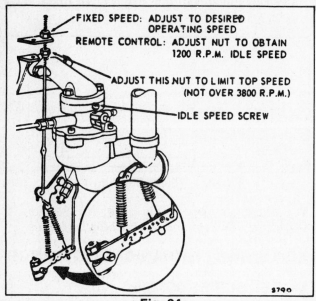

Fig. 24

OBTAINING CLOSER GOVERNING
(Generator Applications Only)

Governor regulation to within two cycles of either 60 or 50 cycles can be obtained if the following procedure is done:

MODEL SERIES 100000, 130000

a. 1800 R.P.M., 60 cycle or 1500 R.P.M., 50 cycle generators — Push speed adjusting nut in and up to release spring tension, Fig. 25. Start engine and pull out on speed adjusting nut to the maximum length of travel. Set engine speed to 2800 R.P.M. by bending governor tang, Fig. 21. With engine still running, return speed adjusting nut to slot and turn nut to obtain 1875 R.P.M., 60 cycle, or 1600 R.P.M., 50 cycle, no load.

b. 3600 R.P.M., 60 cycle or 3000 R.P.M., 50 cycle generators — Push speed adjusting nut in and up to release spring tension, Fig. 25. Start engine and pull out on speed adjusting nut. Set engine speed to 4600 R.P.M. by bending governor tang, Fig. 21. With engine still running, return speed adjusting nut to slot and turn nut to obtain 3700 R.P.M., 60 cycle, or 3100 R.P.M., 50 cycle, no load.

MODEL SERIES 140000, 170000, 190000, 220000, 250000 (Aluminum Cylinders)

a. 1800 R.P.M., 60 cycle or 1500 R.P.M., 50 cycle generators — Push speed adjusting nut in and up to release spring tension, Fig. 25. Start engine and pull out on speed adjusting nut. Set engine speed to 2600 R.P.M. by bending governor tang, Fig. 21. With engine still running, return speed adjusting nut to slot and turn nut to obtain 1875 R.P.M., 60 cycle or 1600 R.P.M., 50 cycle, no load.

b. 3600 R.P.M., 60 cycle or 3000 R.P.M., 50 cycle generators — Push speed adjusting nut in and up to release spring tension, Fig. 25. Start engine and pull out on speed adjusting nut. Set engine speed to 4200 R.P.M. by bending governor tang, Fig. 21. With engine still running, return speed adjusting nut to slot and turn nut to obtain 3700 R.P.M., 60 cycle or 3100 R.P.M., 50 cycle, no load.

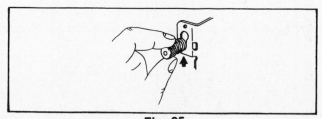

Fig. 25

Section 6
COMPRESSION

COMPRESSION

Briggs & Stratton does not publish any compression pressures, as it is extremely difficult to obtain an accurate reading without special equipment.

It has been determined through extensive testing, a simple and accurate indication of compression can be made as follows:

Spin the flywheel counterclockwise (flywheel side) against the compression stroke, a sharp rebound indicates satisfactory compression. Slight or no rebound indicates poor compression.

Loss of compression will usually be the result of the following:

1. The cylinder head gasket blown or leaking.

2. Valves sticking or not seating properly.

3. Piston rings not sealing, which would also cause the engine to consume an excessive amount of oil.

Carbon deposits in the combustion chamber should be removed every 100 to 300 hours of use (more often when run at a steady load), or whenever the cylinder head is removed.

Remove Cylinder Head and Shield

Always note the position of the different cylinder head screws so that they may be properly reassembled. If a screw is used in the wrong position, it may be too short and not engage enough threads. It may be too long and bottom on a fin, either breaking the fin, or leaving the cylinder head loose.

CYLINDER HEAD TORQUE PROCEDURE

Assemble the cylinder head with a new head gasket, cylinder head shield, screws and washers in their proper places. (A graphite grease or part no. 93963 should be used on aluminum cylinder screws.)

Do not use a sealer of any kind on gasket. Tighten the screws down evenly by hand. Use a torque wrench and tighten head bolts in the sequence shown, Fig. 1, and to the specified torque in Table 1.

Do not turn one screw down completely before the others, as it may cause a warped cylinder head.

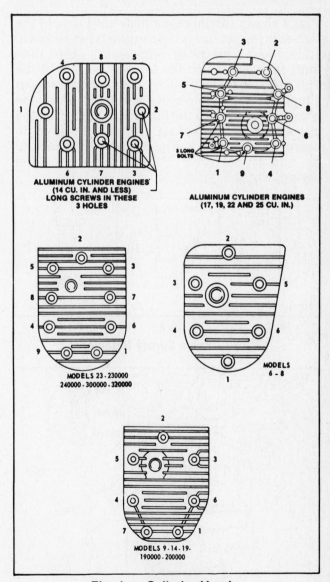

Fig. 1 — Cylinder Heads

COMPRESSION
Valves

TABLE NO. 1
CYLINDER HEAD TORQUE

BASIC MODEL SERIES ALUMINUM CYLINDER	Inch Pounds	Meter Kilopond	Newton Meter
6B, 60000, 8B, 80000, 82000, 92000, 94000, 110000, 100000, 130000	140	1.61	15.82
140000, 170000, 190000, 220000, 250000	165	1.90	18.65
CAST IRON CYLINDER	**Inch Pounds**	**Meter Kilopond**	**Newton Meter**
5, 6, N, 8, 9	140	1.61	15.82
14	165	1.90	18.65
19, 190000, 200000, 23, 230000, 240000, 300000, 320000	190	2.19	21.47

To Remove Valves

Fig. 2 shows the three methods used to hold the valve spring retainers. To remove types shown in Illus. 1 and 2, use 19063 compressor; adjust jaws until they just touch the top and bottom of the valve chamber. This will keep the upper jaw from slipping into the coils of the spring. Push the compressor in until the upper jaw slips over the upper end of the spring. Tighten the jaws to compress the spring. Fig. 3. Remove collars or pin and lift out valve. Pull out compressor and spring. Fig. 4.

To remove valves using retainers, Fig. 2, Illus. 3, slip the upper jaw of 19063 compressor over the top of the valve chamber and lower jaw between spring and retainer. Compress spring. Remove retainer. Pull out valve. Remove compressor and spring. Fig. 5.

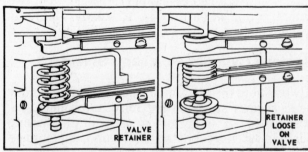

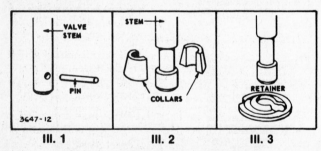

Fig. 2 — Valve Spring Retainers

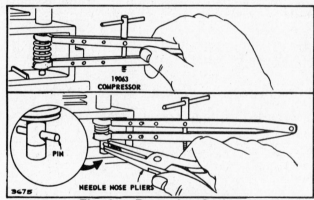

Fig. 4 — Removing Spring

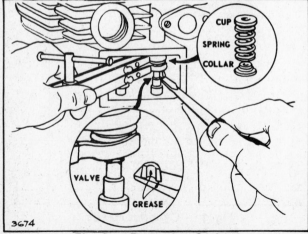

Fig. 3 — Removing Spring

Fig. 5 — Removing Retainer and Spring

Old 19063 valve spring compressors can be modified by grinding as shown in Fig. 6.

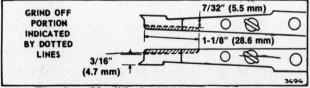

Fig. 6 — Modified #19063 Compressor

TABLE NO. 2
VALVE TAPPET CLEARANCE

MODEL SERIES	INTAKE				EXHAUST			
	MAX.		MIN.		MAX.		MIN.	
ALUMINUM CYLINDER	Inches	Milli-meter	Inches	Milli-meter	Inches	Milli-meter	Inches	Milli-meter
6B, 60000, 8B, 80000, 82000, 92000, 94000, 100000, 110000, 130000, 140000, 170000, 190000, 220000, 250000	.007	0.18	.005	0.13	.011	0.28	.009	0.23
CAST IRON CYLINDER	Inches	Milli-meter	Inches	Milli-meter	Inches	Milli-meter	Inches	Milli-meter
5, 6, 8, N, 9, 14, 19, 190000, 200000	.009	0.23	.007	0.18	.016	0.41	.014	0.36
23, 230000, 240000, 300000, 320000	.009	0.23	.007	0.18	.019	0.48	.017	0.43

To Reface Valves and Seats

Faces on valves and valve seats should be resurfaced with a valve grinder or cutter, to an angle of 45°. NOTE: SOME ENGINE MODELS HAVE A 30° INTAKE VALVE AND SEAT. Valve and seat should then be lapped with a fine lapping compound to remove grinding marks and assure a good seat. Valve seat width should be 3/64" to 1/16" (1.19-1.58 mm). Fig. 7. If the seat is wider, a narrowing stone or cutter should be used. If either the seat or valve is badly burned, it should be replaced. Replace valve if margin is 1/64" (0.4 mm) or less after refacing. Fig. 7.

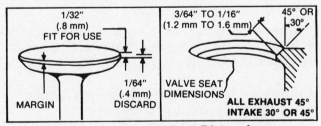

Fig. 7 — Valve and Seat Dimensions

To Check and Adjust Tappet Clearance

Insert the valves in their respective positions in the cylinder. Turn the crankshaft to top dead center, end of compression stroke. Both valves are now closed. Then check clearance on the intake and exhaust valves with feeler gauge. See Table 2. Grind off the end of the valve stem if necessary, to obtain proper clearance.

CAUTION: Piston MUST be at top dead center at the end of compression stroke to assure both valves being closed.

NOTE: Check clearance cold.

To Install Valves

Some engines use the same spring for intake and exhaust side, while others use a heavier spring on the exhaust side. Compare springs before installing.

If retainers are held by a pin or collars, Fig. 2, Illus. 1 and 2, place valve spring and retainer (and cup on Model Series 9, 14, 19, 20, 23, 24 and 32) into valve spring compressor 19063. Compress the spring until it is solid. Insert the compressed spring and retainer (and cup when used) into the valve chamber. Then drop the valve into place, pushing the stem through the retainer. Hold the spring up in the chamber, and the valve down. Insert the retainer pin with a needle nose pliers or place the collars in the groove in the valve stem. Lower the spring until the retainer fits around the pins or collars, then pull out the spring compressor. Fig. 3. Be sure pin or collars are in place.

If self-lock retainer, Fig. 2, Illus. 3, is used, compress retainer and spring with compressor 19063. Large diameter of retainer should be toward front of valve chamber. Fig. 8. Insert compressed spring and retainer into valve chamber. Drop the valve stem through larger area of retainer slot and move the compressor so as to center the small area of the valve retainer slot onto the valve stem shoulder. Release the spring tension and remove the compressor.

6

COMPRESSION
Valves & Guides

NOTE: Apply "LED-PLATE" or Part No. 93963 lubricant to valve stems and guides before installing. Be sure that no "LED-PLATE" or Part No. 93963 is on the ends of the valve stems or tappets.

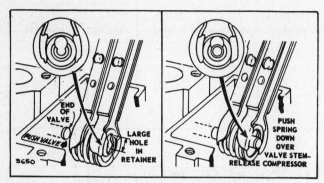

Fig. 8 — Installing Valves

Valve Guides

Models 5, 6, 8, 6B, 60000, 8B, 80000, 82000, 92000, 94000, 100000, 110000, 130000

If the flat end of valve guide plug gauge 19122 can be inserted into the valve guide for a distance of 5/16" (7.94 mm), the valve guide is worn and should be rebushed in the following manner. Fig. 9.

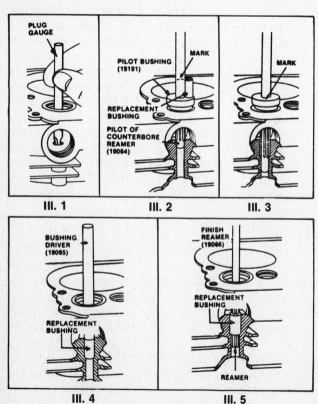

Fig. 9 — Bushing Valve Guides

Place pilot of counterbore reamer no. 19064 in valve guide, Fig. 9, Illus. 1. Install pilot bushing 19191 over counterbore reamer and lower pilot bushing to rest in valve seat. Hold replacement valve guide bushing 63709 on top of pilot bushing next to reamer. Make a mark on reamer 1/16" (1.59 mm) above top of replacement bushing, Fig. 9, Illus. 2.

Ream out valve guide until mark on counterbore reamer is level with top of pilot, Fig. 9, Illus. 3. (Lubricate reamer with kerosene or equivalent lubricant.)

Place replacement bushing in reamed-out hole, Fig. 19. Press replacement bushing down until it is flush with the top of the hole with valve guide bushing driver 19065, Fig. 9, Illus. 4.

Finish ream the replacement bushing with a valve guide bushing finish reamer 19066, Fig. 9, Illus. 5. (Lubricate reamer with kerosene or equivalent lubricant.)

NOTE: It is usually not necessary to bush factory installed brass valve guides. However, if bushing is required, DO NOT REMOVE ORIGINAL BUSHING — follow standard procedure outlined.

Models 9, 14, 19, 23, 140000, 170000, 190000, 200000, 220000, 230000, 240000, 250000, 300000, 320000

Checking Valve Guide Wear

If the flat end of valve guide plug gauge no. 19151 can be inserted into the valve guide for a distance of 5/16" (7.9 mm) the guide is worn and should be rebushed in the following manner. Fig. 9, Illus. 1.

Removing Valve Guide Bushings Using Kit 19232 (Aluminum Engines)

To remove factory or field installed guide bushings on aluminum engines, rotate nut no. 19239 up to head of 19238 puller screw. Center washer on valve seat. (Larger washer may be required on some model intake seats.) Lubricate cutting surface of screw and inside of guide bushings with Stanisol or kerosene. Insert screw 19238 thru washer 19240, centering washer on seat. See Fig. 10. Use 3/4" socket to turn screw clockwise to a depth of 1/4" (6.5 mm) or until bushing starts to turn — and —STOP. While holding screw stationary, turn nut down onto washer until bushing is free.

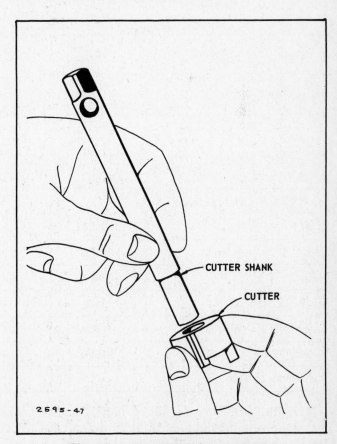

Fig. 10

Repairing Worn Aluminum or Sintered Iron Guides

Place piloted counterbore reamer, 19231, into worn guide. Slide reamer guide, 19234, down shank of 19231 and center on valve seat, Fig. 9, Illus. 2. Place bushing 231218 next to reamer on reamer guide, Fig. 9, Illus. 2, and mark reamer 1/16" (1.6 mm) above bushing.

Use Stanisol or kerosene to lubricate reamer while turning clockwise. Continue reaming until mark on reamer is flush with top of reamer guide bushing, 1-1/32" (26.19 mm), Fig. 9, Illus. 3.

Installing Replacement Bushing

Clean out all chips. Place grooved end of service bushing, 231218, into valve guide, Fig. 9, Illus. 4. Use bushing driver, 19204, to press bushing into guide until flush with top of guide or until it bottoms. Place reamer guide bushing, 19234, on valve seat and slide finish reamer, 19233, thru center of bushing. Fig. 9, Illus. 5. Use Stanisol or kerosene as lubricant while turning reamer clockwise. Continue reaming until reamer enters tappet chamber. After reaming is done, continue to turn reamer clockwise while removing. Clean out all chips before reassembling engine.

Repairing Worn Valve Guides Using 19183 Reamer and Reamer Guide Bushing 19192

Place piloted counterbore reamer, 19183 into worn guide. Slide reamer guide bushing, 19192, down shank of reamer and center in valve seat, Fig. 9, Illus. 2. Slide replacement bushing, 230655, next to reamer shank on reamer guide bushing. Mark reamer 1/16" (1.6 mm) above bushing Fig. 9, Illus. 3. Use Stanisol or kerosene to lubricate reamer while turning clockwise. Continue reaming until mark on reamer is flush with top of bushing. DO NOT REAM THROUGH THE WHOLE GUIDE. Continue to turn reamer clockwise while withdrawing reamer.

Installing Replacement Bushing 230655

Clean out all chips. Press in valve guide bushing, 230655, using bushing driver, 19204, until flush with top of guide or until it bottoms. Fig. 9, Illus. 4.

The bushing 230655 is finish reamed to size at the factory, no further reaming is necessary, and a standard valve can be used.

NOTE: Cast iron engines use sintered (gray colored) valve guide bushings. DO NOT REMOVE THESE BUSHINGS. See reaming valve guide (230655 or 231218 bushing) to install service brass bushings.

CAUTION
Valve seating should be checked after bushing the guide, and corrected if necessary by refacing the seat.

Valve Seat Inserts

Cast iron cylinder engines are equipped with an exhaust valve seat insert which can be removed and a new insert installed. The intake side must be counterbored to allow installation of an intake valve seat insert. Fig. 12, 13 & 14.

CUTTER SHANK

CUTTER

2595-47

Fig. 12 — Inserting Cutter Shank

6

COMPRESSION
Valve Seat Inserts

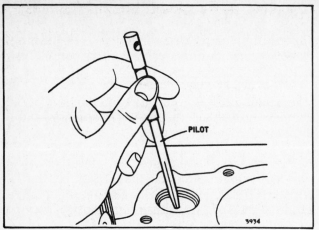

Fig. 13 — Inserting Pilot

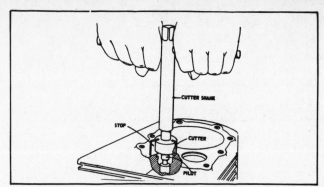

Fig. 14 — Counterboring for Valve Seat

Aluminum alloy cylinder models are equipped with inserts on exhaust and intake side. See Table 3.

TABLE NO. 3
VALVE SEAT INSERTS

BASIC MODEL SERIES	INTAKE STANDARD	EXHAUST STANDARD	EXHAUST STELLITE	INSERT # PULLER ASSEMBLY	PULLER NUT
ALUMINUM CYLINDER					
6B, 8B	211291	211291	210452	19138	19140 Ex. 19182 In.
60000, 80000	210879*	211291	210452	19138	19140 Ex. 19182 In.
82000, 92000, 94000, 110000	210879	211291	210452	19138	19140 Ex. 19182 In.
100000, 130000, 131000	211787	211172	211436	19138	19182 Ex. 19139 In.
140000, 170000, 190000	211661	211661	210940††	19138	19141
251000	211661	211661	210940	19138	19141
220000, 252000, 253000	261463	211661	210940		
CAST IRON CYLINDER					
5, 6, N	63838	21865		19138	19140
8	210135	21865		19138	19140
9	63007	63007		19138	19139
14, 19, 190000	21880	21880	21612	19138	19141
200000, 23, 230000	21880	21880	21612	19138	19141
240000	21880	21612	21612	19138	19141
300000, 320000		21612	21612	19138	19141

*211291 used before Serial No. 5810060 – 210808 used from Serial No. 5810060 to No. 6012010.
#Includes puller and no. 19182, 19141, 19140 and 19139 nuts.
††Before Code No. 7101260 replace cylinder.

To Remove Valve Seat Insert

Use valve seat puller 19138 as shown in Fig. 15, and select the proper puller nut. See Table 3. Be sure the puller body does not rest on the valve seat insert. Fig. 16. Turn the 5/16" bolt with a wrench until insert is pulled out of the cylinder. Fig. 16.

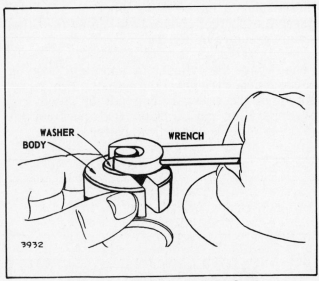

Fig. 15 — Removing Valve Seat

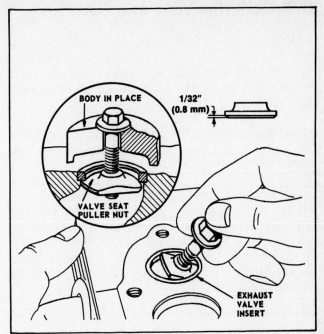

Fig. 16 — Inserting Valve Seat Puller

NOTE: On aluminum alloy cylinder models, it may be necessary to grind the puller nut until the edge is 1/32" (0.8 mm) thick in order to get the puller nut under the valve insert. Fig. 16.

TABLE NO. 4
VALVE SEAT INSERT AND COUNTERBORE TOOLS

BASIC MODEL SERIES	COUNTERBORE CUTTER	SHANK	CUTTER & DRIVER PILOT	INSERT DRIVER
ALUMINUM CYLINDER				
6B, 8B			19126	19136
60000, 80000			19126	19136
82000, 92000, 94000			19126	19136
100000, 130000			19126	19136
140000, 170000, 190000			19127	19136
CAST IRON CYLINDER				
5, 6, N	19133	19129	19126	19136
8	19132	19129	19126	19136
9	19132	19129	19127	19136
14, 19, 190000	19131	19129	19127	19136
200000, 23	19131	19129	19127	19136
230000, 240000	19131	19129	19127	19136
300000, 320000			19127	19136

COMPRESSION
Valve Seat Inserts

To Drive in New Valve Seat Insert

Select the proper valve seat insert and the correct pilot and driver according to Table 3 & 4. You will note that one side of the seat insert is chamfered at the outer edge. This side should go down into the cylinder.

Insert the pilot into the valve guide. Then drive the valve insert into place with the driver, as shown in Fig. 17. The seat should then be ground lightly and the valves and seats lapped lightly with grinding compound. Clean thoroughly. NOTE: Aluminum alloy cylinder models. Use the old insert as a spacer between the driver and the new insert. Drive new insert until it bottoms. Top of insert will be slightly below cylinder head gasket surface. Then peen around the insert as shown in Fig. 18.

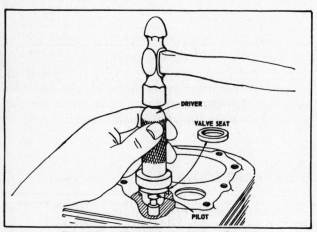

Fig. 17 — Driving in Valve Seat

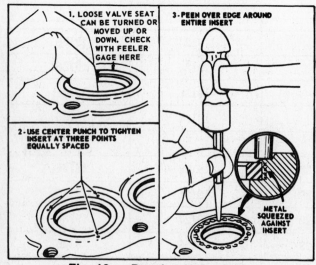

Fig. 18 — Peening Valve Seat

NOTE: Replace Cylinder if a .005" (0.13 mm) Feeler Gauge enters between Valve Seat and Cylinder.

To Counterbore Cylinder for Intake Valve Seat Cast Iron Cylinder Models

These models must be counterbored to allow installation of the intake valve seat insert. Select proper seat insert, cutter shank, counterbore cutter, pilot and driver according to Table 4.

Insert pilot in intake valve guide. See Fig. 19. Assemble correct counterbore cutter to cutter shank as shown in Fig. 20.

Counterbore the cylinder by hand until stop on cutter touches the top of the cylinder. Fig. 21. Do not force the cutter to one side or it will cut oversize. Blow out all chips. Use knock out pin 19135, to remove cutter from cutter shank.

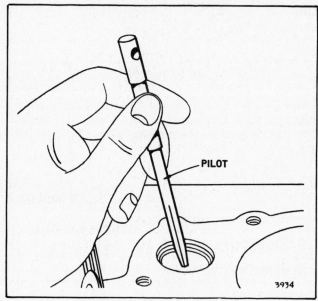

Fig. 19 — Inserting Pilot

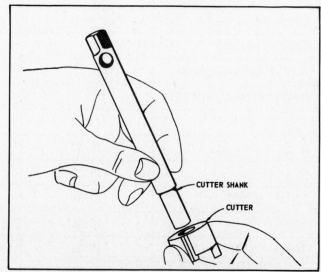

Fig. 20 — Inserting Cutter Shank

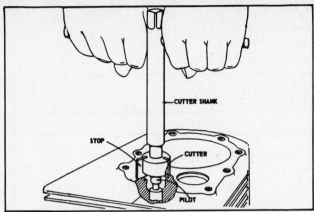

Fig. 21 — Counterboring for Valve Seat

Valves, Valve Conversions

The life of a valve is considered to be the period of time the valve will operate before repair or replacement is necessary. The life of a standard exhaust valve is often shortened because of burning, which occurs when pieces of combustion deposit lodge between the valve seat and valve face, preventing the valve from closing completely. This is most likely to occur on engines which are operated at constant speed and constant load, for long periods of time. Exhaust valve life can be extended by using:

1. A Rotocap (Valve Rotator), which turns the exhaust valve a slight bit on each lift, wiping away any deposits which tend to lodge between the valve face and seat, or,

2. A Stellite® Exhaust Valve which has a greater resistance to heat.

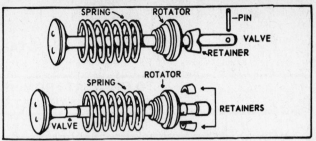

Standard Valve and Rotocap

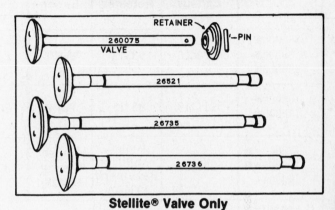

Stellite® Valve Only

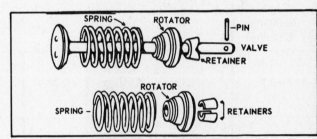

Stellite® Valve and Rotocap

Use Table 5 below, Table 6 on page 10 or Table 7 on page 11 for Part Numbers.

TABLE NO. 5

BASIC MODEL SERIES	STELLITE® VALVE AND ROTOCAP CONVERSION				
		ROTOCAP ONLY CONVERSION			
	STELLITE® VALVE	SPRING	ROTOCAP	RETAINER	PIN
ALUMINUM CYLINDER					
60000*, 80000*, 82000*, 92000*, 94000*	260443	26826	292259	230127	230126
100000, 130000	260860	26826	292259	230127	230126
140000, 170000, 190000, 200000, 250000	390420	26828	292260	93630	
CAST IRON CYLINDER					
14, 19, 190000, 200000	26735	26828	292260	68283	
23, 230000	261207	26828	292260	68283	
240000, 300000, 320000	261207	26828	292260	68283	(Stellite® Std.)

*To use Rotocap only #26973 standard valve must be used.
NOTE: Rotocap not used with LP Gas on 6, 8 and 10 cu. in. engine.

TABLE NO. 6

MODEL Series	TO CONVERT FROM STANDARD EXHAUST VALVE TO STELLITE® EXHAUST VALVE WITH VALVE ROTATOR							
	REMOVE			ADD				
	Standard Exhaust Valve	Retainer	Spring	Stellite® Exhaust Valve	Rotator	Retainer	Spring	Pin
60000■ 80000■ 90000■	296676	93312	26478	260443	292259	230127 (Sleeve Type)	26826	230126
100000■ 130000■	211119	93312	26478	260860	292259	230127 (Sleeve Type)	26826	230126
170000● ■ 190000● ■ 400000★	390419	Reuse Split Retainers (93630)	Reuse Spring (26828)	390420	Reuse Rotator (292260)	Reuse Split Retainers (93630)	Reuse Spring (26828)	Not Used
220400★ 221400★ 250000★ 420000★	Stellite® Exhaust Valve and Seat With Rotator Standard							
200000	23835	68293 (Collar Type)	65906	26735	292260	Reuse Split Retainers (68283)	26828	Not Used
233000	23923	68293 (Collar Type)	65906	261207	292260	Reuse Split Retainers (68283)	26828	Not Used
243000★ 300000★ 320000★	Stellite® Exhaust Valve and Seat With Rotator Standard							

■Some standard with Stellite® exhaust valve and seat with valve rotator. Stellite® valves are usually marked "TXS" on head.

●Valve rotator standard with standard exhaust valve.

★Standard with Stellite® exhaust valve and seat with valve rotator.

NOTE: APPLY BRIGGS & STRATTON PART NO. 93963 "VALVE GUIDE LUBRICANT" TO VALVE STEMS AND GUIDES BEFORE INSTALLING VALVES ESPECIALLY WHEN OPERATING WITH LP FUEL OR NATURAL GAS.

6

TABLE NO. 7

TO CONVERT FROM STELLITE® EXHAUST VALVE WITH ROTATOR TO STELLITE® EXHAUST VALVE WITHOUT ROTATOR						
REMOVE				ADD		
Rotator	Retainer	Spring	Pin	Retainer	Spring	Pin
292259	230127 (Sleeve Type)	26826	230126	23184 (Collar Type)	26478	23187
292259	230127 (Sleeve Type)	26826	230126	23184 (Collar Type)	26478	23187
292260	Reuse Split Retainers (93630)	Reuse Spring (26828)	Not Used	68293 (Collar Type)	Reuse Spring (26828)	Not Used
292260	Reuse Split Retainers (93630)	Reuse Spring (26828)	Not Used	68293 (Collar Type)	Reuse Original Spring (26828)	Not Used
292260	Reuse Split Retainers (68283)	26828	Not Used	68293 (Collar Type)	65906	Not Used
292260	Reuse Split Retainers (68283)	26828	Not Used	68293 (Collar Type)	65906	Not Used
292260	Reuse Split Retainers (68283)	26828	Not Used	68293 (Collar Type)	65906	Not Used

6

6

Section 7
STARTERS & CHARGING SYSTEMS

REWIND STARTERS

Various rewind starter assemblies are illustrated below.

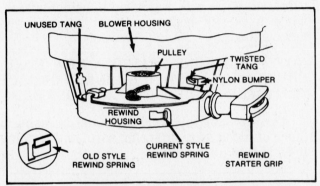

Fig. 1 — Old Style Model Series: 60000, 80000, 92000, 100000 and 110000

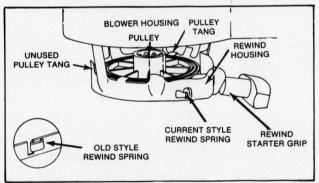

Fig. 2 — Model Series: 60000, 80000, 92000, 100000 and 110000

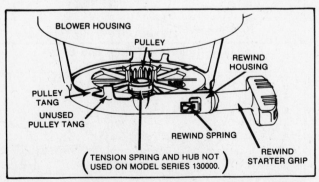

Fig. 3 — Model Series: 130000, 140000, 170000, 190000, 220000 and 250000

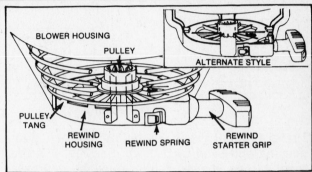

Fig. 4 — Model Series: 140000, 170000, 190000, 250000 and 300000

Repair procedure is similar except as indicated.

TO REPLACE A SPRING

Remove Spring

Cut knot at starter pulley to remove rope. With rope removed, grasp outer end of rewind spring with pliers, see Fig. 5, and pull out of housing as far as possible. Turn spring 1/4 turn and remove from pulley or bend one of the tangs up and lift out starter pulley to disconnect spring.

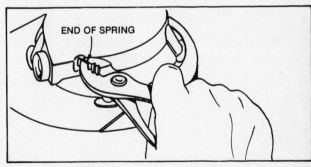

Fig. 5 — Remove Spring

Install Spring

Clean rewind housing, pulley and rewind spring in solvent. Wipe clean with cloth. Straighten spring to allow easier installation and restore tension. Oil spring. Insert either end of spring into blower housing slot and hook into pulley. Fig. 6.

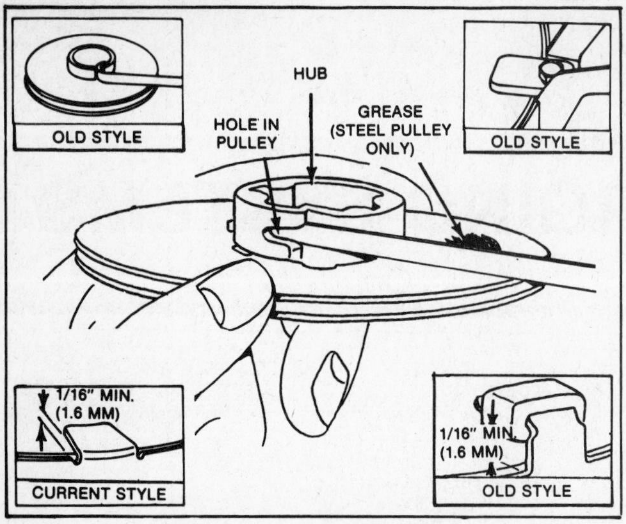

STARTERS
Rewind Starters

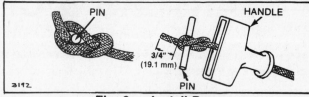

Fig. 6 — Install Spring

Place a dab of grease on pulley. Set pulley into housing and bend tang down. See Fig. 6. Adjust tang gap as shown. Pulley must be depressed fully into rewind housing when measuring tang gap.

NOTE: Do not remove nylon bumper from old style tang when replacing metal pulley with nylon pulley. Replace nylon bumpers if worn.

Wind Spring

Place a 3/4″ square piece of stock into center of pulley hub or make rewind tool similar to one shown in Fig. 7. GRASPING STOCK WITH A WRENCH, WIND PULLEY COUNTERCLOCKWISE UNTIL SPRING IS WOUND TIGHT. Then back off pulley one turn or until hole in pulley for rope knot and eyelet in blower housing are in alignment. See Fig. 11 or 12.

Spring should be securely locked in smaller portion of tapered hole. See Fig. 8.

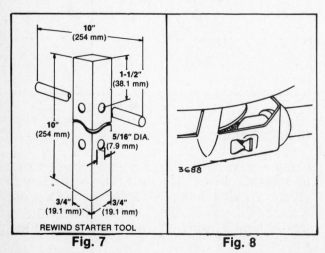

Fig. 7   **Fig. 8**

Install Rope

Inspect rope. Replace if frayed. Insert rope through handle and tie a figure eight knot. Insert pin through knot and pull tightly into handle. Fig. 9. ALWAYS SEAL BOTH ENDS OF KNOT.

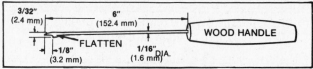

Fig. 9 — Install Rope

If re-using old rope, burn pulley end of rope with a match. Wipe with waste cloth, using caution, while it is still hot, to prevent swelling and unravelling.

NOTE: WHEN INSTALLING A NEW ROPE, CHECK PARTS LIST TO BE SURE CORRECT DIAMETER AND LENGTH ROPE IS USED.

A rope inserter tool may be made by using a piece of music wire or spring wire, and forming it as shown in Fig. 10.

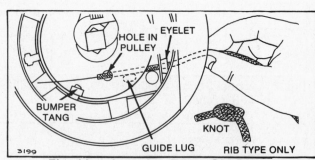

Fig. 10 — Rope Inserter

Thread wire and rope through rope eyelet in housing and out pulley hole. (CAUTION: Rope must pass inside a guide lug on metal pulley.) Fig. 11.

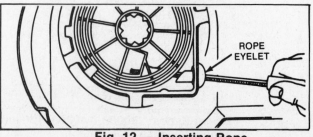

Fig. 11 — Inserting Rope, Old Style

Fig. 12 — Inserting Rope

7
A

Old Style with Guide Lug

Tie a knot in rope and pull tight. Fig. 13. Make sure knot in pulley does not contact bumper tangs. Fig. 11.

Current Style without Guide Lug

Tie a knot in rope and pull tight. Manipulate knot so it can be pulled down into knot cavity. Fig. 13.

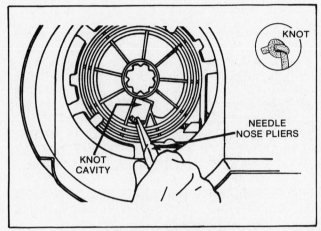

Fig. 13 — Tie Knot

Replace Rewind Assembly

If original starter housing is spot welded to blower housing, drill out spot welds using a 3/16″ diameter drill. Drill deep enough to loosen spot welds ONLY. Locate replacement rewind assembly in desired position. Install screws from inside blower housing up through starter housing mounting leg. Fasten securely with nuts as shown in Fig. 14.

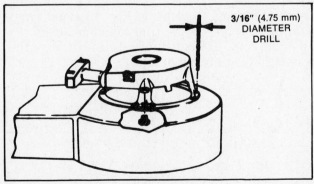

Fig. 14

Starter Clutch (Old Style)

Inspect and clean starter clutch assembly as necessary. Fig. 15 and 16. Do not oil ball cavity area.

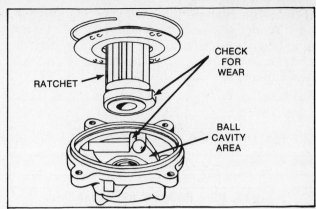

Fig. 15 — Starter Clutch (Old Style)

Starter Clutch (Sealed)

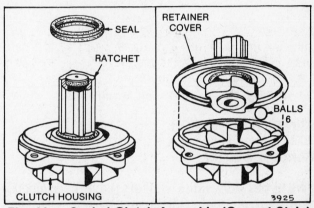

Fig. 16 — Sealed Clutch Assembly (Current Style)

If necessary, the sealed clutch can be disassembled by using a screwdriver or wedge to pry the retainer cover from the housing, as shown in Fig. 17. Place one drop of engine oil on end of crankshaft before replacing clutch assembly on crankshaft. Tighten clutch to torque noted on specification sheet for your model engine. DO NOT run engine without screen screws assembled to clutch.

NOTE: Clean ratchet by wiping with cloth only.

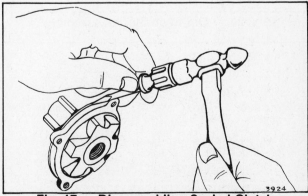

Fig. 17 — Disassembling Sealed Clutch

7
A

STARTERS
Windup Starters

NOTE: The sealed clutch may be installed on older model engines, by modifying the starter pulley and crankshaft. The old pulley can be made to fit the new clutch by cutting off the hub to a dimension of 1/2" as shown in Fig. 18.

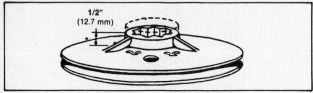

Fig. 18 — Pulley Modification

The crankshaft must be shortened 3/8" and the end chamfered as shown in Fig. 19. A new screen #221661 is required with the new clutch.

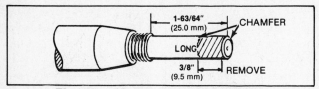

Fig. 19 — Crankshaft Modification

WINDUP STARTER

Windup Starter

Two types of windup starters have been used. The control knob release was used with the unsealed four ball clutch. The control lever release can only be used with a sealed six ball clutch. See Fig. 20 and Fig. 21.

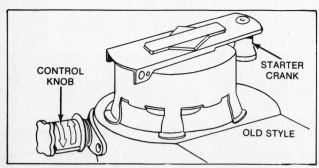

Fig. 20 — Old Style Starter Assembly

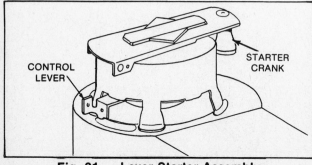

Fig. 21 — Lever Starter Assembly

Before working on equipment, remove spark plug from engine. Make sure starter spring is not wound. This can be determined by attempting to turn starter crank clockwise.

If wound tight, release tension by placing control knob or lever to "Start" position. If starter spring does not release, place control at "Crank" position. To prevent injury, hold crank handle with one hand while removing Phillips head screw and handle assembly from starter housing. This will release spring. Fig. 22.

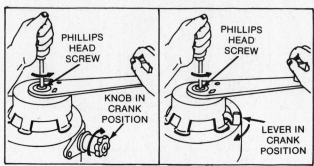

Fig. 22 — Releasing Spring

Broken Spring, Windup Starter

To check starter for a broken spring, while unit is still on engine, place control knob or lever to "Start" position. Turn cranking handle ten turns clockwise. If engine does not turn over, either the spring is broken or the starter clutch balls are not engaged. While turning the cranking handle, watch the starter clutch ratchet; if it does not move the starter spring is probably broken.

Disassemble Windup

Remove blower housing. Remove screw holding cranking handle to housing. Fig. 22. Bend tangs holding starter spring and housing assembly upward and lift retainer plate, spring and housing assembly out of blower housing. Fig. 23.

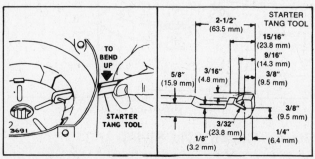

Fig. 23 — Removing Spring Housing

CAUTION: Do not attempt to remove starter spring from its housing.

Inspect Starter Parts

Inspect spring and housing assembly for spring breakage or other damage. Inspect ratchet gear on outside of blower housing for wear or damage.

Do not remove retaining plate from spring and cup assembly.

Check movement of control knob or control lever for ease of operation and damage or wear. (Clean and oil.) Fig. 24.

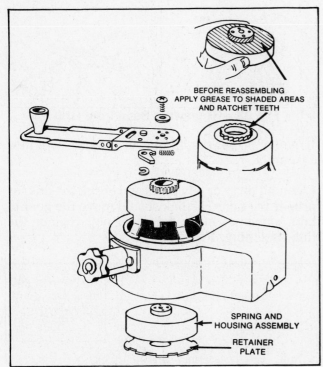

Fig. 24 — Inspecting Parts & Replacing Spring Cup

When re-assembling, be sure to re-install spring washer in housing before placing cup, spring and release assembly into housing. Bend retaining tangs down securely, Fig. 25.

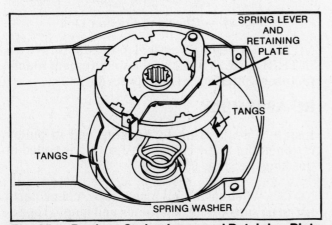

Fig. 25 — Replace Spring Lever and Retaining Plate

VERTICAL PULL STARTER

REMOVING AND INSTALLING A ROPE OR SPRING

Before servicing starter, all tension must be removed from rope.

Use a screwdriver to lift the rope up approximately one foot (304.8 mm). Wind the rope and pulley counterclockwise 2 or 3 turns, as shown in Fig. 26. This will completely release tension from the starter spring.

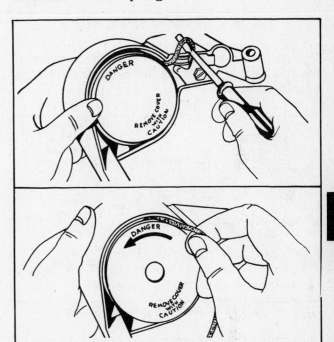

Fig. 26 — Providing Slack

Note the warning on the plastic cover, then use a screwdriver as shown in Fig. 27, to remove the cover.

CAUTION: Do not pull rope with the pulley cover removed, unless the spring is detached from spring anchor.

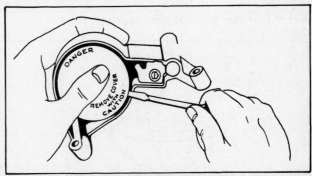

Fig. 27 — Removing Cover

7 A

STARTERS
Vertical Pull

Remove anchor bolt and anchor. Fig. 28. Inspect starter spring for kinks or damaged ends. If the starter spring is to be replaced, carefully remove it from the housing at this time.

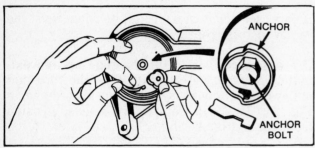

Fig. 28 — Removing Spring Anchor

Remove the rope guide and note the position of the link before removing the assembly from its housing. Fig. 29.

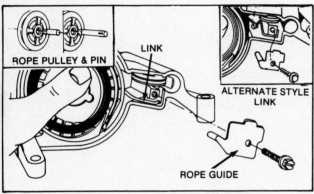

Fig. 29 — Removing Rope Guide

Rope pulley and pin may be replaced if worn or damaged.

Make a rope inserter tool, as shown in Fig. 30. Use the rope inserter tool and/or pliers to remove rope from pulley. Fig. 31 and 32.

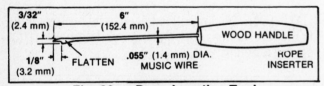

Fig. 30 — Rope Inserting Tool

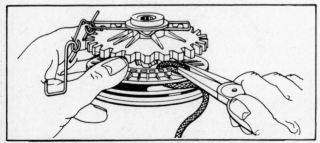

Fig. 31 — Removing Rope from Pulley

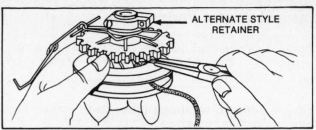

Fig. 32 — (Alternate Style) Removing Rope from Pulley

Remove rope from grip, as shown in Fig. 33.

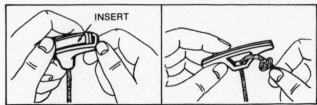

Fig. 33 — Removing Rope from Grip

If pulley or gear is damaged, replace with new assembly.

Clean all dirty or oily parts and check the link for proper friction. The link should move the gear to both extremes of its travel; if not, replace the link assembly. Fig. 34.

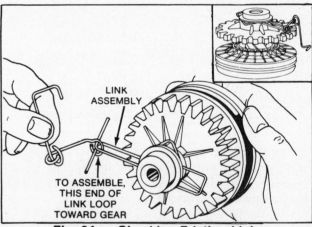

Fig. 34 — Checking Friction Link

NOTE: To repair vertical pull starters with INTERLOCK SYSTEM, follow equipment manufacturers interlock repair procedure.

RE-ASSEMBLY

Install a new spring by hooking end in pulley retainer slot and winding until spring is coiled in the housing. Fig. 35.

NOTE: When installing a new rope, check parts list to be sure correct diameter and length rope is used.

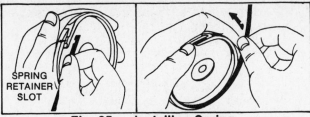

Fig. 35 — Installing Spring

Thread rope through grip and into insert. Tie a small, tight knot. Heat seal the knot to prevent loosening. Pull knot into insert pocket and snap insert into grip. Fig. 36.

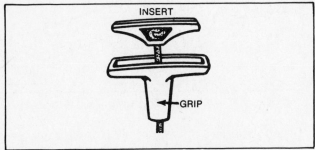

Fig. 36 — Installing Rope

Insert the rope through the housing and into the pulley, using the rope inserter tool. Tie a small knot, heat seal and pull tight into the recess in the rope pulley. Rope must not interfere with gear motion. Fig. 37.

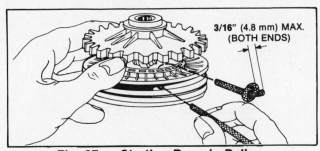

Fig. 37 — Starting Rope in Pulley

Install pulley assembly in the housing, with link in pocket or hole of casting, as shown. Install rope guide. Fig. 38.

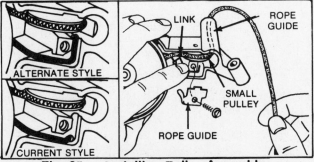

Fig. 38 — Installing Pulley Assembly

Rotate pulley in a counterclockwise direction until the rope is fully retrieved. Fig. 39.

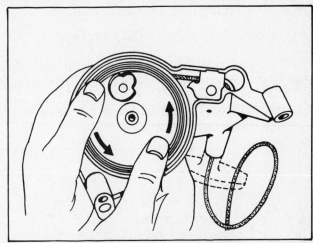

Fig. 39 — Retracting Rope

Hook the free end of spring to spring anchor, and install the screw, torque to 75 to 90 inch pounds (8.5 – 10.2 Nm). Lubricate spring with a small quantity of engine oil or lubricate. Fig. 40.

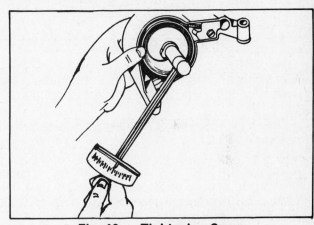

Fig. 40 — Tightening Screw

Snap the cover in place. Wind starter spring by pulling rope out approximately one foot (304.8 mm); wind rope and pulley 2 or 3 turns, clockwise to achieve proper rope tension. Fig. 41.

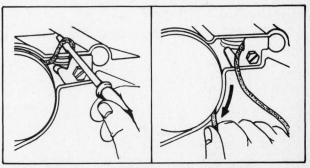

Fig. 41 — Adding Tension to Rope

7
A

7

STARTERS
Test Equipment

Equipment to Test Starter Motors

The following equipment is recommended for test and repair of starter motors.

Volt/Ohm/Ampere (VOA) Meter

The suggested VOA meter is available from your Briggs & Stratton source of supply. Order as part No. 19236. The meter may be used to read volts. ohms or amperes when leads are attached to appropriate connector. Fig. 42.

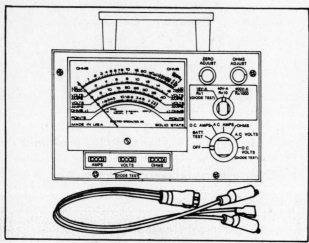

Fig. 42 — VOA Meter

A growler or armature tester is available from an Automobile Diagnostic Service supplier.

A known good 12 volt or 6 volt battery is required for some tests.

A Trysit Sirometer is available from your Briggs & Stratton source of supply. Order as part No. 19200. The Sirometer measures from 800 to 25000 revolutions per minute (RPM). Fig. 43.

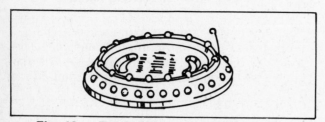

Fig. 43 — Trysit Sirometer (Tachometer)

A starter motor test bracket may be made as shown in Fig. 44.

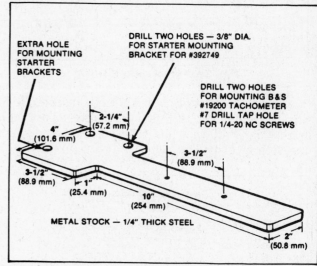

Fig. 44 — Starter Mounting Test Bracket

Brush retainers may be made from scrap pieces of rewind starter spring as shown in Fig. 45. Select the retainer required.

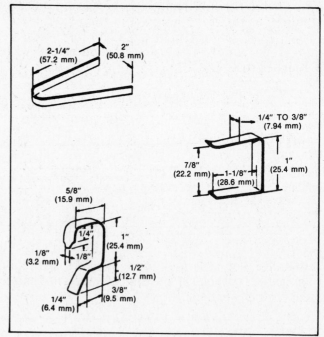

Fig. 45 — Brush Retainers

7
B

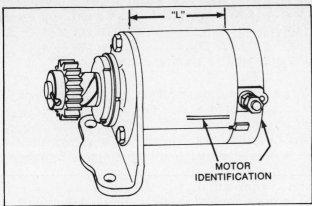

Fig. 46 — Typical 12 VDC Starter Motor

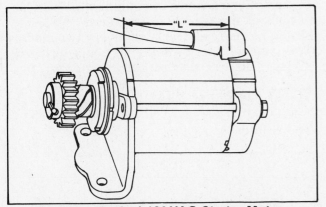

Fig. 47 — Typical 120 VAC Starter Motor

TROUBLESHOOTING 12 VOLT & 120 VOLT STARTING SYSTEMS

The following list is given to aid in diagnosing problems for 12 volt and 120 volt systems.

NOTE: If a starting problem is encountered, the engine itself should be thoroughly checked to eliminate it as the cause of starting difficulty. It is a good practice to check the engine for freedom of rotation by removing the spark plug and turning the crankshaft over by hand, to be sure it rotates freely.

1. Cranks Engine Slowly —
   A. Additional load affecting performance (see note).
   B. Discharged battery (page 11 and 17).
   C. Faulty electrical connection (battery circuit).
   D. Discharged battery (see alternators).
   E. Dirty or worn starter motor commutator, bearing, weak magnets, etc.
   F. Worn brushes or weak brush spring.
   G. Wrong oil viscosity for temperature expected.
   H. Extension cord longer than 25 feet. (120 volt AC only)

7 B

Manufacturer Name	Motor Identification (Fig. 46 and 47)	Motor Voltage	Page Number
Briggs & Stratton	3-1/16" L	12	23
Briggs & Stratton	3-3/4" L	12	23
Briggs & Stratton	3-1/2" L	120	23
American Bosch	SMH-12-A11	12	30
American Bosch	SME-12-48	12	30
American Bosch	01965-23-MO-30-SM	12	30
American Bosch	SME-110-C3	120	30
American Bosch	SME-110-C6	120	30
American Bosch	SME-110-C8	120	30
American Bosch	06026-28-M030SM	120	30
Mitsubishi	MMO-5ML	12	30
Mitsubishi	MMO-4FL	12	30
Mitsubishi	M001T02271	12	30
Mitsubishi	V282188	120	30
Motor Products	None	12	10

Fig. 48 — Starter Motor Identification

2. Engine Will Not Crank —
  A. Faulty safety interlocks.
  B. Discharged or defective battery.
  C. Faulty electrical connections.
  D. Faulty starter motor switch (open circuit).
  E. Open circuit in starter motor.
  F. Defective rectifier assembly (120 VAC only).
  G. Brushes sticking, etc.
  H. Faulty solenoid.
  I. Power source inoperative (wall outlet – 120 VAC only).

3. Starter Motor Spins;
But Does Not Crank Engine —
  A. Sticking pinion gear due to dirt.
  B. Damaged pinion or ring gear.
  C. Battery faulty or damaged.
  D. Incorrect rotation due to reversed motor polarity — all motors rotate counterclockwise viewed from pinion gear.

4. Starter Motor Blows Fuses —
(120 Volt Starter Motor Only)
  A. Shorted starter motor switch.
  B. Shorted rectifier assembly.
  C. Shorted 120 volt extension cord to starter motor.
  D. Armature shorted.
  E. Overloaded circuit.

5. Starter Motor Spins;
Will Not Stop
  A. Defective starter switch.

NICKEL-CADMIUM STARTING SYSTEM SERIES 92000 and 110900 ENGINES

This Briggs & Stratton starter system consists of a starter motor and a starter switch, a wiring harness and a nickel cadmium rechargeable battery and battery charger. When the ignition key is turned to START, the battery supplies power to the starter motor, cranking the engine similar to the system used in an automobile. Under normal conditions, the battery will provide 40 to 60 starts before recharging is necessary.

NOTE: Some equipment manufacturers use a battery and charger of a different style than illustrated. In such cases, follow the equipment manufacturer's recommendations.

When the battery needs recharging, the charger is plugged into a 120 volt AC household outlet, and then connected to the battery. The battery will be fully charged within a 14 to 16 hour period. It is not recommended the battery be recharged if temperatures are below 40° F (4° C). Continual charging may be harmful to this battery. For best results, charge the battery within temperature limits of 40° F (4° C) to 105° F (40° C) and after each use of equipment. When long periods of storage are encountered, the battery should be charged over night every two months. This type of battery will lose its charge when not in use. This will shorten battery life.

NOTE: The battery is shipped in a discharged state and must be charged 14 to 16 hours prior to its initial use.

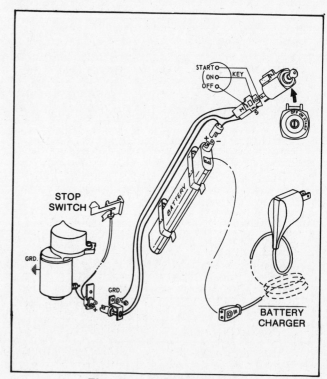

Fig. 49 — Wiring Diagram

NOTE: If a starting problem is encountered, the engine itself should be thoroughly checked to eliminate it as the cause of starting difficulty. It is a good practice to check the engine for freedom of rotation by removing the spark plug and turning the crankshaft over by hand, to be sure it rotates freely.

7 B

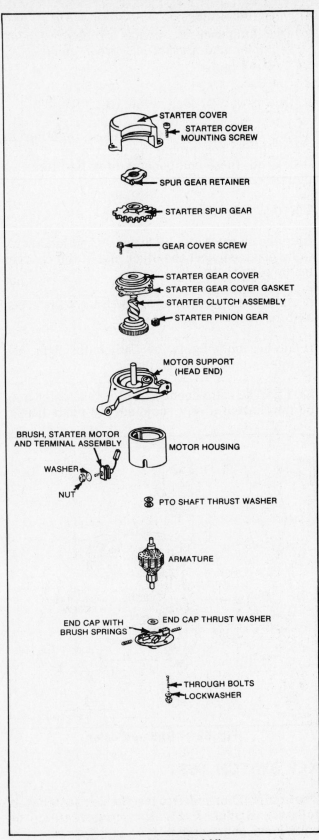

Fig. 50 — Exploded View

The following list is provided to aid in diagnosing problems.

1. Cranks Engine Slowly —
A. Additional starting load affecting performance. See Note, page 10.
B. Battery discharged. See Fig. 51.
C. Faulty battery charger. See Fig. 52.
D. Poor electrical connection (wiring harness). See Fig. 49.
E. Starter motor clutch slipping. See page 13.
F. Brushes sticking in brush holders or worn brushes. See Fig. 58.
G. Dirty or worn starter motor commutator. See page 14 and 15.
H. Weak magnets.

2. Engine Will Not Crank —
A. Discharged or faulty battery. See page 12.
B. Faulty wiring harness (open circuit). See Fig. 49.
C. Faulty starter switch (open circuit). See Fig. 53.
D. Open circuit in starter motor itself. See page 13.
E. Brushes sticking, etc. See Fig. 58.

3. Starter Motor Spins; But Does Not Crank Engine —
A. Sticking nylon spur gear, due to dirt. See page 13.
B. Damaged pinion or starter clutch gear. See page 13.
C. Starter motor clutch slipping. See page 13.
D. Incorrect rotation due to reversed motor polarity — all motors rotate counterclockwise at the pinion gear.

TESTING THE NICKEL CADMIUM BATTERY AND CHARGER

The following paragraphs describe an inexpensive battery load tester and a battery charger tester which may be easily constructed.

BATTERY TESTER

Parts Needed

1. Two GE sealed beam headlight bulbs #4001.

2. Briggs & Stratton VOA meter; page 8 or use a 0 to 15 volt DC voltmeter.

3. Two #70 Miller alligator clips, with #62 insulators, or a battery connector plug from a wiring harness.

Solder the two headlights together with wires, and connect the voltmeter as shown in the accompanying illustration. Fig. 51.

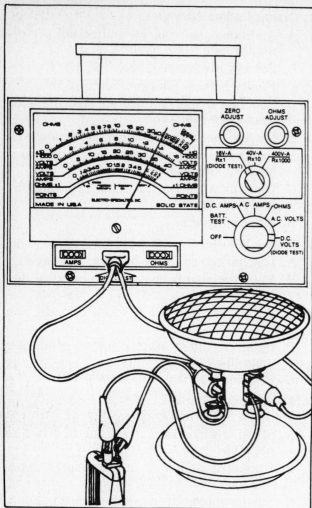

Fig. 51 — Battery Charger Tester

1. One IN4005 diode.
2. Two lamp sockets, such as a Dialco #0931-102, red color and a #0932-102, green color.
3. Two #53 bulbs.
4. One #6-32, 3/4" long screw (m3.5 x 0.6).
5. One #3-48, 3/4" long screw (m2.5 x 0.45).

These components are soldered together as shown in the accompanying illustration, Fig. 52. if desired, these components may be fitted to a plastic case.

The test procedure is as follows:

Plug the charger into a 120 volt AC outlet, known to be good, connect the other end of the charger to the tester.

A charger in good condition will light the green bulb only.

If neither bulb lights, or both bulbs light, the charger would be defective.

NOTE: The component parts for this tester may be purchased at any radio supply parts house.

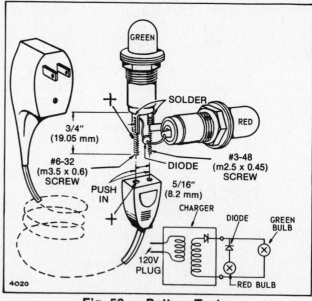

Fig. 52 — Battery Tester

A fully charged battery, when connected to this headlight set up will light the bulbs brightly for at least five minutes. The voltmeter reading should be 13.5 volts minimum after one minute, using the headlight load. A voltmeter reading of 13 volts, or less, within a one minute period indicates a defective cell in the battery. Replace battery.

NOTE: The battery must be in a fully charged condition, prior to the above test. If the battery is not fully charged, it will require charging for a 14 to 16 hour period before proceeding with the above test. This voltmeter test is valid only after a one minute period, when using the lights as a load, because the voltage continues to drop slowly throughout most of the test.

BATTERY CHARGER TESTER

The parts needed to construct a battery charger tester are as follows. (See following for parts ordering information.)

KEY SWITCH TEST

The equipment needed to test the key switch is as follows: Briggs & Stratton meter #19236 or equivalent ohmmeter.

Test key switch as noted in Fig. 53. Replace switch if not as shown under column, "Check Continuity."

7
B

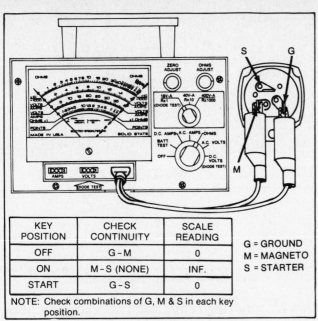

KEY POSITION	CHECK CONTINUITY	SCALE READING
OFF	G - M	0
ON	M - S (NONE)	INF.
START	G - S	0

NOTE: Check combinations of G, M & S in each key position.

G = GROUND
M = MAGNETO
S = STARTER

Fig. 53 — Starter Key Switch

CHECKING THE STARTER MOTOR DRIVE AND CLUTCH

When the starter switch is activated, the nylon spur gear should rise, engaging the flywheel ring gear, and crank the engine. This action can be observed by removing the starter cover. If the starter motor drive does not react properly, inspect the helix and the nylon spur gear for freeness of operation. If any sticking occurs, this must be corrected. Proper operation of the starter is dependent on the nylon spur gear freely moving on the helix. See Fig. 54.

NOTE: Do not oil nylon spur gear or clutch helix.

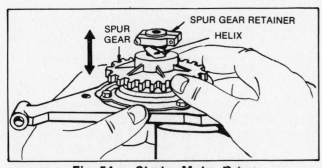

Fig. 54 — Starter Motor Drive

The starter motor clutch is designed to prevent damage from shock loads such as an engine backfire. The clutch should not slip during normal engine cranking. This can be checked by blocking the mower blade and engaging the starter motor. If the clutch assembly slips at this time, it should be replaced.

CAUTION: Remove spark plug high tension wire prior to this test if starter motor is mounted on engine.

CHECKING THE STARTER MOTOR

A performance test of the starter motor may be made in the following manner.

Equipment Needed —

A tachometer capable of reading 1500 RPM.
An ammeter capable of reading 0 to 5 amps.
A fully charged battery.

Connect the starter motor, battery and ammeter, as shown in the illustration. See Fig. 55.

Insert the tachometer in the end of the starter clutch helix and activate the starter motor.

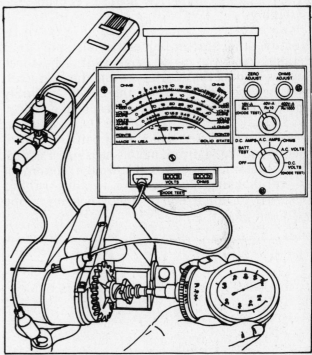

Fig. 55 — Performance Test

A starter motor in good condition will be within the following specifications.

Starter Motor RPM — 1000 minimum
Current — 3½ Amperes maximum

If the starter motor does not perform satisfactorily, the following should be checked, and corrected if necessary.

1. A binding condition between the pinion and clutch gear or mis-alignment of motor bearings.

7B

2. Starter motor brushes sticking in brush holders.

3. A dirty or worn armature commutator.

4. A shorted, open or grounded armature.

   A. Shorted armature (worn insulation, wires touching each other) will be indicated by slow speed and high current.

   B. Open armature (broken wire) may not turn or will have low RPM.

   C. Grounded armature (worn insulation, wire touching armature) will not turn or may turn slowly and will have excessive current (amperes).

5. Weak magnets.

DISASSEMBLY OF STARTER MOTOR

Study Fig. 50 prior to Starter Motor Disassembly.

Remove the starter cover, nylon spur gear retainer and the nylon spur gear. The three screws holding the gear cover and the gear itself may now be removed. Lift the clutch assembly and the pinion gear off their respective shafts.

Remove the starter motor thru bolts. Separate motor end head from motor housing. Fig. 56. Push motor armature out through bottom of starter housing, taking care to slide rubber mounted terminal out of motor housing along with end cap. Fig. 57.

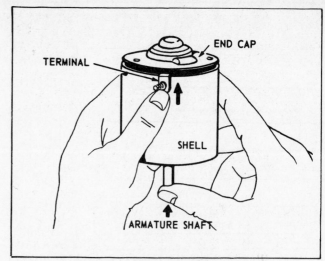

Fig. 57 — Removing Armature

Before removing armature from end cap, check brushes for freedom of movement. If brushes are found to be sticking in their retainers, this must be corrected, or poor starter motor performance will result. Fig. 58. If brushes are worn to a length of 1/4″ (6.4 mm) or less, the brushes should be replaced. Check brush springs for proper tension (sufficient force to keep brush in firm contact with commutator).

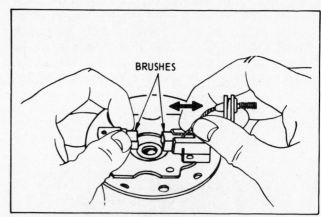

Fig. 58 — Checking Brushes

Clean all dirt accumulations from armature, end cap, motor support, gears, etc. The end cap bearings and armature should not be soaked in a solvent. The armature commutator may be cleaned with a fine sandpaper or commutator paper. Do not use aluminum oxide paper or emery cloth, as emery will embed in the commutator and cause rapid brush wear.

If the armature is suspected to be defective, a new armature should be tried in the motor. If proper testing equipment is available, check the suspected armature to determine if it is defective.

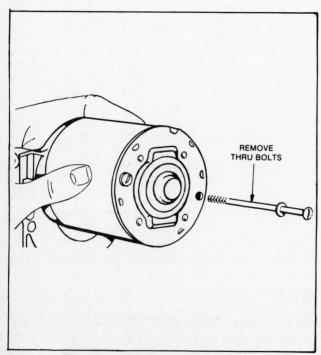

Fig. 56 — Removing Thru Bolts

7
B

Starter motor armatures have very low resistance. Usually below detection on available multimeters (volts – amperes – ohms). To check for shorted armatures, a piece of equipment known as a "growler" may be used. If this equipment is not available, a known good armature should be used and performance checked.

If the magnets are suspect, a new motor housing should be tried to test motor performance.

ASSEMBLY OF STARTER MOTOR

When all parts have been thoroughly inspected, lightly lubricate bearings with a #20 oil and re-assemble in the following manner.

Insert brush springs and brushes in holders as far as possible, and hold them in this position with tool shown in Fig. 59. Place thrust washers on armature shaft, using care to insure brushes clear commutator, slide armature shaft into end cap bearing. See Fig. 59.

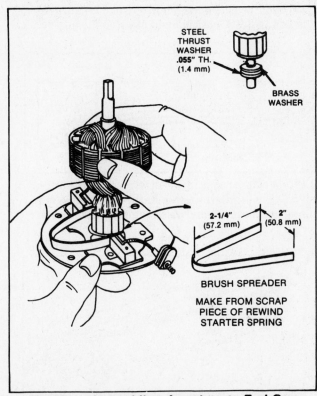

Fig. 59 — Assembling Armature to End Cap

Support armature shaft and slide it slowly into starter housing, as shown in Fig. 60. Insert rubber mounted terminal into starter housing at this time.

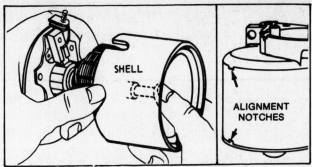

Fig. 60 — Inserting Armature

Place remaining thrust washers on motor PTO shaft, install end head cover and thru bolts. Notches in end cap, housing and end head must be aligned. Fig. 60. Check for end play to be sure armature is free. Slip pinion and starter motor clutch gear on shaft, add a small amount of gear lubricant to gears and install gear cover and gasket. Fig. 61.

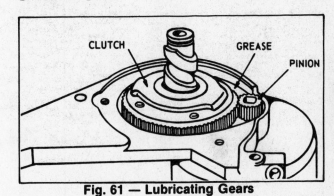

Fig. 61 — Lubricating Gears

Tap end cap edge lightly using a soft hammer as this will align the bearings. See Fig. 62.

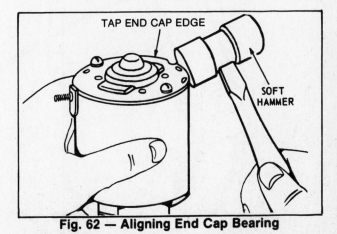

Fig. 62 — Aligning End Cap Bearing

Replace nylon spur gear and retainer assembly, tighten retainer screws securely. NOTE: Do not oil nylon spur gear or clutch helix. Install starter cover. The starter motor assembly is now ready for re-installation to the engine.

7
B

ELECTRIC STARTER KEY SWITCH AND WIRING RECOMMENDATIONS
FOR 12 VOLT NICKEL CADMIUM BATTERY STARTING SYSTEM — SERIES 92000 AND 110900 ENGINES

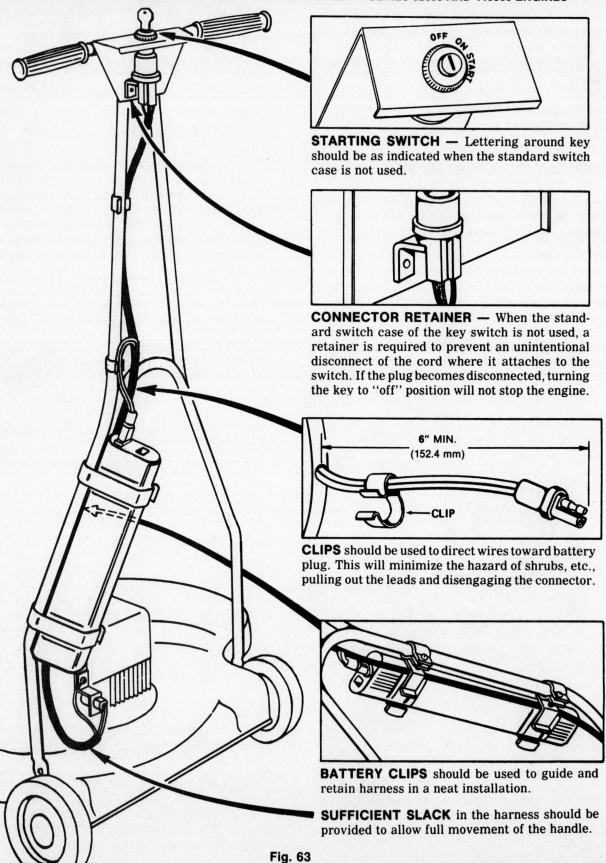

STARTING SWITCH — Lettering around key should be as indicated when the standard switch case is not used.

CONNECTOR RETAINER — When the standard switch case of the key switch is not used, a retainer is required to prevent an unintentional disconnect of the cord where it attaches to the switch. If the plug becomes disconnected, turning the key to "off" position will not stop the engine.

CLIPS should be used to direct wires toward battery plug. This will minimize the hazard of shrubs, etc., pulling out the leads and disengaging the connector.

BATTERY CLIPS should be used to guide and retain harness in a neat installation.

SUFFICIENT SLACK in the harness should be provided to allow full movement of the handle.

Fig. 63

7
B

The battery used to operate starter motors on most Briggs & Stratton engines above 4 horsepower, is of the 12 volt, lead acid — wet cell type. This type is available as a wet charge or dry charge battery.

The wet charged maintenance-free battery is filled with electrolyte at the time of manufacture. The level of electrolyte can not be checked.

The dry charge battery is manufactured with fully charged plates. Electrolyte must be added at the time that the battery is placed in service. Before activating a dry charge battery, read and follow the manufacturer's recommended procedure. Fig. 66.

BATTERY GAS IS EXPLOSIVE. DO NOT store, charge or use a battery near an open flame or devices which utilize a pilot light or can create a spark.

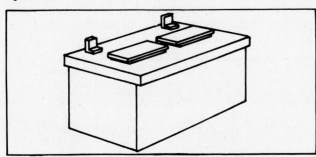

Fig. 64 — Typical Dry Charge Battery

Installation:

1. Before installing battery, connect all equipment to be operated.
2. Place battery in holder with a flat base. Tighten hold downs evenly until snug. DO NOT overtighten.
3. Connect positive terminal to positive post FIRST to prevent sparks from accidental grounding. Tighten connectors securely.
4. Connect negative terminal to negative battery terminal. Tighten connectors securely.

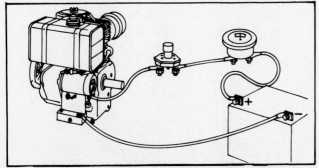

Fig. 65 — Typical 12V Wiring Diagram

Checking Battery

1. Physical check — clean if necessary.
   A. Corrosion
   B. Dirt
   C. Terminal and clamps
      (secure — good conditions)
2. Bring battery to full charge.

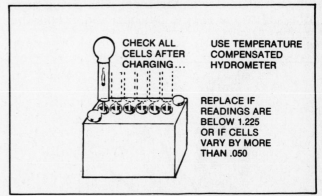

CHECK ALL CELLS AFTER CHARGING . . .

USE TEMPERATURE COMPENSATED HYDROMETER

REPLACE IF READINGS ARE BELOW 1.225 OR IF CELLS VARY BY MORE THAN .050

Fig. 66 — Checking 12V Battery Cells
(Lead Acid — Wet Cell — Dry Charge)

DANGER: DO NOT EXCEED CHARGE RATE OF 1/10 AMPERE FOR EVERY AMPERE OF BATTERY RATING. Consult battery manufacturer for maximum charge recommendations.

A. Use a taper charger (automatically reduces charge rate).
B. Fill battery cells with distilled water or tap water after charging (for batteries that have been in service).

NOTE: If battery gets "Hot" to the touch or is spitting acid (gassing) excessively, unplug charger periodically.

3. With battery fully charged, check specific gravity readings of each cell with a Battery Hydrometer and record readings (Fig. 66).

All readings should be above 1.250 (compensating for temperature). If specific gravity readings varied .050 or if ALL cells read less than 1.225, replace battery.

Attach voltmeter clips to the battery posts, positive lead (+) to positive post of battery, negative lead (–) to negative post of battery. With ignition switch "Off" press starter button. If ignition switch and starter switch are the same switch, disconnect spark plug lead from plug and turn switch to "Start." Voltmeter should read 9 volts or more while cranking engine. If less than 9 volts, replace battery.

7
B

STARTERS
Gear Drive 12V & 120V

GEAR DRIVE STARTER MOTOR USED ON MODEL 130000

This starting system incorporates a permanent magnet motor and back gearing. A gear type engagement method similar to an automobile starter is used. When the starter motor is activated, the helix on the back gear shaft drives a pinion gear into engagement with a ring gear attached to the engine flywheel and cranks the engine.

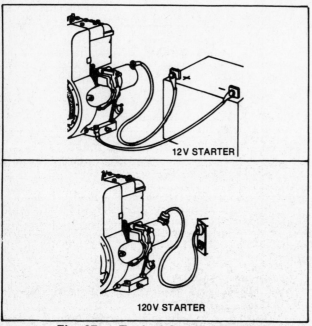

Fig. 67 — Typical Starter Motors

A LIST IS GIVEN TO AID YOU IN DIAGNOSING PROBLEMS FOR 12 VOLT AND 120 VOLT SYSTEMS. SEE PAGE 9.

The service procedures for both the 12 volt and 120 volt starter motors are similar and will be covered together except where noted otherwise.

The 120 volt electric starter is equipped with a three-prong plug for safety. The longer prong in this plug is connected to the starter motor housing. When the starter motor is plugged into the three-wire cord supplied, and the cord is plugged into a properly grounded receptacle, it will protect the user from shock should the starter-motor insulation fail for any reason. If a longer extension cord is used with this starter, it should also have three-prong and three-hole plugs. Fig. 68.

CAUTION: 120 volt starter motor should be Hi-Pot tested before reassembly to engine to determine if a shock hazard exists.

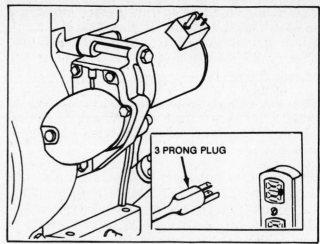

Fig. 68 — 120 Volt Gear Drive Starter

CAUTION: DO NOT run starter motor for more than one minute without cooling 15 minutes.

A 12 ampere hour battery is suggested for warm temperature operation and a 24 ampere hour battery should be used in cold service. See page 17.

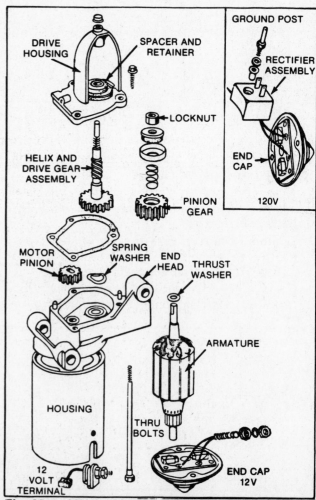

Fig. 69 — 12V & 120V Starter Motor, Exploded View

NOTE: If a starting problem is encountered, the engine itself should be thoroughly checked to eliminate it as the cause of starting difficulty. It is a good practice to check the engine for freedom of rotation by removing the spark plug and turning the crankshaft over by hand, to be sure it rotates freely.

CHECKING STARTER MOTOR DRIVE

When the starter motor is activated, the pinion gear should rise, engaging the flywheel ring gear, and crank the engine. This action can be observed by removing the starter motor. If the starter motor drive does not react properly, inspect the helix and pinion gear for freeness of operation. If any sticking occurs, this must be corrected. Proper operation of the starter is dependent on the pinion gear freely moving on the helix. See Fig. 70.

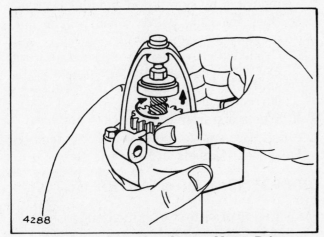
Fig. 70 — Checking Starter Motor Drive

DISASSEMBLY OF STARTER MOTOR DRIVE

Remove drive housing from end head. Fig. 69.

To remove the drive gear assembly for cleaning or replacement, clamp the drive gear in a vise having brass jaws, to prevent damage to the gear teeth. The lock nut may then be removed and the starter drive disassembled for cleaning or replacement.

The pinion gear should be inspected for damaged teeth. If a sticking condition exists between the pinion gear and the helix, the parts may be washed in a solvent such as Stanisol or Varsol. If the sticking condition is not corrected by cleaning, the complete drive assembly must be replaced. Individual parts of the drive assembly are not available.

ASSEMBLING STARTER MOTOR DRIVE

Reversing disassembly procedure for assembling. See Fig. 71. Use care to insure drive spacer and retainer are correctly positioned in drive housing. Note: Do not lubricate drive assembly. A dry silicone spray may be used if necessary.

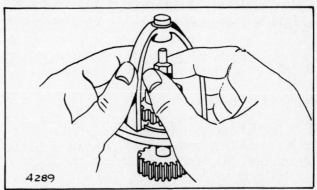
Fig. 71 — Assembling Starter Motor Drive

CHECKING 12 VOLT DC MOTORS

A performance test of the 12 volt starter motor may be made in the following manner.

Equipment Needed —

1. A tachometer capable of reading 10,000 RPM.
2. A 12 volt battery ± 0.3 volts.
3. An ammeter capable of reading 25 amperes.

Connect the starter motor, battery and ammeter as shown on the accompanying illustration. Fig. 72.

NOTE: To test starter motor ON ENGINE, refer to Briggs & Stratton #19236 VOA meter Instruction Manual.

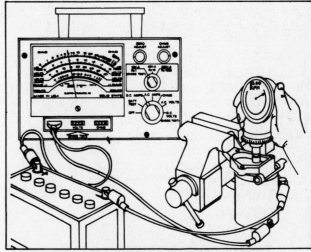
Fig. 72 — Checking 12 Volt Starter Motor Performance

7 B

STARTERS
Gear Drive 12V & 120V

Insert the tachometer in the end of the starter motor shaft and activate the starter motor. A starter motor in good condition will be within the following specifications.

1. Starter motor RPM — 5,600 minimum.
2. Current — 6 amperes maximum (disregard surge current)

CHECKING THE 120 VOLT AC STARTER MOTOR

A performance test of the 120 volt starter motor may be made in the following manner.

Equipment Needed —

1. A tachometer capable of reading 10,000 RPM.
2. An ammeter capable of reading 0 to 10 amperes AC (RMS).

DANGER: The performance test of this starter requires the use of an ammeter, connected in the 120 volt AC starter motor circuit. Extreme care should be used in making this test to minimize the hazard of electrical shock.

Clamp the starter motor in a vise as shown. An ammeter may be connected as shown in the accompanying illustration. Fig. 73. Plug the electrical cord into a 120 volt outlet and insert the tachometer in the end of the starter motor shaft.

CAUTION: Starter motor housing contains two powerful ceramic magnets that may crack if motor housing is clamped in a vise or struck with a hammer or a hard object.

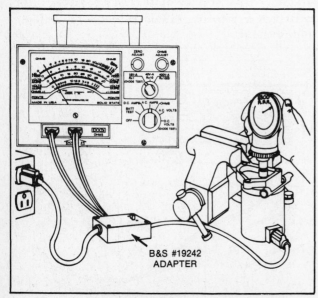

Fig. 73 — Checking 120 Volt Starter Motor Performance

A starter motor in good condition will be within the following specifications.

1. Starter Motor RPM — 8,300 minimum.
2. Current — 1½ amperes maximum AC.

If either the 120 volt AC or 12 volt DC starter motor does not perform satisfactorily, the following should be checked and corrected if necessary.

1. Binding condition between the pinion gear, helix and drive gear assembly.
2. Misalignment or binding between motor bearings.
3. Starter motor brushes sticking in brush holders.
4. Dirty or worn commutator.
5. Shorted, open or grounded armature.
   A. Shorted armature (wire insulation worn and wires touching one another) will be indicated by slow speed and high current.
   B. Open armature (wire broken) will be indicated by low or no RPM.
   C. Grounded armature (wire insulation worn and wire touching armature lamination or shaft) will be indicated by excessive current or no RPM.
6. A defective starter motor switch (in cord).
7. A defective starter motor rectifier assembly.
8. Weakened magnets.

DISASSEMBLY OF STARTER MOTOR

Study Fig. 69 prior to starter motor disassembly.

NOTE: END HEAD, END CAP AND HOUSING MUST BE PLACED IN THE SAME POSITION AS WHEN REMOVED, OR INTERFERENCE MAY RESULT. See Fig. 74.

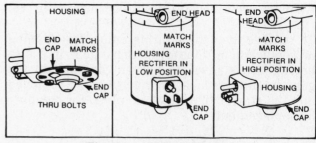

Fig. 74 — Match Marks

Remove thru bolts. Fig. 75. The end cap may then be removed.

(See checking starter motor drive if repair, cleaning or replacement of drive assembly is necessary.)

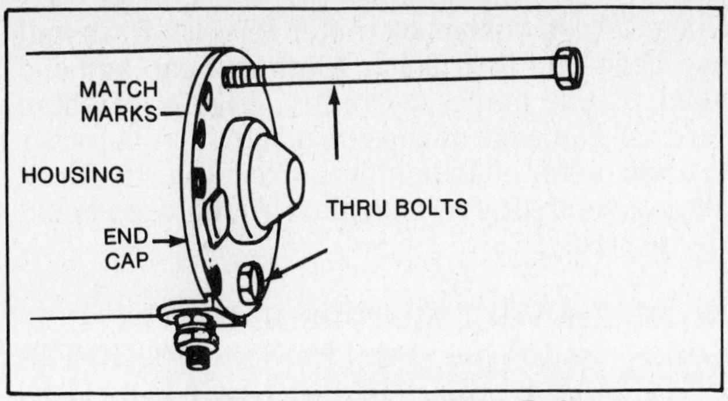

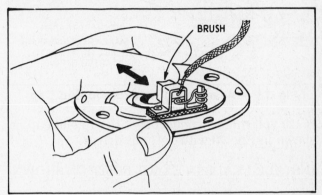

Fig. 75 — Removing Thru Bolts

CAUTION: Do not clamp the motor housing in a vise or strike the motor housing with a hammer. These motors contain two powerful ceramic magnets which can be broken or cracked if the motor housing is deformed or dented.

Remove armature and end cap as shown in Fig. 76. (If 120 volt motor, remove ground post with 1/4″ nut driver to free rectifier assembly. Fig. 79.)

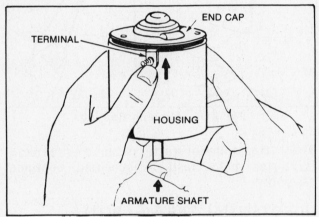

Fig. 76 — Removing Armature

Clean all dirt or corrosion accumulations from the armature, end cap, end head, etc. The bearings, motor housing and armature should not be soaked in a cleaning solution. The armature commutator may be cleaned with a fine sand paper or commutator paper. Do not use emery cloth, as emery will embed in the commutator and cause rapid brush wear. If it is suspected that the armature is defective, a new armature should be tried in the motor. If proper testing equipment is available, check the suspected armature to determine if it is defective.

Starter motor armatures have very low resistance, usually below detection on available multimeters (volt-ampere-ohm). To check for shorted armatures, a piece of equipment known as a ''growler'' may be used.

The brushes should be checked for poor seating, weak brush springs, dirt, oil or corrosion. See Fig. 77.

If the magnets are suspect, a new motor housing should be tried to test motor performance (Figs. 72 and 73).

Fig. 77 — Check Brushes

CHECKING THE RECTIFIER ASSEMBLY 120 VAC STARTER MOTOR

Disconnect rectifier from end cap by removing leads from terminals.

Test rectifier with multimeter (VOA meter, page 8) set on resistance (R x 1 ohm) scale. Touch meter leads to red and black rectifier lead, then reverse meter leads and recheck. The meter should indicate a reading in one direction only. Touch meter leads to black rectifier lead shown in Fig. 79 and both AC posts, then reverse meter leads. The meter should show a reading in one direction only. Touch meter leads to red rectifier lead and both AC posts, then reverse meter leads. The meter should show a reading in one direction only.

If a meter reading is indicated in both directions or no reading is indicated in either direction, the rectifier assembly is defective and must be replaced.

ASSEMBLY OF STARTER MOTORS

When all parts have been thoroughly inspected, lightly lubricate the bearings with #20 oil, and reassemble in the following manner.

Insert the brushes in their respective holders. NOTE: A tool such as shown in Fig. 45 and 78 should be used to hold the brushes clear of the armature commutator when assembling the armature to end cap.

7
B

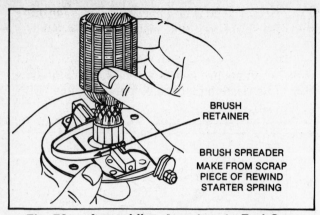

Fig. 78 — Assembling Armature to End Cap

If 120 volt motor, connect rectifier to end cap as shown in Fig. 79 with 1/4″ nut driver.

INSTALL LEADS IN EXACT POSITION SHOWN.

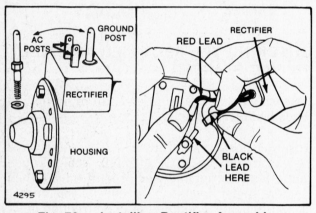

Fig. 79 — Installing Rectifier Assembly

Support armature shaft and slide it slowly into housing, as shown in Fig. 80. Insert rubber mounted terminal into housing at this time.

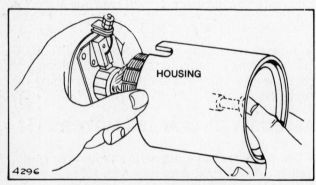

Fig. 80 — Inserting Armature

Place thrust washer on motor PTO shaft. Install end head and thru bolts. Align end cap and end head match marks correctly. Fig. 74. Tighten screws. Tap edge of end cap using a soft hammer to align motor bearings if required. Fig. 81. Check armature shaft for end play. Armature should rotate freely.

NOTE: 120 VOLT MOTORS HAVE TWO POSSIBLE HOUSING POSITIONS. INTERFERENCE MAY RESULT IF CORRECT POSITION IS NOT USED. FIG. 74.

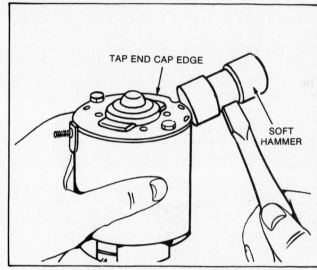

Fig. 81 — Aligning Bearings

Test performance of starter motor. Page 19 or 20. If starter motor tests as specified, continue assembly.

HI-POTENTIAL TEST (HI-POT)

WARNING: A Hi-Potential Test of the 120 Volt AC starter motor must be conducted prior to installation of starter motor to engine.

DANGER: High voltage is used in this test. Exercise extreme care to minimize the hazard of electrical shock.

If test equipment is not available, take starter motor to a local electrical motor repair shop for test. Failure to perform this test may present an electrical hazard. If starter motor tests are positive, continue assembly.

Slip motor pinion gear on armature shaft. Add a small amount of gear lubricant to gear teeth. Position gasket, spring washer and drive housing assembly. Fig. 69. Fasten drive housing to end head securely with three screws. The starter motor assembly is now ready for installation to the engine.

GEAR DRIVE STARTERS

120 VOLT AC; 12 VOLT DC
STARTER MOTOR — USED ON MODEL
SERIES: 170000, 190000, 220000, 240000, 250000 and 320000.

The 120 volt electric starter is equipped with a three-prong plug for safety. The longer prong in this plug is connected to the starter motor housing. When the starter motor is plugged into the three-wire cord supplied, and the cord is plugged into a properly grounded receptacle, it will protect the user from shock should the starter-motor insulation fail for any reason. If a longer extension cord is used with this starter, it should also have three-prong and three-hole plugs. Fig. 68. DO NOT USE extension cords longer than 25 feet (7.62 m).

These starter motors use a gear type engagement method, similar to an automobile starter. When the starter motor is activated, the helix on the starter motor is activated, the helix on the starter motor shaft drives a pinion gear into engagement with a ring gear attached to the engine flywheel and cranks the engine.

CAUTION: 120 volt starter motor should first be Hi-Pot tested before re-assembly to engine to determine if a shock hazard exists.

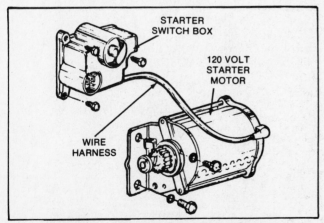

Fig. 82 — 120 Volt Gear Drive Starter

CAUTION: DO NOT run starter motors for more than one minute without cooling 15 minutes.

It is recommended a battery of 32 ampere hour capacity be used with the 12 volt starter. The battery cable size should be #4 or #6.

NOTE: A battery of higher amperage may be required for extremely cold weather starting conditions.

Replacing a Ring Gear

To replace a worn or damaged flywheel ring gear, proceed as follows:

A steel ring gear must be used on the flywheel if the pinion gear on the starter motor is made of steel, An aluminum ring gear must be used on the flywheel if the pinion gear on the starter motor is made of nylon.

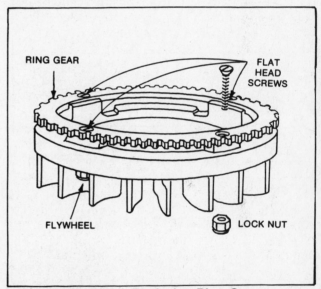

Fig. 83 — Replacing Ring Gear

WARNING: DO NOT strike flywheel with a hard object or metal tool as this may cause flywheel to shatter in operation, causing personal injury or property damage.

STARTERS – Briggs & Stratton Gear Drive 12V & 120V

Mark the center of the rivets holding the ring gear to flywheel, with a center punch. Drill out the rivets using a 3/16" (4.8 mm) drill. Clean holes after drilling. Fig. 83.

Attach new gear to flywheel using four screws and lock nuts provided with gear.

CHECKING STARTER MOTORS

If a starting problem is encountered, check the engine thoroughly to be sure it is not the cause of starting difficulty. It is a good practice to remove the spark plug and rotate the crankshaft by hand, to be sure it rotates freely. Any belt, clutch or other parasitic load will affect cranking performance.

Service procedures for both the 12 volt and 120 volt starter motors are similar and will be covered together, except where noted otherwise.

A list is provided to aid in diagnosing problems for 120 volt DC and 120 volt AC systems. See page 9 and 10.

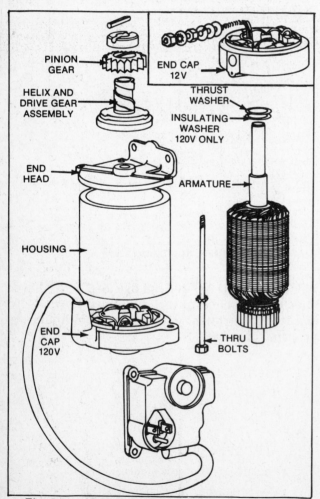

Fig. 84 — 12 Volt & 120 Volt Starter Motor — Exploded View

CHECKING STARTER MOTOR DRIVE

When the starter motor is activated, the pinion gear should rise, engaging the flywheel ring gear and crank the engine. This action can be observed by removing the starter shield. If the starter motor drive does not react properly, inspect the helix and pinion gear for freeness of operation. If any sticking occurs, this must be corrected. Proper operation of the starter is dependent on the pinion freely moving on the helix. See Fig. 85.

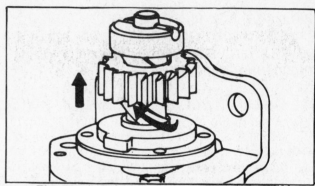

Fig. 85 — Checking Starter Motor Drive

DISASSEMBLING STARTER MOTOR DRIVE

To remove the drive assembly for cleaning or replacement, disconnect and remove starter from engine. Place in "V" block as shown in Fig. 87. Drive the roll pin out with a hammer and 1/8" (3.2 mm) diameter punch to remove the retainer.

NOTE: Some starter drive assemblies utilize a gear return spring. These are protected with a plastic cap over the drive assembly. Carefully snap the plastic cap from the cup using two screwdrivers. See Fig. 86.

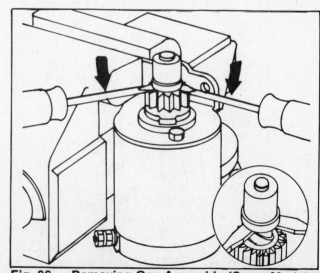

Fig. 86 — Removing Cap Assembly (Some Models)

7
B

The pinion gear should be inspected for damaged teeth. If a sticking condition exists between the pinion gear and the helix, this must be corrected. The parts may be washed in a solvent such as Stanasol or Varsol. The gear, retainer, roll pin and clutch assembly are available from your Briggs & Stratton source of supply if required.

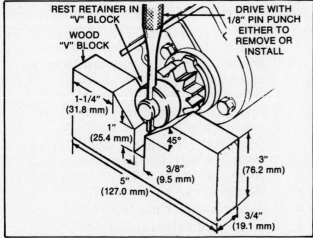

Fig. 87 — Disassembling Starter Motor Drive

ASSEMBLING STARTER MOTOR DRIVE

Reverse disassembly procedure for assembling. Assemble the pinion gear with beveled edge on the gear as shown in Fig. 88. Assemble cup and spring on gear if original assembly was so equipped. Press or drive the roll pin through retainer slot and armature shaft hole with roll pin slot positioned as shown. The roll pin should be centered in shaft within 1/32″ (0.8 mm).

NOTE: ASSEMBLE WITH NEW ROLL PIN ONLY.

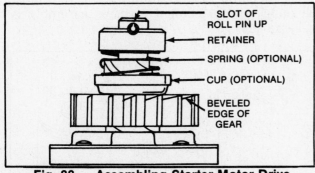

Fig. 88 — Assembling Starter Motor Drive

If the original assembly is equipped with a spring cap assembly, assemble cap as follows:

To install plastic cap, use a socket approximately the same diameter as the plastic cap, for a driver as shown in Figure 89. Press cap in position, cap should lock in position when properly assembled.

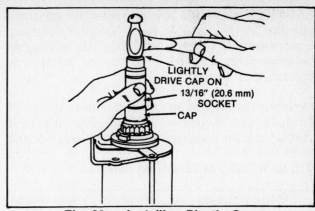

Fig. 89 — Installing Plastic Cap

CHECKING THE STARTER MOTOR PERFORMANCE

A performance test of the 12 volt DC and 120 volt AC starter motors may be made in the following manner.

12 VOLT DC STARTER MOTOR

Equipment Needed — (Page 8)

1. A tachometer capable of reading 10,000 R.P.M.
2. An ammeter capable of reading 0 to 25 amperes.
3. A 12 volt ± 0.3 battery.

Connect the starter motor, battery and ammeter as shown on the accompanying illustration. See Fig. 90. Refer to Fig. 91 for specifications.

NOTE: To test starter motor ON ENGINE, refer to Briggs & Stratton #19236 VOA meter Instruction Manual.

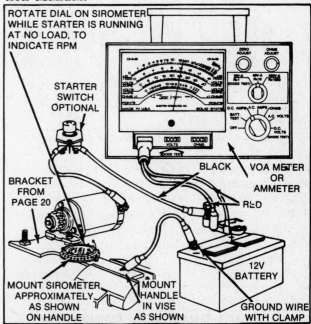

Fig. 90 — Checking Starter Motor Performance

7B

STARTERS – Briggs & Stratton
Gear Drive 12V & 120V

CAUTION: DO NOT clamp motor housing in a vise or strike with a steel hammer. Starter motors contain two powerful magnets which can be broken or cracked if the motor housing is deformed or dented.

Activate the starter motor and note readings of ammeter and tachometer (RPM). Note length of starter motor housing as shown on page 9 and refer to Fig. 91. A starter motor in good condition will be within specifications listed.

Motor Housing Length	Minimum Motor RPM	Maximum Amperes
3-1/16″ (77.8 mm)	6500	18
3-3/4″ (95.3 mm)	6900	19

Fig. 91 — 12 Volt DC Starter Motor Specifications

120 VOLT AC STARTER MOTOR

Connect the starter motor and ammeter as shown in Fig. 92.

DANGER: It is recommended that the starter motor be Hi-Pot tested after final re-assembly.

CAUTION: The performance test of this starter requires the use of an ammeter, connected in the 120 volt AC line cord. Extreme care should be used in making this test to minimize the hazard of electrical shock.

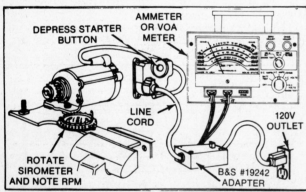

Fig. 92 — Checking Starter Motor Performance

Plug the electrical cord into a 120 volt outlet and press the starter motor button. Note the readings of tachometer or sirometer (RPM) and ammeter. A starter motor in good condition will be within the following specifications. Fig. 93.

Motor Housing Length	Minimum RPM	Maximum Amperes
3-1/2″ (88.9 mm)	6500	2.7

Fig. 93 — Starter Motor Specifications

If either the 120 VAC or 12 VDC starter motor does not perform satisfactorily, the following should be checked and corrected if necessary.

1. A binding or seizing condition in the starter motor bearings.
2. Starter motor brushes sticking in brush holders.
3. A dirty or worn armature commutator or brushes.
4. A shorted, open or grounded armature.
   A. Shorted armature (wire insulation worn and wires touching one another). Will be indicated by low or no R.P.M.
   B. Open armature (wire broken) will be indicated by low or no RPM.
   C. Grounded armature (wire insulation worn and wire touching armature lamination or shaft). Will be indicated by excessive current or no RPM.
5. A defective starter motor switch.
6. A defective starter motor rectifier assembly. (120 volt AC only).
7. Weakened magnets.

DISASSEMBLY OF STARTER MOTORS

Study Fig. 84 prior to starter motor disassembly. Remove thru bolts. The drive head end may now be removed. Inspect bushing for wear. If worn, replace drive head end assembly. Fig. 94.

NOTE: MATCH MARKS AND THRU BOLTS MUST BE PLACED IN THE SAME POSITION AS WHEN REMOVED OR INTERFERENCE MAY RESULT.

(See checking starter motor drive if repair, cleaning or replacement of drive assembly is necessary.)

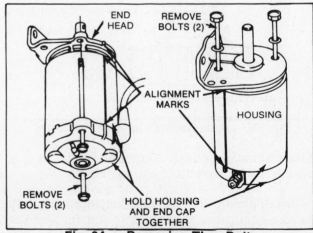

Fig. 94 — Removing Thru Bolts

CAUTION: DO NOT clamp motor housing in a vise or strike with a steel hammer. Starter motors contain two powerful magnets which can be broken or cracked if the motor housing is deformed, dented or dropped.

Hold the armature and commutator end cap against a work surface while sliding housing off the armature. Note: This allows the armature to remain in the end cap for inspection of brush contact to armature. Fig. 95.

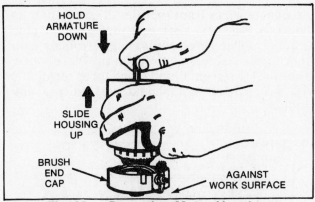

Fig. 95 — Removing Motor Housing

Remove armature from commutator end cap.

Clean all dirt or corrosion accumulations from the armature, end cap, motor support, etc. The bearings, housing and armature should not be soaked in a cleaning solution. The armature commutator may be cleaned with a fine sand paper. Do not use emery cloth, as emery will embed in the commutator and cause rapid brush wear. The commutator may also be machined with the use of a diamond cutting tool to no less than 1.23 (31.24 mm) inches outside diameter. Slots between commutator bars should be cleaned as shown in Fig. 96 after cleaning or machining. If it is suspected that the armature, field coil, magnets or motor housing is defective, a new part should be tried in the motor. If proper testing equipment is available, check the suspected armature or field coil to determine if it is defective (opens or grounds).

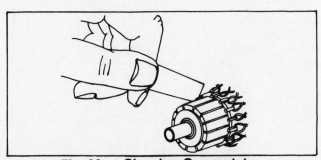

Fig. 96 — Cleaning Commutator

The brushes should be checked for poor seating, weak brush springs, dirt, oil or corrosion. Brush spring pressure should measure from 4.0 to 6.0 ounces. If brushes are worn as shown in Fig. 97, replace. Check to be sure brushes are not sticking in their holders. Use holders to retain brushes and spring during assembly.

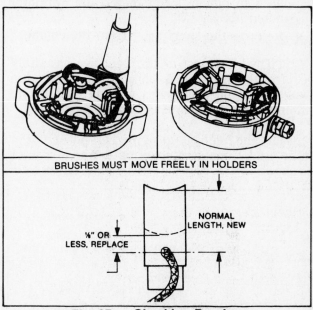

Fig. 97 — Checking Brushes

CHECKING THE BRIGGS & STRATTON RECTIFIER CONTROL ASSEMBLY — 120 VOLT AC STARTER MOTOR

The control assembly consists of a spring loaded switch assembly, cord assembly and rectifier assembly contained in a housing assembly which is provided with an AC three wire ground receptacle. Fig. 98. The test procedure for checking the rectifier control assembly is as follows:

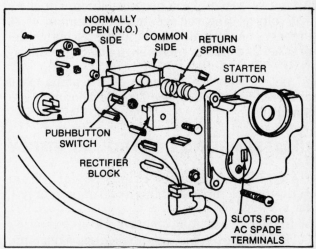

Fig. 98 — Exploded View — Control Assembly

7
B

STARTERS – Briggs & Stratton
Gear Drive 12V & 120V

Equipment Needed —

1. An AC volt meter capable of measuring 120 volts AC.
2. An AC ammeter capable of measuring 25 amperes AC.
3. A VOA meter as shown on page 20 may be used in place of volt meter and ammeter noted above.
4. Remove the spark plug from the engine.

CAUTION: The test of this rectifier assembly requires the use of a 120 volt AC circuit. Extreme care should be used when making this test to minimize the hazard of electrical shock.

Measure the line voltage of the 120 volt AC outlet to be used. Connect the voltmeter and ammeter as shown in Fig. 99 prior to removal from engine.

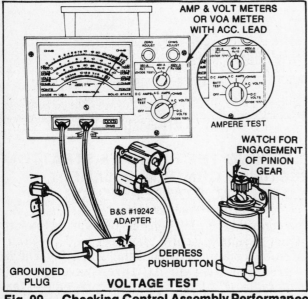

Fig. 99 — Checking Control Assembly Performance

A control assembly in good condition will show 120 volts of line voltage and a maximum of 15 amperes on the ammeter with starter button depressed and starter motor engaged. Fig. 99 inset.

If meters show no readings or a reading of 20 amperes is exceeded, see Troubleshooting, page 9 and 10.

DISASSEMBLING CONTROL ASSEMBLY

DANGER: Disconnect extension cord from outlet before disassembling control assembly.

With control assembly removed from mounting surface, remove three screws holding back plate to housing. Fig. 100. Note position of wires.

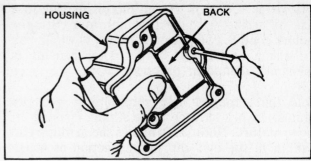

Fig. 100 — Removing Back Plate

Disconnect wires from rectifier. Test rectifier as shown in Fig. 101. With one probe on (+) plus terminal, touch three remaining terminals with other probe. Reverse procedure. Place other probe on (+) terminal and touch three terminals with probe. One test should not indicate any reading.

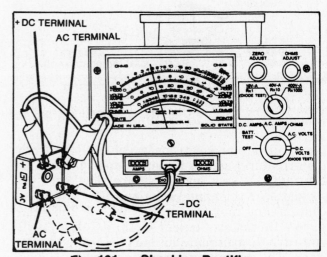

Fig. 101 — Checking Rectifier

To replace rectifier assembly, remove retainer spring washer. Note rectifier position and remove. If rectifier post should break, drill a 3/16″ diameter hole in post location. Connect rectifier with plastic screw and nut. Assemble as noted in Fig. 102 and 104.

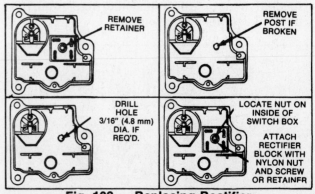

Fig. 102 — Replacing Rectifier

7
B

Test switch assembly as noted in Fig. 103.

ASSEMBLY OF STATOR MOTOR

When all parts have been thoroughly inspected, lightly lubricate the bearings with #20 oil and re-assemble in the following manner. (Assemble wiring in commutator end cap as shown in Fig. 105, 120 volt AC.)

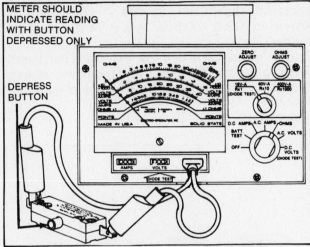

Fig. 103 — Testing Switch Assembly

When re-assembling switch, position starter button and return spring as noted in Fig. 98.

The cord assembly continuity may be tested with the VOA meter noted on page 8.

ASSEMBLY OF 120 VOLT CONTROL ASSEMBLY

Connect wires as shown in Fig. 104.

CAUTION: Incorrect assembly of black and white wires from cord to rectifier will cause motor to run backwards.

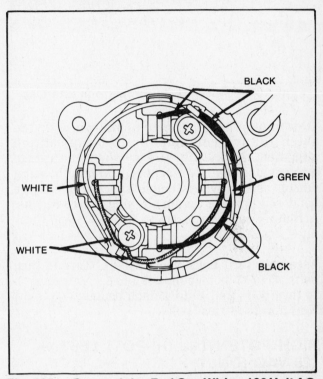

Fig. 105 — Commutator End Cap Wiring 120 Volt AC

Insert brushes and springs in their respective holders.

NOTE: A tool as shown in Fig. 45 and 106 should be used to hold the brushes clear of the armature commutator during assembly.

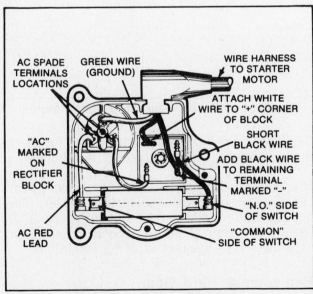

Fig. 104 — Wiring Diagram

Re-assemble backplate to housing. Fig. 100.

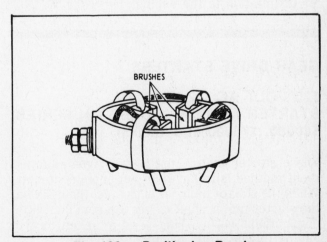

Fig. 106 — Positioning Brushes

STARTERS
Gear Drive 12 V & 120 V

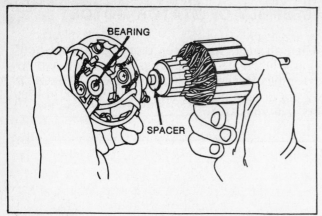

Fig. 107 — Assembling Armature to End Cap

Slide motor housing over armature with the notch toward commutator end cap. Match alignment marks. Fig. 94. Care should be used to prevent damage to magnets in motor housing during assembly. Assemble spacers and drive head end bracket, again aligning match marks. Armature end play is .006 to .038" (.15 to .97 mm) after assembly.

Assemble thru bolts and washers. Torque thru bolts, 45 to 55 inch pounds (5.1 to 6.2 Nm) for 1/4-20 thru bolts and 40 to 45 inch pounds (4.5 to 5.1 Nm) for 10-24 thru bolts.

HIGH POTENTIAL (HI-POT) TEST — 120 VAC (ONLY)

Before and after repairing the 120 volt AC starter motor, a Hi-Pot test must be made to prevent injury. If the proper test equipment is not available, take the starter motor to a qualified electric motor repair shop for testing.

After assembly of the starter motor drive and Hi-Pot test is passed, the starter motor is now ready for installation to the engine.

GEAR DRIVE STARTERS

120 VOLT AC; 12 VOLT DC STARTER MOTOR — USED ON SERIES 140000, 170000 and 190000

These starter motors use a gear type engagement method, similar to an automobile starter. When the starter motor is activated, the helix on the starter motor shaft drives a pinion gear into engagement with a ring gear attached to the engine flywheel and cranks the engine.

Electrical shock is always a hazard with any electrical equipment. To minimize the hazard of electrical shock, the 120 volt starter motor is provided with a three wire power source connection. To maintain the safety provided against electrical shock, the extension cord used between the starter motor and the power source must be a three wire cord, which connects to a properly grounded receptacle. DO NOT USE power cords longer than 25 feet.

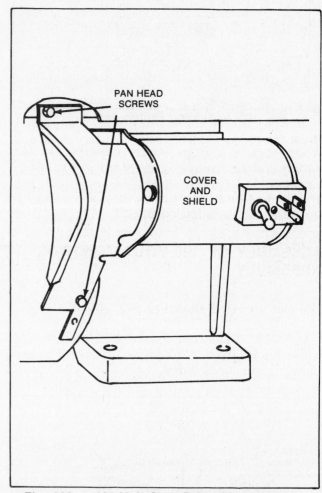

Fig. 108 — 120 Volt Gear Drive Starter Motor

CAUTION: DO NOT run starter motor for more than one minute without cooling 15 minutes.

It is recommended a battery of 32 ampere hour capacity be used with the 12 volt starter. The battery cable size should be #4 or #6. Note: A battery of higher amperage may be required for extremely cold weather starting conditions.

Replacing a Ring Gear

To replace a worn or damaged flywheel ring gear, see page 23, Fig. 82.

7
B

Checking Starter Motors

If a starting problem is encountered, check the engine thoroughly to be sure it is not the cause of starting difficulty. It is a good practice to remove the spark plug and rotate the crankshaft by hand, to be sure it rotates freely. Any belt, clutch or other parasitic load will affect cranking performance.

Service procedures for both the 12 volt and 120 volt starter motors are similar and will be covered together, except where noted otherwise.

A list is provided to aid in diagnosing problems for 12 volt DC and 120 volt AC systems. See page 9 and 10.

CHECKING STARTER MOTOR DRIVE

When the starter motor is activated, the pinion gear should rise, engaging the flywheel ring gear and crank the engine. This action can be observed by removing the starter shield. If the starter motor drive does not react properly, inspect the helix and pinion gear for freeness of operation. If any sticking occurs, this must be corrected. Proper operation of the starter is dependent on the pinion freely moving on the helix. See Fig. 109.

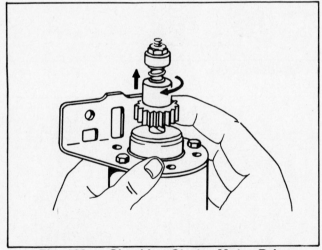

Fig. 109 — Checking Starter Motor Drive

DISASSEMBLING STARTER MOTOR DRIVE

To remove the drive assembly for cleaning or replacement, clamp the pinion gear in a vise having brass jaws, to prevent damage to the gear teeth. The lock nut may then be removed and the starter drive disassembled for cleaning or replacement.

The pinion gear should be inspected for damaged teeth. If a sticking condition exists between the pinion gear and the helix, the parts may be washed in a solvent such as Stanasol or Varsol. If the sticking condition is not corrected by cleaning, the complete drive assembly must be replaced. Individual parts of the drive assembly are not available.

ASSEMBLING STARTER MOTOR DRIVE

Reverse disassembly procedure for assembling. The interior of the shaft screw has a **spline** machined to the center; when assembling, the spline must face the end of the armature shaft. See Fig. 110. Torque the lock nut to **170 inch pounds (19.2 Nm)**. This torque has an effect on pinion travel, so proper torque should be maintained. NOTE: Do not lubricate Drive Assembly.

NOTE: For starter motors equipped with **nylon** pinion gear, page 24 and 25 contains assembly and repair information.

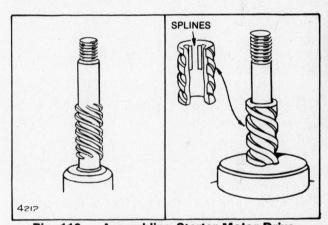

Fig. 110 — Assembling Starter Motor Drive

If sticking occurs during freezing weather, spray a dry silicone spray on helix.

CHECKING STARTER MOTOR PERFORMANCE

120 VOLT AC STARTER MOTORS

A performance test of the 120 volt starter motor may be made in the following manner.

Equipment Needed —

1. A tachometer capable of reading 10,000 RPM.
2. An ammeter capable of reading 0 to 10 amperes.

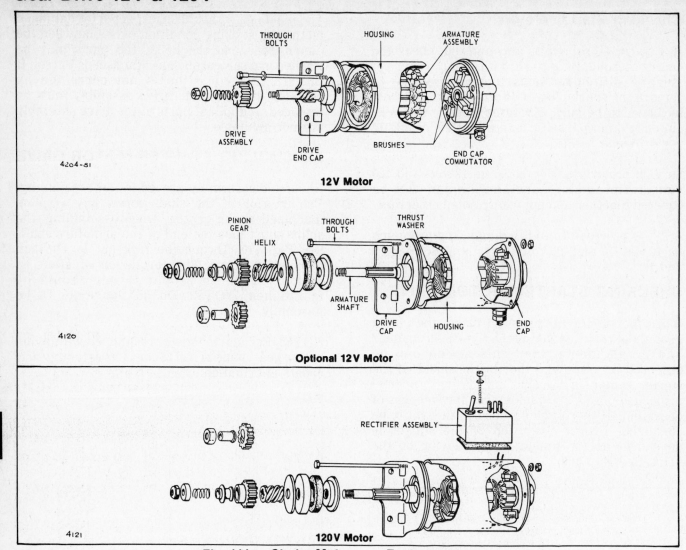

12V Motor

Optional 12V Motor

120V Motor

Fig. 111 — Starter Motors . . . Exploded Views

CAUTION: The performance test of this starter requires the use of an ammeter connected in the 120 volt AC starter motor circuit. Extreme care should be used in making this test to minimize the hazard of electrical shock. It is recommended that a Hi-Pot test be conducted after repairing starter motors to prevent injury.

Clamp the starter motor and connect ammeter as shown in the accompanying illustration. Fig. 112. Plug the electrical cord into a 120 volt outlet, insert the tachometer in the end of the starter motor and press the starter motor switch. Disregard surge current.

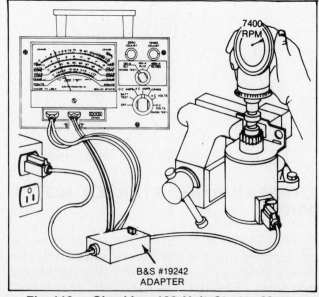

Fig. 112 — Checking 120 Volt Starter Motor Performance

7 B

A starter motor in good condition will be within the following specifications. Fig. 113.

If the starter motor does not meet these requirements a list is given to aid in diagnosing problems. See page 9 and 10.

Starter Motor Identification	Voltage Required	Minimum Motor RPM	Maximum Amperes
American Bosch SME-110-C3 SME-110-C6 SME-110-C8	120	7400	3-1/2
American Bosch 06026-28-M030SM	120	7400	3
Mitsubishi V282188	120	7800	3-1/2

Fig. 113 — 120 Volt Starter Motor Performance Chart

12 VOLT DC STARTER MOTORS

A performance test of the 12 volt starter motor may be made in the following manner.

Equipment Needed —

1. A tachometer capable of reading 10,000 R.P.M.
2. A 6 volt battery ± 0.3 volts.
3. An ammeter capable of reading 40 amperes.
4. A 12 volt battery ± 0.3 volts.

Connect the starter motor, battery and ammeter as shown on the accompanying illustration. See Fig. 114.

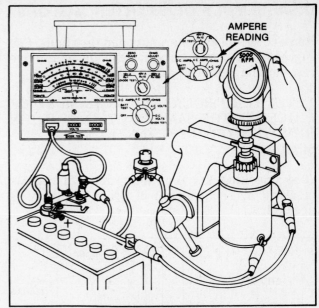

Fig. 114 — Checking 12 Volt Starter Motor Performance

Insert the tachometer in the end of the starter motor and activate the starter motor. A starter motor in good condition will be within the specifications noted in Fig. 115. Disregard surge current.

NOTE: A 6 volt battery is required in some instances for test purposes only. This allows R.P.M. readings to be made on a lower scale. See Fig. 115.

If the starter motor does not perform satisfactorily, a list is given to aid in diagnosing problems. See page 9 and 10.

NOTE: To test starter motor ON ENGINE, refer to Briggs & Stratton #19236 VOA meter Instruction Manual.

7
B

Starter Motor Identification	Voltage Required	Minimum Motor RPM	Maximum Amperes	VOA Scale
American Bosch SME-12A8	6V ± 0.1	5000	25	40 V-A R x 10*
American Bosch SMH-12A-11	12V ± 0.3	4800	16	16 V-A R x 1
American Bosch 01965-23-MO-30-SM	12V ± 0.3	5500	16	16 V-A R x 1
Mitsubishi MMO-4FL MMO-5ML MOO1TO2271	6V ± 0.1	6700	16	16 V-A R x 1

*Note inserts, Fig. 114. **Fig. 115 — 12 Volt Starter Motor Performance Chart**

STARTERS
Gear Drive 12V & 120V

DISASSEMBLY OF STARTER MOTORS

Remove the lockwasher, nuts and thru bolts. See Fig. 116. The armature, drive cap and gear drive can now be removed as an assembly.

NOTE: THRU BOLTS AND NUTS MUST BE PLACED IN THE SAME POSITION AS WHEN REMOVED OR INTERFERENCE MAY RESULT.

(See checking starter motor drive if repair, cleaning or replacement of drive assembly is necessary.)

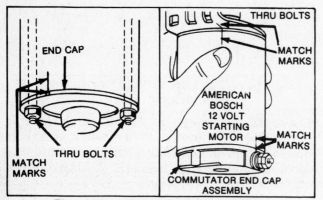

Fig. 116 — Removing Thru Bolts

CAUTION: Do not clamp the motor in a vise or strike the motor with a hammer. Some motors include two powerful ceramic magnets which can be broken or cracked if the motor housing is deformed or dented.

To remove the commutator end cap, lift the brush springs and slide brushes out of the brush holders. The 120 volt AC starter motor rectifier assembly may now be removed by loosening the cover screw and unsoldering the field lead attached to the rectifier assembly. See Fig. 117.

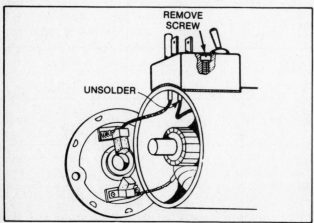

Fig. 117 — Removing Rectifier

Clean all dirt or corrosion accumulations from the armature, commutator end cap, drive end cap, etc. The bearings, housing and armature should not be soaked in a cleaning solution. The armature commutator may be cleaned with a fine sand paper. Do not use emery cloth, as emery will embed in the commutator and cause rapid brush wear. If it is suspected that the armature, field coil or motor housing is defective, new parts should be tried in the motor. If proper testing equipment is available, check the suspected armature or field coil to determine if it is defective. The brushes should be checked for proper seating, weak brush spring, dirt, oil or corrosion. Brush spring pressure should measure from 4 to 6 ounces when pressed to working position. Also check to be sure brushes are not sticking in their respective brush holders. See Fig. 118.

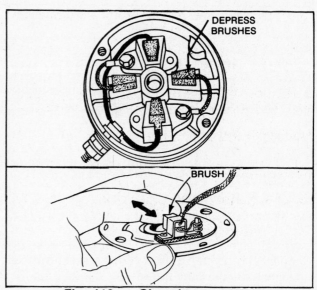

Fig. 118 — Checking Brushes

CHECKING THE RECTIFIER ASSEMBLY 120 VOLT AC STARTER MOTOR

The rectifier assembly consists of a spring loaded switch, which is in a normally "off" position, an AC three wire ground receptacle and four rectifiers encapsuled in an epoxy case. The test procedure for checking the rectifier is as follows:

Equipment Needed —

1. An AC volt meter capable of measuring 120 volts AC.
2. A DC volt meter capable of reading 100 volts DC.
3. A 10,000 ohm resistor (1 watt).

CAUTION: The test of this rectifier assembly requires the use of a 120 volt AC circuit. Extreme care should be used when making this test to minimize the hazard of electrical shock.

Solder the 10,000 ohm resistor to the DC internal terminals of the rectifier, as shown in the accompanying illustration. Fig. 119.

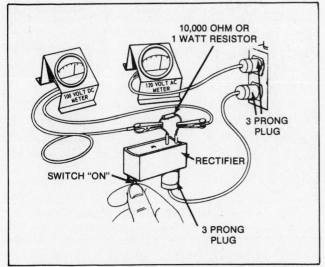

Fig. 119 — Checking Rectifier Assembly

Connect the DC volt meter between the rectifier field terminal and the brush terminal. Fig. 119.

Measure the line voltage of the 120 volt AC outlet to be used. A rectifier assembly in good condition will be within the following specifications:

1. With the switch in the off position, a zero reading should be observed on the DC volt meter.
2. With the switch in the on position, the DC volt meter reading should be 0 to 14 volts lower than the AC line voltage measured previously.

If the drop exceeds 14 volts, the complete rectifier assembly must be replaced, as individual parts for the rectifier assembly are not available.

ASSEMBLY OF STARTER MOTORS

When all parts have been thoroughly inspected, lightly lubricate the bearings with #20 oil and reassemble in the following manner. (Solder the field lead to the rectifier assembly and assemble the rectifier to the housing (120 VAC motor). Fig. 120.

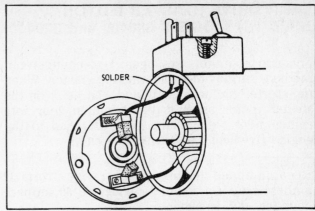

Fig. 120 — Installing Rectifier to Housing

Insert the brushes in their respective holders.

NOTE: A tool such as shown in Fig. 45 should be used to hold the brushes clear of the armature commutator when assembling the commutator end cap to the motor housing.

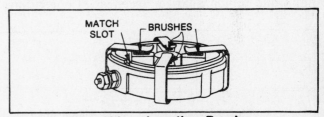

Fig. 121 — Inserting Brushes

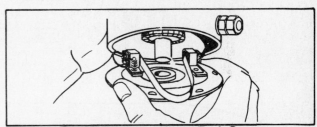

Fig. 122 — Installing End Cap

Slide the armature into the motor housing, being sure to match the drive end cap keyway to the stamped key in motor housing. Assemble end cap, again matching the keyway to key in housing. Care should be used to prevent damage to ceramic magnets where used.

Assemble thru bolts, lockwashers and nuts.

NOTE: THRU BOLTS AND NUTS MUST BE PLACED IN THE SAME POSITION AS WHEN REMOVED OR INTERFERENCE MAY RESULT.

After Hi-Pot test and assembly of the starter motor drive, the starter motor is now ready for installation to the engine.

7
B

STARTERS
Gear Drive 12V

GEAR DRIVE STARTER MOTOR USED ON MODELS 300400 and 320400

This starter motor uses a gear type engagement method, similar to an automobile starter. When the starter motor is activated, the helix on the starter motor shaft drives a pinion gear into engagement with a ring gear attached to the engine flywheel and cranks the engine.

Recommended battery sizes range from 32 ampere hour for normal service to 50 ampere hour for –20° F service.

CHECKING STARTER MOTOR DRIVE

When the starter motor is activated, the pinion gear should engage the flywheel ring gear and crank the engine. This action can be observed by removing the blower housing. If the starter motor drive does not react properly, inspect the helix and pinion gear for freeness of operation.

If any sticking occurs, this must be corrected. Proper operation of the starter is dependent on the pinion freely moving on the helix. See Fig. 123.

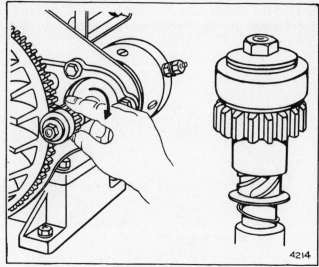

4214

Fig. 123 — Checking Starter Motor Drive

7
B

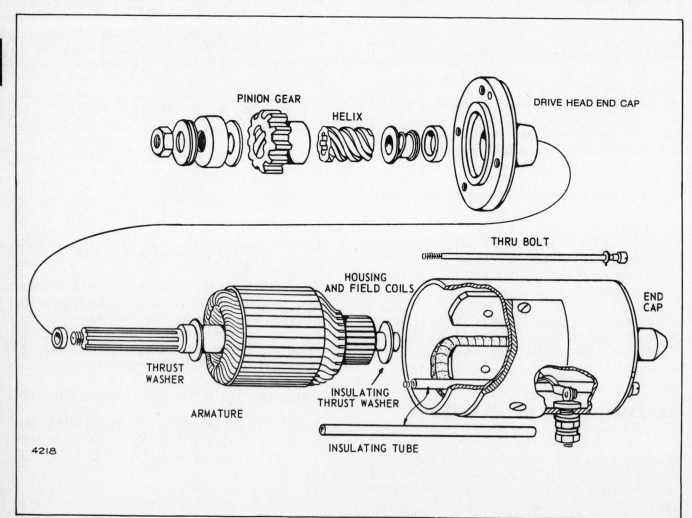

PINION GEAR

HELIX

DRIVE HEAD END CAP

THRU BOLT

HOUSING AND FIELD COILS

END CAP

THRUST WASHER

INSULATING THRUST WASHER

ARMATURE

INSULATING TUBE

4218

Fig. 124 — Exploded View

CHECKING THE STARTER MOTOR

A performance test of the starter motor may be made in the following manner.

Equipment Needed —

1. A tachometer capable of reading 10,000 RPM.
2. A 12 volt battery ± 0.3 volts.
3. An ammeter capable of reading 100 amperes.

Connect the starter motor, battery and ammeter as shown on the accompanying illustration. See Fig. 125.

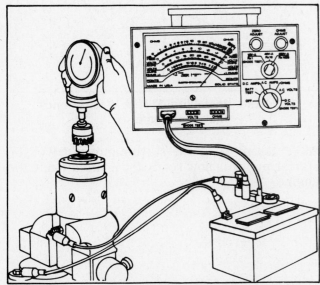

Fig. 125 — Checking Stator Motor Performance

Insert the tachometer in the end of the starter motor and activate the starter motor. A starter motor in good condition will be within the following specifications.

1. Starter motor RPM — 5500 minimum.
2. Current draw (amperes) — 60 maximum (Disregard surge current.)

If the starter motor does not perform satisfactorily, the following should be checked and corrected if necessary.

1. A binding or seizing condition in the starter motor bearings.
2. Starter motor brushes sticking in brush holders.
3. A dirty or worn armature commutator or brushes.
4. A shorted, open or grounded armature or field coil.

DISASSEMBLY OF STARTER MOTOR

(See checking starter motor drive if repair, cleaning or replacement of drive assembly is necessary.)

Remove thru bolts and commutator end cap. The armature, drive cap and gear drive may be removed as an assembly. See Fig. 126.

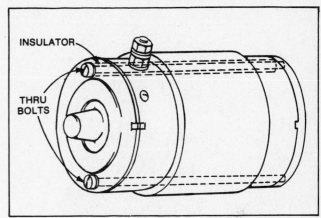

Fig. 126 — Removing Thru Bolts

Clean all dirt accumulations from the armature, end caps, etc. The bearings, housing and armature should not be soaked in a cleaning solution. The armature commutator may be cleaned with a 000 sand paper. Do not use emery cloth, as emery will embed in the commutator and cause rapid wear. If it is suspected that the armature or field coil is defective, a new armature or field coil should be tried in the motor. If proper testing equipment is available, check the suspected armature or field coil to determine if it is defective. The brushes should be checked for poor seating, weak brush springs or dirt and oil. Check to be sure brushes are not sticking in their respective brush holders. See Fig. 127.

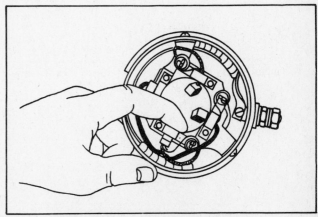

Fig. 127 — Checking Brushes

7
B

STARTERS
Gear Drive 12V

ASSEMBLY OF STARTER MOTOR

When all parts have been thoroughly inspected, lightly lubricate the bearings with #20 oil and re-assemble in the following manner:

Slide the armature into the housing. Drive cap key must match keyway in housing. Insert brushes and brush spring in their respective brush holders as shown in Fig. 128.

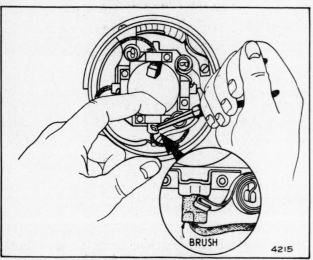

Fig. 128 — Installing Brushes

Install insulator tube on thru bolt close to motor terminal. See Fig. 129. Assemble end cap, matching key to keyway in housing. Tighten thru bolts securely.

NOTE: Insulating thrust washer must be installed on armature shaft or shorting will occur when commutator bars contact end cap. Fig. 129.

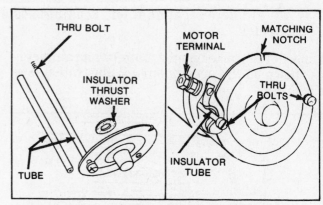

Fig. 129 — Installing Thrust Washer and Insulator Tube

After assembly of the starter motor drive, the starter motor is now ready for installation to the engine.

12 VOLT ELECTRIC STARTER-GENERATOR UNIT

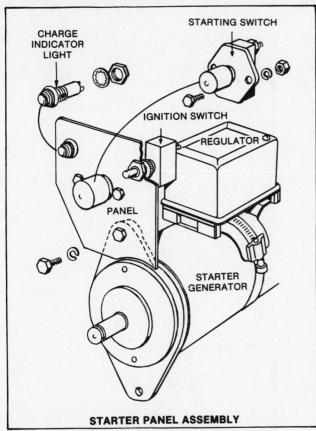

Fig. 130 — Starter Panel Assembly

Removing and Replacing Belts

Remove belt guard. Loosen starter-generator unit mounting bolts and push the unit toward the engine as far as it will go. The belt(s) can then be removed. (Note: Starter-generator units on some models are equipped with two belts. On these units, both belts should be replaced even though only one belt appears to be worn. Use only matched sets of belts.) Do not force belts onto pulleys. There is sufficient adjustment to allow them to be slipped in place. After belt has been installed apply a 30 lb. (13.6 kg) force to the upper pulley and flange.

Tighten mounting bolts securely and replace belt guard. NOTE: Belts are of special high strength design. See Figs. 134 and 135 on page 43. Use only genuine factory replacements obtainable at authorized Briggs & Stratton service station.

Emergency Winter Operation

If run-down batteries are repeatedly experienced due to short or infrequent operation at low temperatures, it is advisable to temporarily increase the generator charge rate.

A simple method of increasing the charge rate is to disconnect the lead to the regulator BAT terminal and reconnect this lead to the regular (L) terminal. This bypasses the current-voltage feature of the regulator automatically increasing the amount of charge to the battery. See Fig. 132.

CAUTION: Operate the regulator with these connected during cold weather when operating periods are short or infrequent. Re-establish the original lead connections as soon as mild weather returns or operating time becomes normal; otherwise the battery will be damaged by over charging.

Battery Size

A 12 volt battery of 50 ampere hour capacity is recommended. CAUTION: Battery must have negative (–) terminal grounded to engine or machine frame.

Maintenance of Battery and Cables (See Fig. 131 for cable size)

Check electrolyte level every 100 hours. Maintain level with distilled or demineralized water. Avoid overfilling. Keep top of battery clean by periodically washing with a brush dipped in ammonia or bicarbonate of soda solution followed by flushing with clean water. Keep battery hold down clamps tight to prevent vibration of battery, but do not overtighten as this may warp case.

Battery cable clamps must be kept tight on terminals to provide a good contact. If corrosion occurs at terminals, disconnect cables and clean clamps and terminals separately. Coat clamps with petroleum jelly and re-install.

Warranty and Service

For warranty and service on all Delco-Remy parts, contact United Motors Service Agencies.

7 B

STARTER-GENERATOR WIRING DIAGRAM

The three drawings shown below illustrate the most common method of wiring 12 volt starter-generator units.

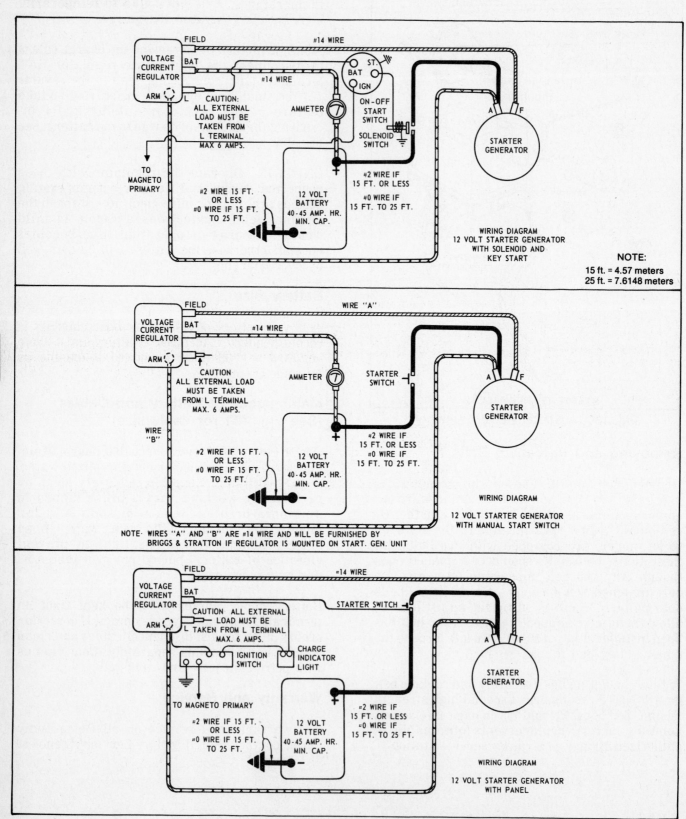

Fig. 131 — Starter Generator Wiring Diagrams

CHECKING 12 VOLT STARTER-GENERATOR SYSTEMS

The following tools and materials should be available.

1. Hydrometer
2. Battery cable and terminal cleaning tool
3. Hand tools for tightening belts and connections
4. Baking soda and water
5. Briggs & Stratton 19236 VOA meter or Eico Model 540 Readi-Tester.
6. 4 to 6 amp taper battery charger

CHECKING BATTERY

Check for clean, corrosion-free and tight connections. Hydrometer reading should be a minimum of 1.225 and each cell should read within less than .050 variation after charging. Battery must meet these conditions before conducting starter-generator tests.

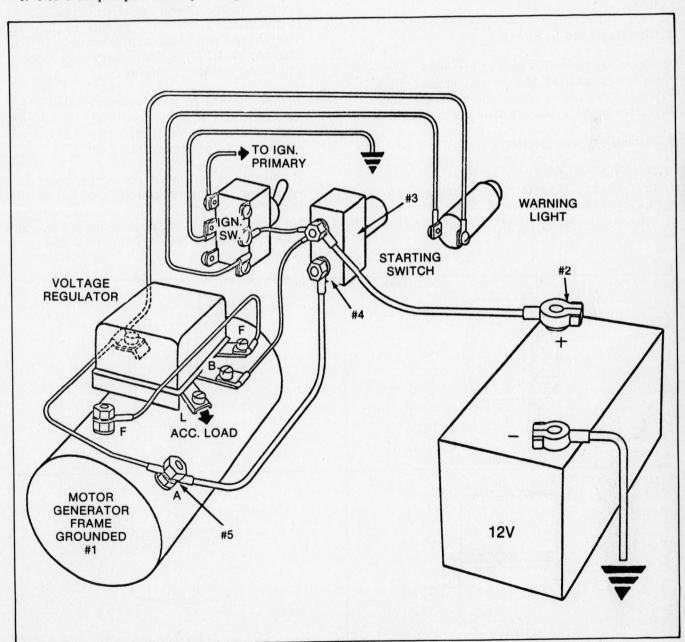

Fig. 132 — Wiring Diagram

STARTERS
Starter Generator 12V

CHECKING STARTER-GENERATOR AND REGULATOR (See Fig. 132)

NOTE: All tests to be made with ignition off and starter switch pressed long enough for meter needle to settle.

1. Checking Ground Resistance (Poor Connection)

Plug black lead in black common meter socket and red lead in VOLTS-OHMS-LEAKAGE socket. Negative test lead to #1 (ground). Positive test lead to #2. Press starter switch. Meter should read 10 volts or more.

2. Checking Lead to Switch

Leave negative test lead at ground #1. Move positive lead to #3. Low or no voltage reading while pressing starter switch indicates defective positive battery cable or connection.

3. Checking Starter Switch

Move the positive test lead to #4. The meter should read "close to battery voltage" when starter switch is pressed. Very low or no voltage indicates a defective starter switch.

4. Checking Lead from Switch to Starter

Move the positive test lead to #5. Press the starter switch. The meter should read "close to battery voltage." If the starter motor does not crank and battery voltage is available, the starter motor is defective. If voltage is not available, cable or connection between test-point #5 and #4 is defective.

5. Generator-Regulator Test

Set test meter at 15 amps, put red lead in AMP socket. Disconnect wire at voltage regulator terminal "B," and connect test instrument in series. The meter will register charge, if any, to the battery when the engine is running. The charge will start approximately 1800 to 2000 engine RPM, and will vary according to the battery state of charge.

If meter reads 10 amps or more, disconnect "F" terminal at regulator. If output remains high, the generator is defective. If output stops, the regulator is defective.

If no charge is shown on meter, short the regulator "F" terminal to ground. Meter should then show a 10 amp or more charge. No charge would indicate a defective generator. A charge would indicate a defective regulator.

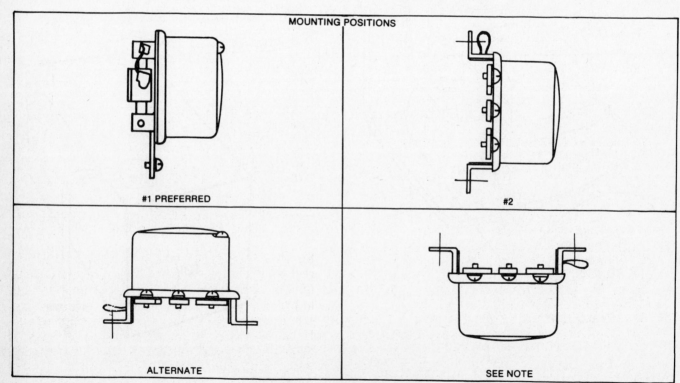

MOUNTING POSITIONS

#1 PREFERRED

#2

ALTERNATE

SEE NOTE

Fig. 133 — Voltage Regulator

Installation of Voltage Regulators

NOTE: Avoid — Regulator will not function in this position.

Regulator should be mounted at a point of minimum vibration.

There must be a good ground connection between regulator mounting feet and equipment frame and between the engine and equipment frame. If this is not possible, a #14 wire must be run from the grounded regulator mounting foot to the engine.

12 Volt Starter-Generator

Belt Adjustment Procedure

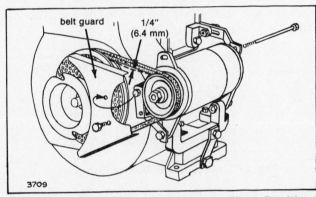

Fig. 134 — 12 Volt Starter-Generator (Low Position)

To adjust, tilt away from blower housing until belts move up and down 1/4″ with thumb pressure at a point midway between pulleys. Tighten screws to hold in place and install guard and tighten in place. Fig. 134 and Fig. 135.

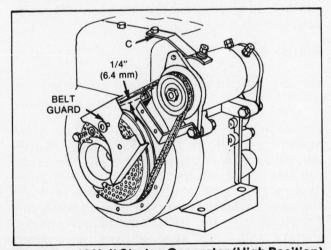

Fig. 135 — 12 Volt Starter-Generator (High Position)

Fig. 136 — Belt Drive 120 Volt Starter

Adjust Belt (120 Volt AC Starter Motor)

Belt adjustment is made by loosening the two nuts shown in Fig. 137, and sliding the motor in the slots. Torque on nuts in 15-20 inch pounds (1.7 to 2.2 Nm).

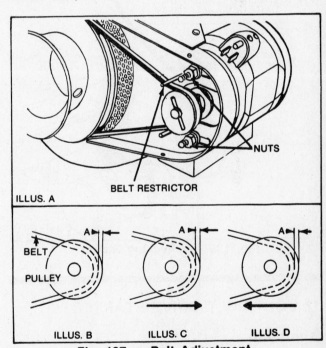

Fig. 137 — Belt Adjustment

Be sure belt is between prongs of the belt restrictor. Crank engine with starter motor and ignition "Off." Observe dimensions as indicated in Fig. 137, Illus. A. If dimension "A" is 3/32″ to 1/8″ (2.4 to 3.2 mm), belt is in proper adjustment. If dimension "A" is less than 3/32″ while cranking, the starter motor must be adjusted away from the engine. If more than 1/8″, the motor must be adjusted toward the engine.

7 B

STARTERS
Starter Generator 12V

Final Check (120 Volt AC Starter Motor)

Starting motor should be tested under maximum load. To do this, turn engine by hand until compression stroke is reached. Plug in starter. Belt should engage and crank engine without slipping. When engine starts, disconnect plug. Belt should not circulate while engine is running. If two prong outlet is the only one available, it should be converted to three prong outlet. See Fig. 138.

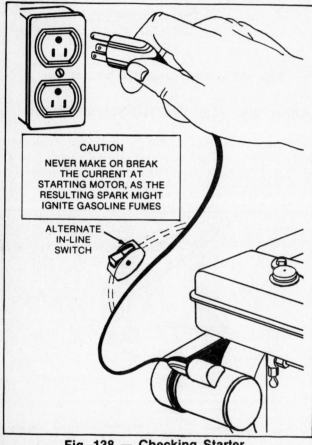

Fig. 138 — Checking Starter

CAUTION

NEVER MAKE OR BREAK THE CURRENT AT STARTING MOTOR, AS THE RESULTING SPARK MIGHT IGNITE GASOLINE FUMES

ALTERNATE IN-LINE SWITCH

---

12 VOLT BELT DRIVE STARTER

Operation

This Briggs & Stratton electric starter automatically engages a belt clutch and cranks engine when a 12 volt battery is connected between the terminal on the starter and engine cylinder. When engine starts, the belt clutch automatically disengages starter motor from engine. Driven equipment should be disengaged from engine prior to engaging electric starter. The starting system is designed to turn over engine only. Fig. 139.

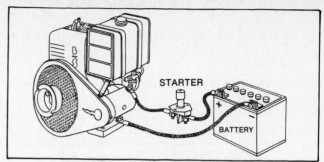

Fig. 139 — Starter Connections

Proper Electric Installation

Negative (–) side of battery must be grounded to engine. This lead must carry starting current and therefore, must be a No. 4 size wire or larger.

Another heavy lead (No. 4 or larger) should be connected from the starter motor terminal through the starter switch and to the positive (+) battery terminal. Fig. 140.

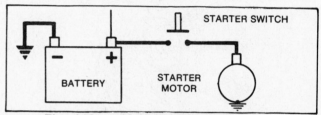

Fig. 140 — 12 Volt Wiring Diagram

Battery Size

A 12 volt battery of 40 to 45 ampere hour capacity is recommended.

Motor Repairs

For warranty and service on starter motors, contact Authorized Representative of Presto-Lite.

Adjust Belt

The two assemblies which had been used are shown below. Fig. 141 and 142. Adjust as follows:

Loosen nut "A" and "B" slightly so the starter motor can just be moved by hand. Move starter motor away from engine as far as possible. Rock engine pulley back and forth and at the same time, slowly slide the starter motor toward engine until the starter motor pulley stops being driven by the vee belt. Move starter motor another 1/16" (1.6 mm) toward the engine. Tighten nuts "A" and "B."

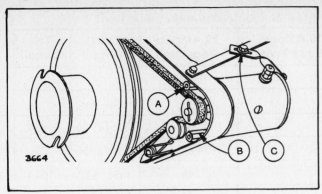

Fig. 141 — Adjust Belt

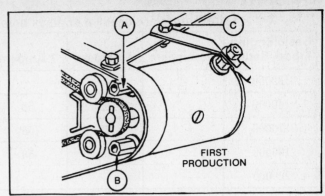

Fig. 142 — Adjust Belt

ALTERNATOR
Identification

Alternators are used on engines noted and may be located on page indicated.

Basic Engine Model Series	1½ Ampere	4 Ampere	7 Ampere	10 Ampere Fuse Type	10 Ampere Regulated	Dual* Circuit	Tri-Circuit
130000	48						
140000		62	58			52, 55	
170000		62	58		66	51, 52, 55	64
190000		62	58		66	51, 52, 55	64
220000					66	51, 52	64
240000					66		64
250000					66	51, 52	64
320000				68	66	51, 52	64

*AC or DC only included with Dual Circuit Alternators.

Fig. 143

ALTERNATOR TROUBLESHOOTING

The following list is provided to aid you in diagnosing problems for alternator systems.

Battery — Not Charging	Alternator defective
	Diode/rectifier defective
	Regulator defective
	Wiring, shorted, broken or corroded
	Stator, damaged
	Battery cables connected to wrong terminals
	Battery defective
	Flywheel magnets, broken or not charged
Battery — Overcharging	Regulator defective (regulated alternator only)
	Battery size too small for alternator
	Vibration/equipment (battery appears to be overcharging when water splashes from battery caps.)
Lights — Not Functioning	Light bulbs, defective
	Wiring, shorted or broken
	Light switch, defective
	Stator defective
	Regulator (regulated alternator), defective
	Battery defective (regulated alternator)

Fig. 144

WARNING: Do not strike flywheel with a hard object or metal tool as this may cause flywheel to shatter in operation, causing personal injury or property damage. Use Briggs & Stratton approved tools only, and if in doubt, contact your Authorized Briggs & Stratton Service Center.

Equipment to Test Alternators

The following list of equipment is recommended for test and repair of alternators.

Volt/Ohm/Ampere (VOA) Meter

The VOA meter is available from your Briggs & Stratton source of supply. Order as part no. 19236. The meter may be used to read volts, ohms or amperes when leads are attached to appropriate connector. Fig. 145.

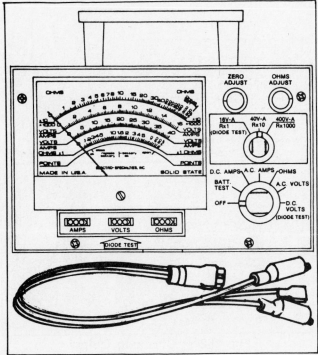

Fig. 145 — VOA Meter

Ammeter

Range 20-0-20; available from automotive parts supplier or use Briggs & Stratton No. 295158. Attach leads and alligator clips as shown in Figure 146.

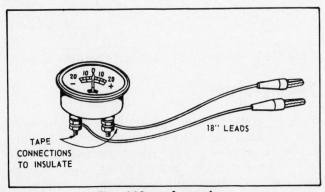

Fig. 146 — Ammeter

Test Lamp

12-volt bulb and bulb holder; available from automotive parts supplier, or use Briggs & Stratton No. 67245 bulb and No. 298586 bulb holder. Attach leads and alligator clips as shown in Figure 147.

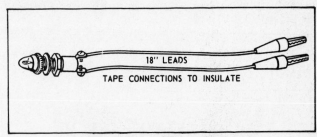

Fig. 147 — Test Lamp

Fuse Cap Test Lead

Part no. 390888 fuse cap. Attach alligator clip as shown in Figure 148.

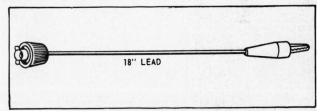

Fig. 148 — Fuse Cap Test Lead

Load Lamp

G.E. No. 4001 sealed beam headlight or equivalent. Available from automotive parts supplier. Attach leads and clips as shown in Figure 149.

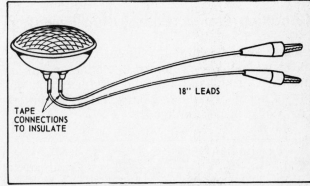

Fig. 149 — Load Lamp

Fuses

AGC or 3AG, 7-1/2 and 15 ampere fuse, available from automotive parts supplier or Briggs & Stratton No. 67125 (7-1/2 amp.) and No. 67345 (15 amp.).

7C

ALTERNATOR
1½ Amp

1-1/2 AMP ALTERNATOR
Used on Model Series 130000

The integral 1-1/2 ampere alternator, with solid state rectifier, is designed for use with a compact battery. A 12 ampere hour battery is suggested for warm temperature operation and a 24 ampere hour battery should be used in cold service.

The alternator is rated at 3600 RPM. At lower speeds available output is reduced.

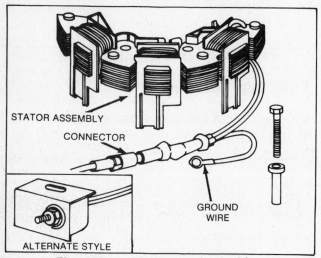

STATOR ASSEMBLY

CONNECTOR

GROUND WIRE

ALTERNATE STYLE

Fig. 150 — Alternator Assembly

WHEN CHECKING ALTERNATOR COMPONENTS, MAKE THE TESTS IN THE FOLLOWING SEQUENCE:

CHECKING 1-1/2 AMP. NON-REGULATED ALTERNATOR

Condition Found (Battery Run Down)

Check battery polarity. Negative (–) side of battery should be grounded to engine or frame; positive (+) side of battery to starter motor and alternator charge lead. Figure 151. If reversed, rectifier will be damaged.

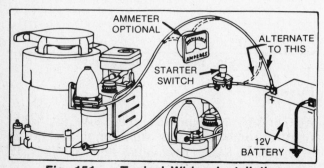

AMMETER OPTIONAL

ALTERNATE TO THIS

STARTER SWITCH

12V BATTERY

Fig. 151 — Typical Wiring Installation

Testing for Output

Disconnect connector or charging lead from charging terminal. Fig. 152 and 153. Do not allow terminal on charging lead to touch engine or equipment. Clip 12 volt load lamp between charging terminal and ground. Start engine. if lamp lights, alternator is functioning. If lamp does not light, alternator system is defective. The same test may be performed using 19236 Briggs & Stratton VOA meter.

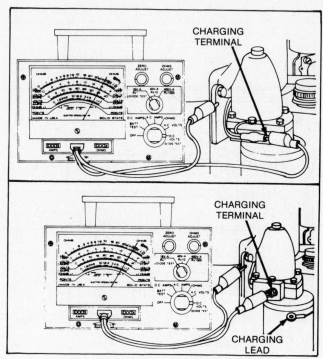

CHARGING TERMINAL

CHARGING TERMINAL

CHARGING LEAD

Fig. 152 — Checking Output

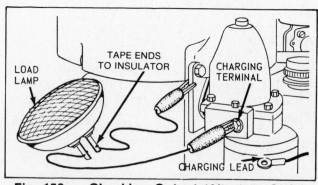

LOAD LAMP

TAPE ENDS TO INSULATOR

CHARGING TERMINAL

CHARGING LEAD

Fig. 153 — Checking Output, (Alternate Style)

Testing Stator

Unplug connector or disconnect charging lead from battery and rectifier assembly on alternate style. Remove screw from ground wire or rectifier assembly from starter motor. Turn rectifier assembly to expose wires attached to soldered terminals on alternate style.

NOTE: Ground wire or rectifier assembly must not touch the engine during this test.

Start engine. With engine running, pierce stator wires with probes from load lamp or touch terminals in rectifier box. Fig. 154 and 155. If load lamp lights, the stator is satisfactory. If load lamp does not light, the flywheel magnet or stator is inoperative. The flywheel should be examined to be sure magnet is charged. If required, replace flywheel or the stator.

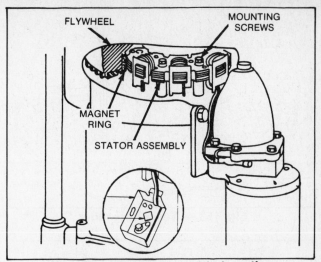
Fig. 156 — Stator Assembly Location

Install new stator assembly with stator mounting screws and bushings. Be sure leads are properly positioned as shown in Figure 157. While tightening mounting screws, push stator toward crankshaft to take up clearance in bushing. Torque mounting screws 18 to 24 inch pounds (1.6 to 2.1 Nm). Before re-assembly, locate stator wires against cylinder in order to clear ring gear and flywheel. Attach ground wire or rectifier assembly to drive housing. Replace flywheel and torque clutch housing as noted on specification chart. Re-assemble rotating screen and blower housing.

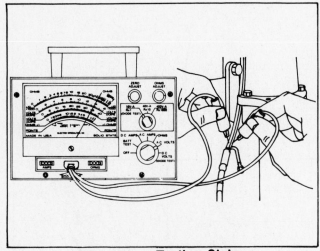
Fig. 154 — Testing Stator

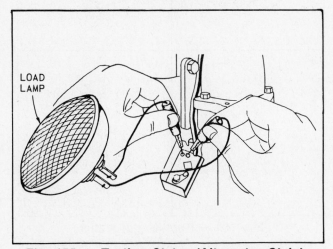
Fig. 155 — Testing Stator (Alternator Style)

Replacing Defective Stator

Remove the blower housing, rotating screen, clutch assembly and flywheel. Note and remember location of stator wires, under one coil spool, then between starter and drive unit housing as shown in Fig. 156. Remove ground wire or rectifier assembly from starter drive housing. Remove the two stator mounting screws and bushings.

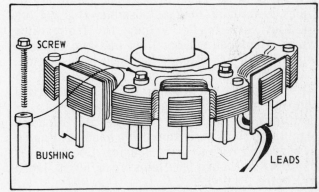
Fig. 157 — Assembling Stator

Testing Rectifier

Do not start engine. Use the #19236 VOA meter to test resistance from charging terminal to ground, as shown in Fig. 158 or 159. Now reverse test leads and recheck. One way there should be a meter reading. The other way there should not be a meter reading. The actual meter readings are not important. If the meter shows a reading both ways, or neither way, the rectifier is defective. Replace rectifier.

7
C

ALTERNATOR
1½ Amp

7
C

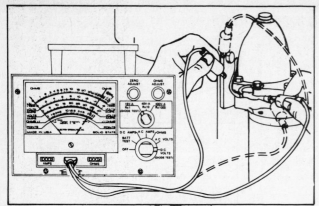

Fig. 158 — Testing Rectifier

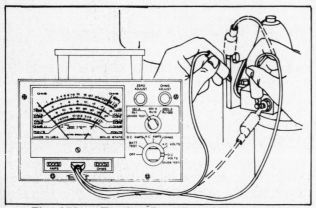

Fig. 159 — Testing Rectifier (Alternate Style)

Replacing Rectifier

Cut stator wires close to rectifier so that stator wires remain as long as possible. Discard old rectifier. Strip insulation back 3/8″ from stator wires. Replacement rectifier has two exposed wires which are already stripped of insulation. Twist and solder each stator wire to a rectifier wire. Insulate each connection with electrical friction tape, keeping connected areas as compact as possible. Remove and discard original ground wire from drive housing. Fasten new ground wire to drive housing. Locate wires as shown in Figure 160. Retest rectifier as shown in Figure 158 or 159.

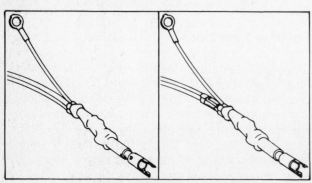

Fig. 160 — Replacing Rectifier

Replacing Defective Rectifier Box

Remove rectifier box from starter motor. Use a screwdriver to pry under the fibre board as shown in Figure 161. Fibre will break, exposing soldered connections between rectifier and stator leads. Cut stator leads close to eyelets so stator leads remain as long as possible. Strip insulation back to expose about 3/8″ of wire. Discard defective rectifier box.

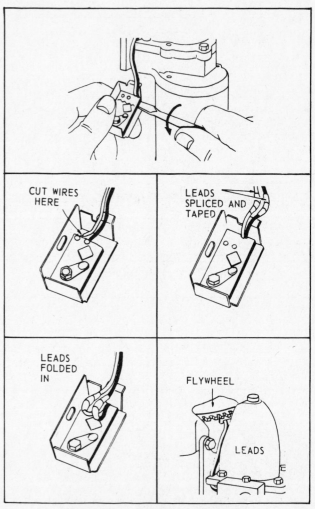

Fig. 161 — Replacing Rectifier

Replacement rectifier box has short leads, the tips of which are already stripped of insulation. Twist and solder each stator lead to a rectifier lead. Insulate each connection with electrical friction tape, keeping splices as compact as possible because of small space available. Form splices into bottom of rectifier box as shown in Figure 161, and re-assemble rectifier box to starter motor. Pull gently on leads to insure a firm connection and locate them as shown in Figure 161, so they cannot rub on flywheel ring gear. Recheck output as shown in Figure 153.

AC Only Alternator

The AC alternator is designed to operate as an integral part of the engine. It provides current for lights normally used on lawn and garden equipment.

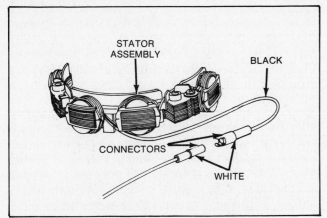

Fig. 162 — AC Circuit Alternator

Current for the lights is available as long as the engine is running. The output depends upon engine speed. Twelve-volt lights with a total rating of 60 to 100 watts may be used. With lights rated at 70 watts, the voltage rises from 8 volts at 2400 RPM to 12 volts at 3600 RPM, so the brightness of the light changes with the engine speed. The 5 amp lighting alternator uses less than .2 of a horsepower at full output.

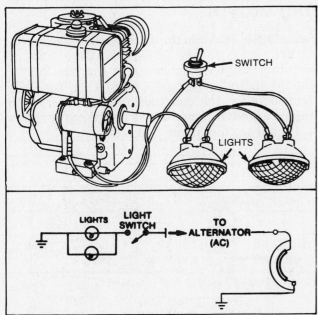

Fig. 163 — Typical AC Wiring Diagram

The test procedure for this alternator is located in the Dual Circuit Alternator Section 7, page 54.

DC Only Alternator

The DC alternator is designed to operate as an integral part of the engine and is separate from the engine starting system. It is intended to provide DC charging current for 12 volt batteries. Recommended battery sizes range from 12 ampere hour for warm temperature service to 24 ampere hour in coldest service for model series 130000. Model series 140000 and up range from 20 ampere hour for warm temperature service to 40 ampere hour in coldest service.

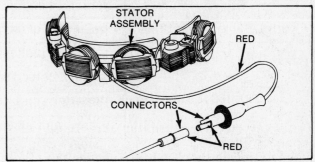

Fig. 164 — DC Circuit Alternator

The current from the battery charging alternator is unregulated and is rated at 3 amperes. The output rises from 2 amperes at 2400 RPM to 3 amperes at 3600 RPM; the alternator uses less than .2 of a horsepower.

WARNING: For electrical safety always remove cable from negative (–) side of the battery before attempting any repairs or maintenance to engine or equipment.

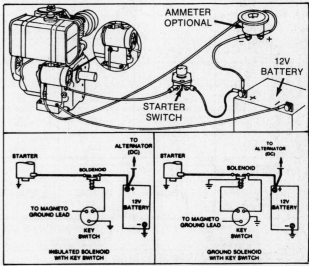

Fig. 165 — Typical DC Wiring Diagram

The test procedure for this alternator is located in the Dual Circuit Alternator Section 7, pages 52 and 53.

7
C

ALTERNATOR
Dual Circuit

5 Amp AC – 3 Amp DC – Rectifier Plug Type

The dual circuit alternator is designed to operate as an integral part of the engine and is separate from the engine starting system. Recommended battery sizes range from 20 ampere hour for warm temperature service to 40 ampere hour in coldest service.

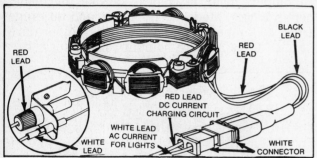

Fig. 166 — Dual Circuit Alternator

The dual circuit alternator is actually two separate alternator systems. A single ring of magnets inside the flywheel supplies the magnetic field for both of them. One alternator system uses a solid state rectifier and provides battery charging current. The other alternator system feeds alternating current directly to the lights. Since the two are electrically independent, use of the lights does not reduce the charge going into the battery.

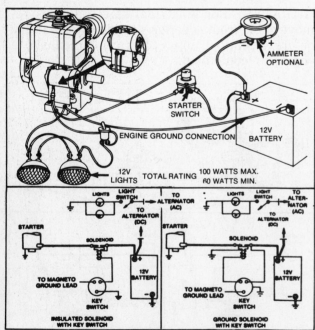

Fig. 167 — Typical Wiring Diagram

The battery is not used for the lights, so lights are available even if the battery is disconnected or removed. The alternator uses less than 0.2 horsepower.

Current for the lights is available as long as the engine is running. The output depends upon engine speed. Twelve-volt lights with a total rating of 60 to 100 watts may be used. With lights rated at 70 watts, the voltage rises from 8 volts at 2400 RPM to 12 volts at 3600 RPM, so the brightness of the light changes with the engine speed.

The current from the battery charging alternator is unregulated and is rated at 3 amperes. The output rises from 2 amperes at 2400 RPM to 3 amperes at 3600 RPM.

There is one external connection. The battery charging current connection is made through one terminal of a two connector plug. Current for lights is available at the second terminal of this plug. The plug is polarized to prevent improper connections. The return circuit for both alternators is through ground to the engine block.

CHECKING BATTERY INSTALLATION

Check if battery polarity is correct. Negative (–) side of battery should be grounded to engine or frame; positive (+) side of battery to alternator output lead. Figure 167.

WHEN CHECKING ALTERNATOR COMPONENTS, MAKE THE TESTS IN THE FOLLOWING SEQUENCE:

TESTING ALTERNATOR CHARGING (DC) OUTPUT

Set #19236 VOA meter to measure amperes. Attach leads in series with positive battery terminal and wire as shown in Fig. 168. Meter should indicate output. The charge range is dependent on the condition of the battery and engine speed. If meter shows no charge or shows a discharge, test diode and stator.

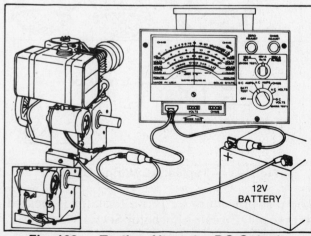

Fig. 168 — Testing Alternator DC Output

TESTING FOR SHORT IN ALTERNATOR SYSTEM

Disconnect charging lead from battery, and connect charge lead test lamp in series between battery and charge lead. (Figure 169) DO NOT START ENGINE. Test lamp should not light. If it does light, stator charging lead is shorted or diode is defective. Disconnect charge lead connector at alternator. If test light does not go out, the lead from the cap to the battery is shorted. If light goes out, diode is defective.

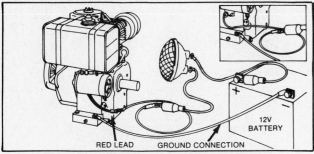

Fig. 169 — Testing for Short in Stator, Diode or Charge Lead

TESTING DIODE

Disconnect connector plug. Set meter on ohm scale. Check diode by attaching one meter lead to red stator lead wire. (A needle may be used to pierce stator lead wire insulation.) Touch the other meter lead to diode join in plastic connector, then reverse meter leads. The meter should show a reading in one direction only. If meter shows a reading in both directions or does not show a reading in either direction, the diode is defective and the connector assembly must be replaced. See Fig. 170.

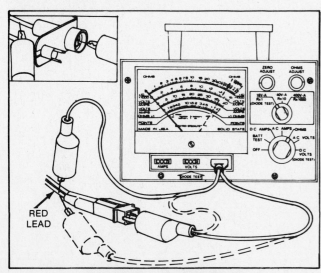

Fig. 170 — Testing Diode

NOTE: Service replacement diodes are pre-assembled to a connector and a short lead wire for ease of installation.

TESTING STATOR CHARGING COILS

Remove blower housing, flywheel etc. and examine red lead wire for cuts, damaged insulation or obvious short on lead. If bare spots are found repair with electrical tape. If short cannot be repaired, replace stator. Stator should also be checked for continuity as follows:

Use VOA meter set on ohm scale. Touch one meter lead to stator laminations, touch the other meter lead to red stator charge lead wire. (Pierce red wire insulation with a needle to insure meter lead contact.) Meter should show continuity. Fig. 171.

Next remove screw which attaches stator ground wires to stator laminations. Be certain ground wire does not touch laminations as shown in Fig. 171 and repeat previous test. Meter should not show continuity. If meter does not show continuity in first test or shows continuity during second test, stator is defective and must be replaced.

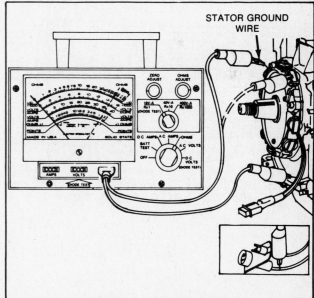

Fig. 171 — Testing Stator

NOTE: Discoloration of stator coils does not mean stator is defective. A shorted diode will pass battery current thru stator coils to ground, which discolors coils due to heat. Replacing diode would normally restore alternator without replacing stator.

7 C

ALTERNATOR
Dual Circuit – Rectifier Plug Type

TESTING ALTERNATOR AC CIRCUIT (Lighting)

Connect load lamp to AC side of connector and ground as shown in Fig. 172. Load lamp should light to full brilliance at medium engine speed. If lamp does not light or is very dim at medium speeds, stop engine and remove blower housing and flywheel. Disconnect stator ground wire as shown in Fig. 171.

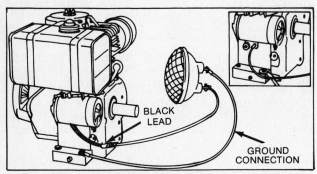

Fig. 172 — Testing AC Lights Circuit Output

With #19236 VOA meter, check for continuity between ground lead wire of AC coil and AC plug of connector as shown in Fig. 173. Meter reading should show continuity.

Next, be sure ground lead terminal is not touching a grounded surface, and check continuity from terminal to ground. Figure 174. Meter should not show continuity. If meter indicates continuity, coils are grounded and defective. Examine black lead to be sure the insulation is not worn or cut. Repair with tape and shellac if a bad spot is found. If ground still exists, or if AC coils do not show continuity, stator must be replaced.

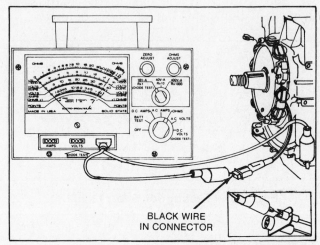

Fig. 174 — Test for AC Output Ground Condition

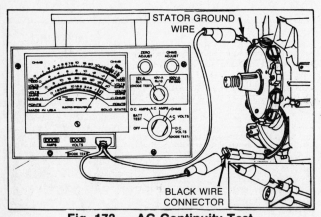

Fig. 173 — AC Continuity Test

Dual Circuit Alternator with Fuse

This efficient gear drive, 12 volt battery powered starter system is compact and powerful. It is available with either a rope or rewind auxiliary starter. Recommended battery sizes range from 20 ampere hour for warm temperature service to 40 ampere hour in coldest service.

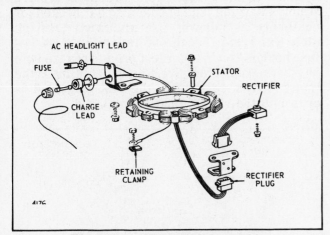

Fig. 175 — Alternator Assembly

DUAL CIRCUIT ALTERNATOR

The dual circuit alternator is actually two separate alternator systems. A single ring of magnets inside the flywheel supplies the magnetic field for both of them. One alternator system uses a solid state rectifier and provides battery charging current. The other alternator system feeds alternating current directly to the lights. Since the two are electrically independent, use of the lights does not reduce the charge going into the battery.

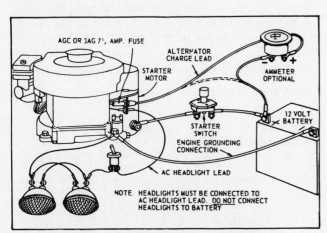

Fig. 176 — Typical Wiring Installation

The battery is not used for the lights, so lights are available even if the battery is disconnected or removed.

Current for the lights is available as long as the engine is running. The output depends upon engine speed. Twelve-volt lights with a total rating of 60 to 100 watts may be used. With lights rated at 70 watts, the voltage rises from 8 volts at 2400 RPM to 12 volts at 3600 RPM, so the brightness of the light changes with the engine speed.

The current from the battery charging alternator is unregulated and is rated at 3 amperes. The output rises from 2 amperes at 2400 RPM to 3 amperes at 3600 RPM.

There are two external connections. The battery charging current connection is made through a 7.5 ampere fuse mounted in a fuse holder beside the starter motor. Current for the lights is available at a plastic connector located below the fuse-holder. The two connections are different so they cannot be accidentally interchanged. The fuse protects the 3 amp charging alternator and rectifier from burnout due to improper (reverse polarity) battery connections. The 5 amp lighting alternator does not require a fuse as a short circuit in its output will not damage it. The return circuit for both alternators is through ground to the engine block. The alternator uses less than 0.2 horsepower.

CHECKING DUAL CIRCUIT ALTERNATOR

Fuse Blown

Check if battery polarity is correct: Negative (–) side of battery should be grounded to engine or frame; positive (+) side of battery to (fused) alternator output lead. Figure 177. If reversed, correct and put in new fuse.

WHEN CHECKING ALTERNATOR COMPONENTS, MAKE THE TESTS IN THE FOLLOWING SEQUENCE:

BATTERY RUNS DOWN

Testing Alternator Charging Output

Install ammeter in series with charging lead, as in Figure 177. Start engine. Ammeter should indicate charge. The charge rate is dependent upon the condition of the battery.

7 C

ALTERNATOR
Dual Circuit – Fuse Type

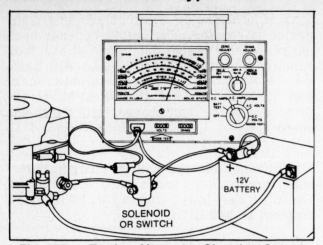

Fig. 177 — Testing Alternator Charging Output

If VOA meter shows no reading, test stator and rectifier.

Testing for Short in Stator or in Rectifier

Disconnect charging lead from battery, and connect small test lamp in series between battery positive terminal and fuse cap, as shown in Figure 178. DO NOT START ENGINE. Test lamp should not light. If it does light, stator's charging lead is grounded or rectifier is defective. Unplug rectifier plug under blower housing. See Figure 179. If test light goes out, rectifier is defective. If test light does not go out, stator charging lead is grounded.

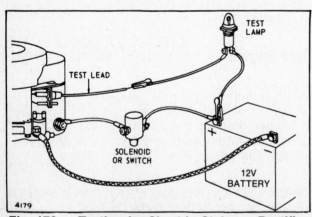

Fig. 178 — Testing for Short in Stator or Rectifier

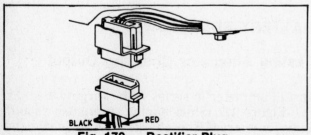

Fig. 179 — Rectifier Plug

Testing Stator Charging Coils

If "short" test indicates stator charging lead is grounded, remove blower housing, flywheel, starter motor and retaining clamp (see figure 175) and examine length of red lead for damaged insulation or obvious shorts on lead. If bare spots are found, repair with electrical tape and shellac. If short cannot be repaired, replace stator. Charging lead should also be checked for continuity as follows: Use multimeter, set on ohm Rx1 scale. Touch one test prod to lead at fuse holder. Touch other test prod to red lead pin in plastic connector: See Figure 180. Unless the meter shows continuity, the charging lead is open and the stator must be replaced.

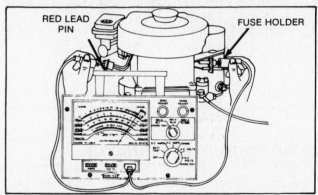

Fig. 180 — Checking Charging Lead for Continuity

The charging coils should be checked for continuity as follows: Using the multimeter, touch one test prod on each of the black lead pins as shown in Figure 181. Unless the meter shows continuity, charging coils are defective and stator must be replaced. Test for grounded charging coils by touching one test prod to a clean "ground" surface on the engine and touching the other test prod on each of the black lead pins as shown in Figure 182. If the meter shows continuity, the charging coils are grounded and stator must be replaced.

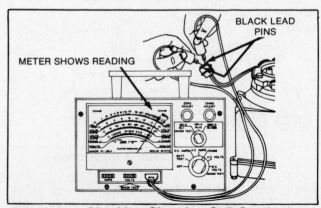

Fig. 181 — Checking Charging Coil Continuity

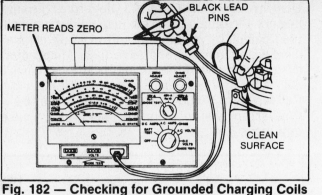

Fig. 182 — Checking for Grounded Charging Coils

Testing Rectifier

Attached to the blower housing baffle is a small black rectifier assembly.

The rectifier is tested with a multimeter as follows: Three leads from the rectifier connect to pins in the detachable plug. See Figure 183. Leave rectifier installed on blower housing. Test rectifier with multimeter (using resistance scale) to check resistance from the red lead pin to blower housing (in an unpainted clean area). See Figure 183.

After checking pin, reverse meter leads and recheck. The meter should show a reading in one direction only. If the rectifier pin shows a meter reading both ways, the rectifier is defective. If the pin shows no reading either way, the rectifier is again defective.

Leaving one probe on blower housing, repeat with each black lead pin. Again meter should show continuity in one direction only, otherwise rectifier is defective. Now try between red lead pin and each black lead pin. Again, when probes are interchanged, meter should show continuity in one direction only.

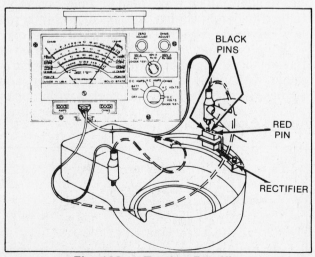

Fig. 183 — Testing Rectifier

Testing Alternator AC Circuit (Lighting)

Connect load lamp to AC output plug and ground as shown in Figure 184. Load lamp should light to full brilliance at medium engine speed. If lamp does not light, or is very dim at medium speeds, remove blower housing and flywheel. Disconnect ground end of AC coil, which is attached to the retaining clamp screw as shown in Figure 185.

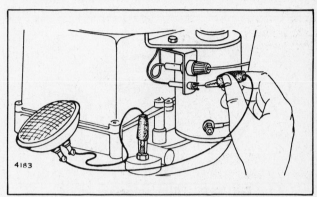

Fig. 184 — Testing AC Light Circuit Output

With multimeter, check continuity between ground lead of AC coil and AC output terminal as shown in Figure 185. Meter should show continuity.

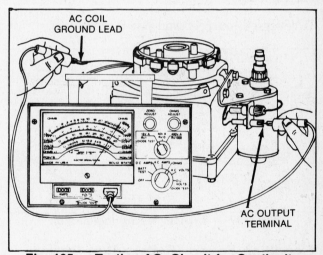

Fig. 185 — Testing AC Circuit for Continuity

Next, be sure ground lead terminal is not touching a grounded surface, and check continuity from terminal to ground.

Meter should not show continuity. If meter indicates continuity, coils are grounded and defective. Examine both (white) leads to be sure the insulation is not worn or cut. Repair with tape and shellac if a bad spot is found. If ground still exists, or if AC coils do not show continuity, stator must be replaced.

7 C

ALTERNATOR
7 Amp

7 AMP REGULATED ALTERNATOR
Used on Model Series 140000, 170000 and 190000

The 7 ampere regulated alternator uses both a rectifier and a solid state electronic regulator for rapid charging or extra electrical loads. The regulator protects the battery from overcharge. The alternator requires less than 0.2 horsepower.

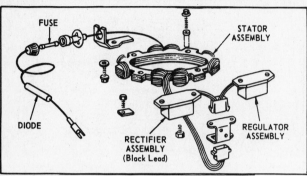

Fig. 186 — Alternator Assembly

Condition Found (Fuse Blown)

Check if battery polarity is correct. Negative (–) side of battery should be grounded to engine or frame; positive (+) side of battery to alternator output lead.

If reversed, correct and put in new fuse.

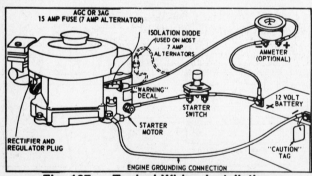

Fig. 187 — Typical Wiring Installation

Condition Found (Battery Run Down)

Certain operating conditions could cause the regulator to malfunction, permitting the battery to discharge even after then engine is stopped. To prevent such a malfunction, and the possible inconvenience of a "dead" battery, an isolation diode assembly (an electronic check-valve) is installed in the alternator output lead, on engines with 7 ampere regulated alternators.

The isolation diode assembly is installed at the time of production, or may be added with kit #390607 described as follows:

Disconnect cable from (–) negative (ground) battery terminal. Unscrew fuse holder cap from fuse holder by pushing in and twisting counter-clockwise. Remove and save fuse. Mount diode assembly in one of the various positions shown in Fig. 188. Use 1/2" long screw, lockwasher and flat washer. If diode assembly is mounted on tank strap, install clamp between lock washer and strap.

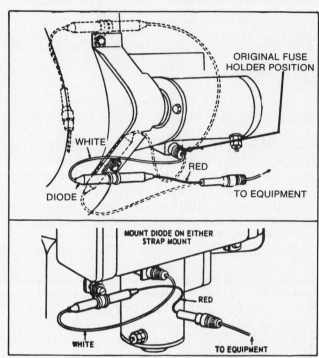

Fig. 188 — Diode Mounting Positions

The body of the isolation diode assembly should not rub against any metal part. Repeated contact with a metal part could wear through the insulation, causing a short.

Insert fuse in fuse holder on engine. Assemble fuse holder cap on white lead of diode assembly to fuse holder on engine. Attach connector on red lead of diode assembly to original fuse cap, which was disconnected above. No fuse is used at this connection. Wrap two turns of wire, provided with diode assembly, between cap and socket. Secure the wires and socket with tape to prevent rubbing or interference with other parts. See Fig. 189.

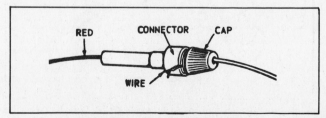

Fig. 189 — Wiring Connector

Reconnect (–) negative (grounded) cable to battery post. If necessary, recharge battery with a battery charger, or by running engine 3 to 5 hours.

NOTE: An isolation diode is not required if the equipment manufacturer routes the alternator output lead through a special ignition switch, which disconnects the alternator when the switch is in the "OFF" position.

WHEN CHECKING ALTERNATOR COMPONENTS, MAKE THE TESTS IN THE FOLLOWING SEQUENCE:

Testing Isolation Diode

Unplug cap from fuseholder and connect small test lamp between tip of white wire and battery negative terminal, as shown in Figure 190. Lamp should not light. If lamp lights, isolation diode is defective. Now disconnect test lamp, and check continuity from the tip of white diode lead to tip of red diode lead with multimeter. The meter should show continuity in one direction and not in the other — reverse leads to check this, as shown in Figure 191. If indication is incorrect, diode is defective and must be replaced.

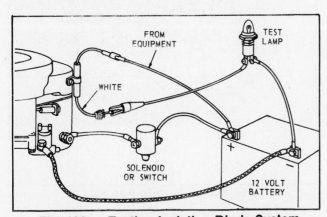

Fig. 190 — Testing Isolation Diode System

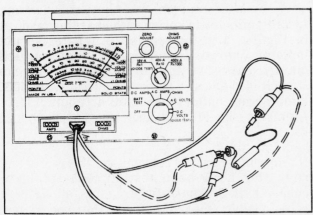

Fig. 191 — Testing Isolation Diode

Testing for Shorts or Ground in Stator, Regulator or Rectifier

Disconnect charging lead from battery, and connect small test lamp in series between battery positive terminal and fuse cap, as shown in Figure 192. (Test lead must not include an isolation diode.) DO NOT START ENGINE. Test lamp should not light. If it does light, stator or regulator or rectifier is defective. Unplug rectifier-regulator plug under blower housing. See Figure 193. If test light goes out, rectifier or regulator is shorted. If test light does not go out, stator is grounded.

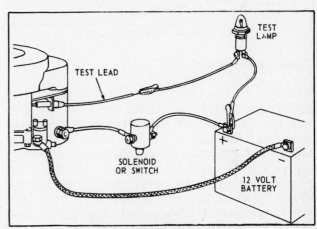

Fig. 192 — Testing for Shorts

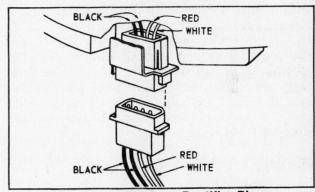

Fig. 193 — Regulator Rectifier Plug

Testing Stator

If test indicates stator is grounded, look for obvious defects on leads. If bare leads are found, repair with friction tape and shellac. If shorted leads are not visible, replace stator. Stator should also be checked for continuity as follows: Use multimeter, set on resistance scale. Touch one test prod to lead at fuse holder. Touch other test prod to each of the four pins in plastic connector. Unless the meter shows continuity at each of the four pins, the stator winding is open and the stator must be replaced. Figure 194.

7 C

ALTERNATOR
7 Amp

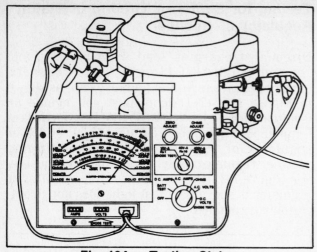

Fig. 194 — Testing Stator

Testing Rectifier

Attached to the blower housing baffle are two small black boxes; one (the rectifier box) has two black leads, and the other (the regulator box) has one red lead and one white lead. These leads connect to four pins in the detachable plug. Leave boxes installed on blower housing. Test rectifier with multimeter (using resistance scale) to check resistance from each black lead pin to blower housing (in an unpainted clean area). See Figure 195. After checking each pin, reverse meter leads and recheck. The meter should show a reading in one direction only. If either of the rectifier pins shows a meter reading both ways, the rectifier is defective. If either of the pins shows no reading either way, the rectifier is again defective. Remove rectifier lead pins from detachable plug and replace rectifier box. Instruction sheet packed with rectifier assembly shows how to remove lead pins from detachable plug.

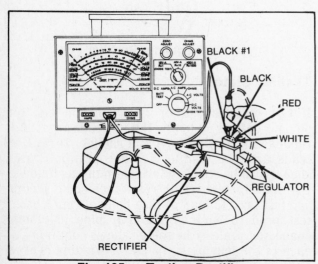

BLACK #1

BLACK

RED

WHITE

REGULATOR

RECTIFIER

Fig. 195 — Testing Rectifier

Testing Regulator

Test regulator with multimeter (using resistance scale) as described in "Testing Rectifier," except touching red lead pin and white lead pin, as shown in Figure 196. If the red lead pin shows a reading in either direction, the regulator is defective. The white lead pin must show a weak reading in one direction only. If meter indicates otherwise, regulator is defective. Replace regulator by removing rectifier pins from plug and installing rectifier pins in new plug furnished with new regulator. Instruction sheet packed with regulator assembly shows how to replace pins in plug.

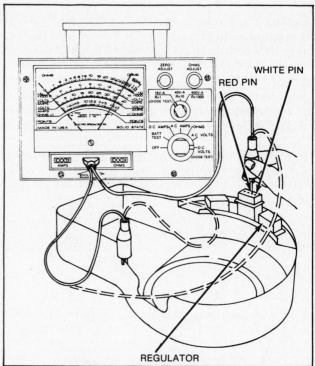

WHITE PIN

RED PIN

REGULATOR

Fig. 196 — Testing Regulator

Testing Alternator Output

Install ammeter in series with charging lead, as in Figure 197. Start engine. Ammeter should indicate charge. If battery is fully charged, ammeter will show little or no needle deflection. If such is the case, connect a 12 volt headlight lamp across battery terminals to apply a load. Ammeter should then show increased charge rate.

If ammeter shows no charge, and if rectifier and regulator have been tested, look for loose connections, broken or frayed wires, etc. If there is no visible fault, replace stator and re-test alternator output.

7 C

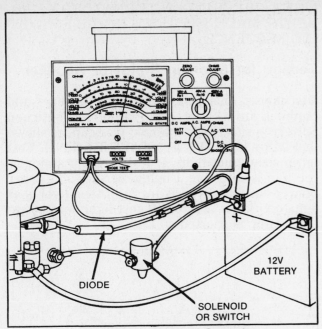

Fig. 197 — Testing Output

ALTERNATOR
4 Amp

4 AMP NON-REGULATED ALTERNATOR

The 4 ampere non-regulated alternator is entirely self-contained. It incorporates a solid state rectifier and a fuse, and uses less than 0.2 horsepower.

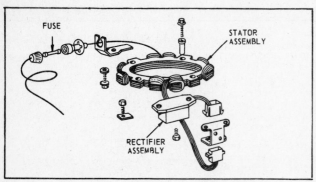

Fig. 198 — Alternator Assembly

CHECKING 4 AMP NON-REGULATED ALTERNATOR

Condition Found (Fuse Blown)

Check if battery polarity is correct: Negative (–) side of battery should be grounded to engine or frame; positive (+) side of battery to alternator output lead. Figure 199. If reversed, correct and put in new fuse.

Condition Found (Battery Run Down)

WHEN CHECKING ALTERNATOR COMPONENTS, MAKE THE TESTS IN THE FOLLOWING SEQUENCE:

Testing for Short in Stator or Rectifier

Disconnect charging lead from battery, and connect small test lamp in series between battery positive terminal and fuse cap, as shown in Figure 200. DO NOT START ENGINE. Test lamp should <u>not</u> light. If it does light, stator or rectifier is defective. Unplug rectifier plug under blower housing. See Figure 201. If test light goes out, rectifier is shorted. If test light does not go out, stator is shorted.

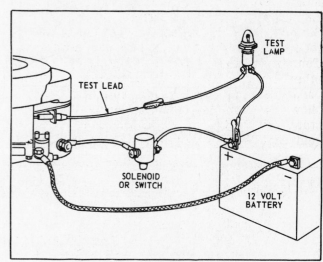

Fig. 200 — Testing for Shorts

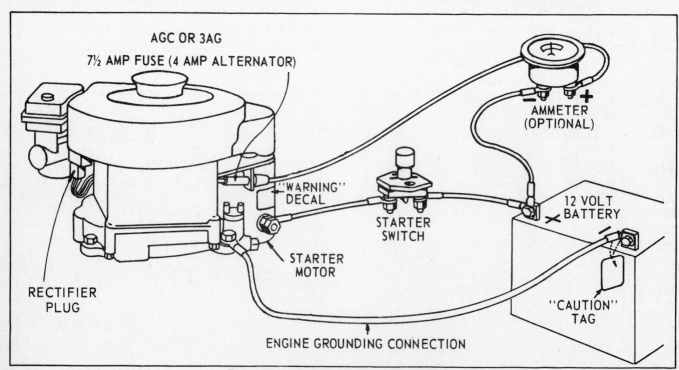

Fig. 199 — Typical Wiring Installation

7
C

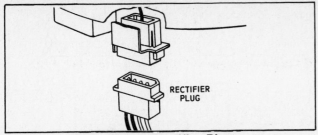

Fig. 201 — Rectifier Plug

Testing Stator

If "short" test indicates stator is shorted, look for obvious shorts on leads. If bare leads are found, repair with friction tape and shellac. If shorted leads are not visible, replace stator. Stator should also be checked for continuity as follows: Use VOA meter, set on resistance scale. Touch one test prod to lead at fuse holder. Touch other test prod to each of the four pins in plastic connector. See Figure 202. Unless the meter shows continuity at each of the four pins, the stator winding is open and the stator must be replaced.

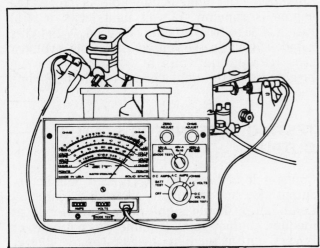

Fig. 202 — Testing Stator

Testing Rectifier

Attached to the blower housing baffle is a small black rectifier box. A lead from the box connects to a single pin in the detachable plug. See Figure 201. Leave box installed on blower housing. Test rectifier with multimeter (using resistance scale) to check resistance from the pin to blower housing (in an unpainted clean area). See Figure 203. After checking pin, reverse meter leads and recheck. The meter should show a reading in one direction only. If the rectifier pin shows a meter reading both ways, the rectifier is defective. If the pin shows no reading either way, the rectifier is again defective.

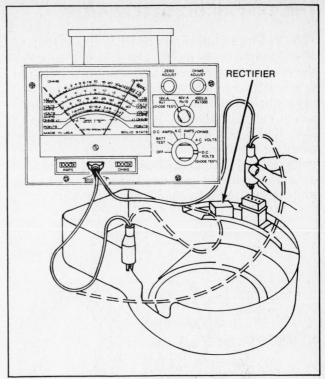

Fig. 203 — Testing Rectifier

Testing Alternator Output

Install ammeter in series with charging lead, as in Figure 204. Start engine. Ammeter should indicate charge.

If ammeter shows no charge, and if rectifier has been tested, look for loose connections, broken or frayed wires, etc. If there is no visible fault, replace stator and re-test alternator output.

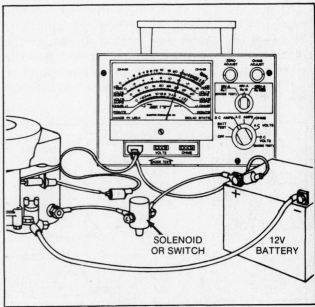

Fig. 204 — Testing Output

7C

ALTERNATOR
Tri-Circuit

THE TRI-CIRCUIT ALTERNATOR

The Tri-Circuit alternator consists of a single ring of magnets inside the flywheel, which supplies the magnetic field for a stator having one output lead which produces AC voltage. The output lead connects to a charge lead that contains one diode which rectifies minus –12 volts DC (5 amps at 3600 RPM) for lights. This same charge lead contains a second diode that rectifies plus +12 volts DC (5 amps at 3600 RPM) for battery charging and external loads. See Fig. 205. The alternator uses less than 0.2 horsepower.

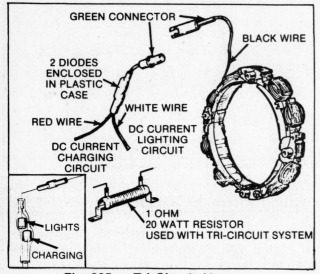

Fig. 205 — Tri-Circuit Alternator

If an accessory such as an electric clutch is used on the equipment, 3.5 amps powers the clutch, and up to 1.5 amps charges the battery, thus not over-charging the battery. A two-pole clutch switch is used on the vehicle when an electric clutch is an accessory. When the clutch is switched on, one circuit is used to engage the clutch, and the other circuit bypasses the resistor, thus allowing full alternator output to be applied to the battery and clutch. Fig. 206 and 207.

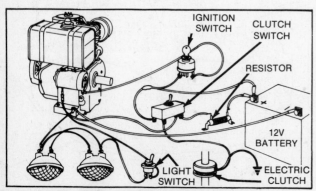

Fig. 206 — Typical Wiring Diagram

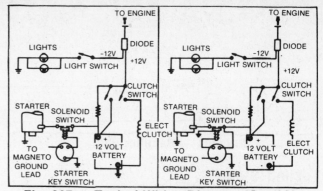

Fig. 207 — Typical Wiring Diagram (Cont'd.)

If the clutch is not engaged, a resistor is placed in series with the alternator charge lead, thereby limiting the charge current to about 3 amps. See Fig. 207. The resistor (20 watts), becomes hot and must be mounted somewhere on the vehicle by the manufacturer.

The battery is not used for the lights, so lights are available even if the battery is disconnected or removed.

Current for the lights is available as long as the engine is running. 12 volt lights with a total rating of 60 to 100 watts may be used. With lights rated at 70 watts, the voltage rises from 8 volts at 2400 RPM to 12 volts at 3600 RPM, so the brightness of the light changes with the engine speed.

TESTING ALTERNATOR STATOR OUTPUT

Connect load lamp to AC (green connector) output plug and ground as shown in Figure 208. Load lamp should light to full brilliance at medium engine speed. If lamp does not light, or is very dim at medium speeds, remove blower housing and flywheel. Disconnect the ground terminal end of AC coil, which is attached to the stator laminations with screw.

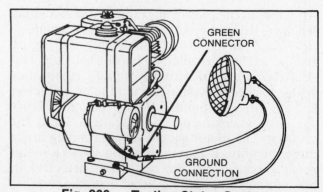

Fig. 208 — Testing Stator Output

7 C

TESTING STATOR COILS

With multimeter, check continuity between ground lead to stator coil and output connector lead shown in Figure 209. Meter should show continuity. If meter does not indicate continuity, replace stator.

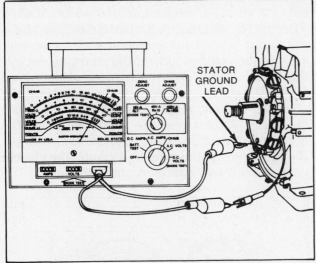

Fig. 209 — Checking Continuity

Next, be sure ground lead terminal is not touching a grounded surface. Check continuity from terminal to ground. See Fig. 210.

Meter should not show continuity. If meter indicates continuity, coils are grounded and defective. Examine lead to be sure the insulation is not worn or cut. Repair with tape and shellac if a bad spot is found. If ground still exists, sator must be replaced.

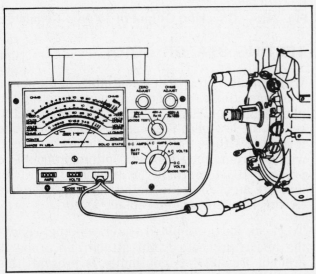

Fig. 210 — Checking for Grounded Wire in Stator Assembly

CHECKING DIODES

Disconnect charge lead from stator output lead. Using a multimeter set on resistance scale, check diodes by attaching one meter lead to connector pin. Touch the other meter lead to the white wire (light circuit diode), then reverse meter leads. Meter should show continuity in one direction only. Repeat this procedure for the red wire (battery charging diode). Meter should show continuity in one direction only. If meter shows continuity in both directions or does not show continuity in either direction, the diode harness must be replaced. See Fig. 211.

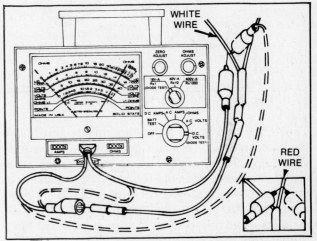

Fig. 211 — Checking Diodes in Wire Harness

The resistor that reduces battery charging current should also be checked when testing alternator. See Fig. 212. An acceptable resistor should have approximately one ohm resistance. Also check to be certain the double pole switch is operating properly. See Fig. 207.

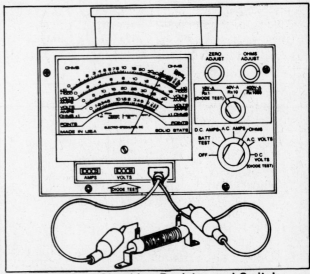

Fig. 212 — Checking Resistor and Switch

7
C

ALTERNATOR
10 Amp

10 AMP REGULATED ALTERNATOR

The 10 amp regulated alternator incorporates a system in which the charging rate is regulated to the battery. The stator is located under the flywheel and is similar to the Dual Circuit stator and Tri-Circuit stator.

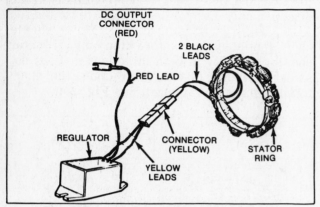

Fig. 213 — 10 Amp Alternator Assembly

There are two leads from the stator, similar to the dual circuit alternator, but of the same color. Fig. 213. The charge rate to the battery is 10 amps and less than 0.2 horsepower is used to operate the system. In the regulator box assembly there are diode rectifiers and S.C.R. (Silicon Controlled Rectifiers) which convert alternating current to direct current for charging the battery, and regulating the voltage.

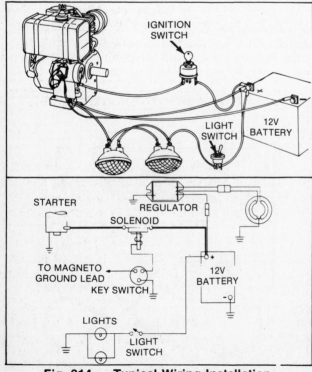

Fig. 214 — Typical Wiring Installation

CHECKING ALTERNATOR OUTPUT

NOTE: There will be no charging output unless a 12 volt battery with a minimum of 5 volts charge is connected to the output side of the regulator. See Fig. 214.

To check the 10 amp system, first make sure the battery is at a minimum of 5 volts. With a VOA meter, check the amperage output of the regulator. Attach the meter in series (see Fig. 215) on the positive side of the charging circuit. Start the engine and run at normal operating RPM. If battery voltage is at its maximum the charging current will be less. An example would be if the battery voltage reads 14 volts, the amperage would probably read less than 3 amps. If the battery voltage reads 10 volts, the charge current will read approximately 10 amps.

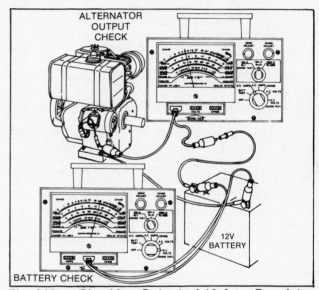

Fig. 215 — Checking Output of 10 Amp Regulator

TESTING STATOR COILS

With a multimeter, check continuity of the stator windings; this can be done by disconnecting the plug connector. See Fig. 216. Use a VOA meter set on the low ohm resistance scale. Touch one terminal with a probe and the other terminal with the remaining probe. Continuity should be present. If no continuity is present, this would indicate an open in the stator windings. Remove flywheel and repair or replace stator.

To check for a grounded stator winding, repeat the above procedure, but attach one probe to ground, Fig. 217. If continuity is present, this would indicate a grounded or "shorted" stator winding.

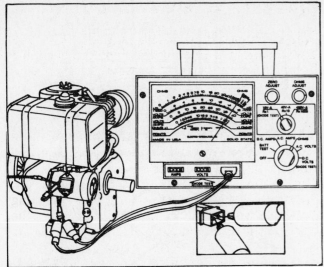

Fig. 216 — Testing Stator Coils for Continuity

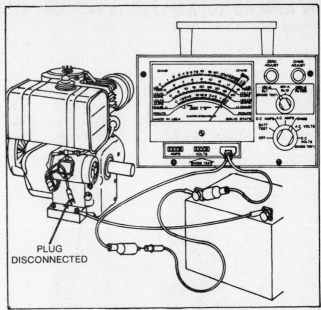

Fig. 218 — Checking Continuity of
DC Output Lead to Battery

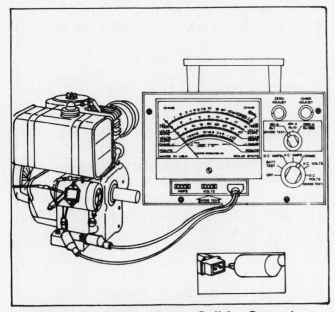

Fig. 217 — Testing Stator Coil for Grounds

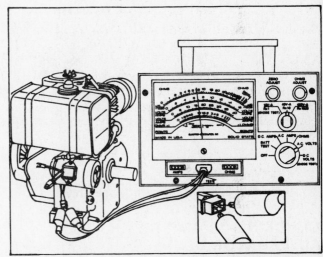

Fig. 219 — Checking Output Voltage (AC)

CHECK STATOR ASSEMBLY (OUTPUT VOLTAGE)

If there is no current flow on the DC output side of regulator, check to insure the stator is functioning. Disconnect the regulator to stator plug, Fig. 219. Attach the leads from a #19236 VOA meter to the pins in the stator plug. Start and run the engine at normal operating speed (minimum 3200 RPM). The voltmeter should read at least 17 volts (20 volts at 3600 RPM). If meter does not show a reading, check the stator for an open or ground condition, Fig. 217. If voltage is present, first make sure there is continuity in the charging lead (rectifier to battery wire), Fig. 218. If continuity exists, replace the regulator.

OVERCHARGING

If battery seems to be in a state of overcharge (boiling out of water), first check to ensure the battery is not vibrating or shaking in the battery holder or case. If battery seems secure, check battery voltage. If voltage is more than 16 volts, it is being overcharged. This could be either the fault of the battery which is due to a high resistance or the regulator which is continually putting current into the battery. If the battery is replaced and the voltage still is above 16 volts, this would indicate the regulator is at fault. Replace the regulator in that case. If upon replacement of the battery the voltage stays below 16 volts, this would indicate the battery was at fault.

ALTERNATOR
10 Amp – Fuse Type

10 AMP REGULATED ALTERNATOR
Used on Model Series 320400

This completely self-contained 10 ampere regulated alternator uses both solid state rectifier and electronic regulating elements. It provides rapid charging and handles extra electrical loads without overcharging the battery. Its output rises from 4.2 amperes at 2000 RPM to 10 amperes at 3600 RPM. It uses less than 0.2 horsepower.

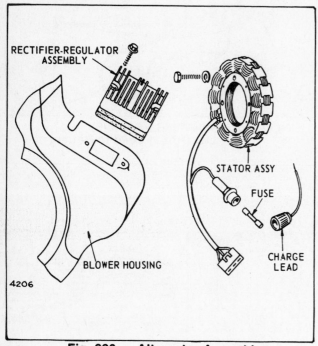

Fig. 220 — Alternator Assembly

CHECKING 10 AMP REGULATED ALTERNATOR

Condition Found (Fuse Blown)

Check if battery polarity is correct. Negative (–) side of battery should be grounded to engine or frame; positive (+) side of battery to alternator output lead.

If reversed, correct and put in new fuse.

WHEN CHECKING THE ALTERNATOR COMPONENTS, MAKE THE TESTS IN THE FOLLOWING SEQUENCE:

Condition Found (Fuse Blown)

Disconnect charging lead from battery. Connect a DC ammeter between charging lead and battery, as shown in Fig. 221.

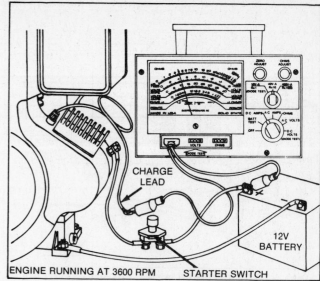

Fig. 221 — Testing for Output

Start engine and run at 3600 RPM. An ammeter reading of 10 amps or above indicates alternator is functioning. Check battery, cables, etc.

If ammeter reading is less than 10 amps, stator or rectifier-regulator is defective.

Testing Stator

Disconnect plug from regulator-rectifier assembly. Start engine and run at 3600 RPM. Connect AC volt meter to AC terminals at stator plug. See Fig. 222. A meter reading above 20 volts indicates stator is good. A volt meter reading less than 20 volts indicates stator is defective. Check for shorted leads or obvious defects. If shorted leads are found, repair with electrical tape. If visible defect is not found, replace stator.

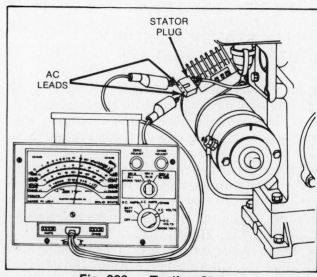

Fig. 222 — Testing Stator

Testing Rectifier-Regulator Assembly

With changing lead connected to battery, check voltage across battery terminals with DC voltmeter. See Fig. 223. If voltmeter reads 13.8 volts or higher, reduce battery voltage by connecting 12 volt load lamp across battery terminals.

When battery voltage is below 13.5 volts, note voltage. Start engine and run at 3600 RPM. Voltmeter reading should rise. If battery is fully charged reading should rise about 13.8 volts. If voltage does not increase and stator has been checked previously, rectifier-regulator assembly is defective and must be replaced.

Condition Found (Continuous High Charge Rate)

Start engine and run at 3600 RPM. (Charge lead must be connected to battery.) Measure voltage across battery terminals with DC voltmeter. See Fig. 223. Voltmeter reading should not be above 14.7 volts. If voltage is higher regulator-rectifier assembly is defective and must be replaced.

NOTE: A high charge rate with voltage below 14.7 volts indicates battery condition is poor. Test battery!

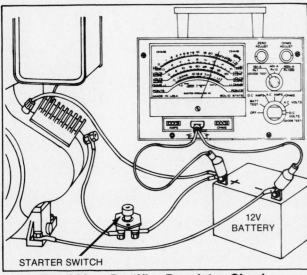

STARTER SWITCH

Fig. 223 — Rectifier-Regulator Check

7
C

7
C

Section 8
LUBRICATION

Oil has four purposes. It cools, cleans, seals and lubricates. Briggs & Stratton engines are lubricated with a gear driven splash oil slinger or a connecting rod dipper.

OIL

Capacity Chart

BASIC MODEL SERIES	CAPACITY	
ALUMINUM	PINTS	LITERS
6, 8, 9, 11 cu. in. Vert. Crankshaft	1-1/4	.6
6, 8, 9 cu. in. Horiz. Crankshaft	1-1/4	.6
10, 13 cu. in. Vert. Crankshaft	1-3/4	.8
10, 13 cu. in. Horiz. Crankshaft	1-1/4	.6
14, 17, 19 cu. in. Vert. Crankshaft	2-1/4	1.1
14, 17, 19 cu. in. Horiz. Crankshaft	2-3/4	1.3
22, 25 cu. in. Vert. Crankshaft	3	1.4
22, 25 cu. in. Horiz. Crankshaft	3	1.4
CAST IRON		
9, 14, 19, 20 cu. in. Horiz. Crank.	3	1.4
23, 24, 30, 32 cu. in. Horiz. Crank.	4	1.9

Oil Recommendations

Use a high quality detergent oil classified "For Service SC, SD, SE or MS." Detergent oils keep the engine cleaner and retard the formation of gum and varnish deposits. Nothing should be added to the recommended oil.

RECOMMENDED SAE VISCOSITY GRADES

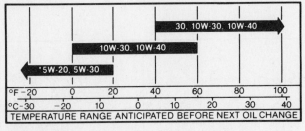

*If not available, a synthetic oil may be used having 5W-20, 5W-30 or 5W-40 viscosity.

Change Oil (Crankcase)

Change oil after first 5 hours of operation. Thereafter change oil every 25 hours of operation; more often under dirty operating conditions. Remove oil drain plug, Fig. 1, Ill. 1 or 2 and drain oil while engine is warm. Replace drain plug. Remove oil fill plug or cap and refill with new oil of proper grade. Replace oil fill plug or cap. Check oil level regularly — at least after five hours of operation.

BE SURE OIL LEVEL IS MAINTAINED.

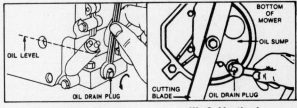

Ill. 1 Horizontal   **Ill. 2 Vertical**

Fig. 1 — Change Oil Crankcase

Check Oil (6 to 1 Gear Reduction Models)
6, 8, 60000, 80000, 100000, 130000

Remove the oil plug in lower half of gear cover every 100 hours of operation to check the oil level. Fig. 2.

Add SAE 10W-30 oil at upper oil fill plug until oil runs out of lower hole. Replace both plugs.

NOTE: Filler plug has vent hole and must be placed in top opening.

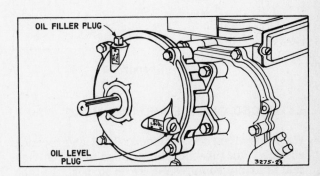

Fig. 2 — Check Oil Level

LUBRICATION
Extended Oil Fill and Dipsticks

Check Oil (Gear Reduction)
Aluminum Engines
Models 140000, 170000, 190000

Remove drain plug in bottom of gear case cover and drain oil every 100 hours of operation. Fig. 3. Replace plug. To refill, remove oil check plug and oil fill plug and pour oil (same grade as used in crankcase) into filler hole until it runs out level check hole. Replace both plugs. Oil fill plug has a vent hole and must be installed on top of gear case cover.

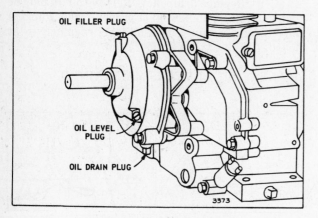

Fig. 3 — Check Oil Level

Change Oil (Gear Reduction) Cast Iron Engines

The reduction gears are lubricated by engine crankcase oil. Remove drain plug from gear case cover to drain oil remaining in gear case. See Fig. 4.

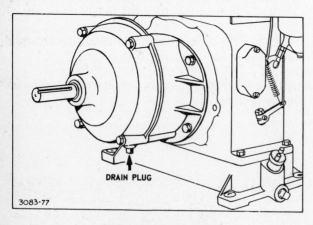

Fig. 4 — Change Oil

EXTENDED OIL FILL AND DIPSTICKS

When installing the extended oil fill and dipstick assembly, the tube must be installed so the "O" ring seal is firmly compressed. To do so, push the tube downward toward the sump, then tighten blower

housing screw, which is used to secure the tube and bracket. When the cap and dipstick assembly is fully depressed or screwed down, it seals the upper end of the tube. See Fig. 5.

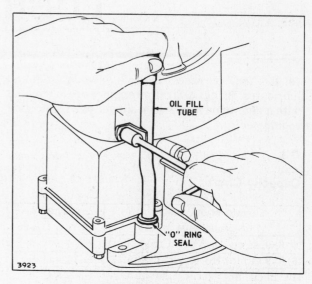

Fig. 5 — Extended Oil Fill and Dipstick

A LEAK AT THE SEAL BETWEEN THE TUBE AND SUMP, OR AT THE SEAL AT THE UPPER END OF THE DIPSTICK CAN RESULT IN A LOSS OF CRANKCASE VACUUM, AND A DISCHARGE OF SMOKE THROUGH THE MUFFLER.

Caution owners not to overfill the sump or crankcase with oil when using the extended filler and dipstick. The dipstick is marked "DO NOT OVERFILL." Excessive oil will cause a smoking condition, as the engine attempts to discharge the surplus oil.

Various styles of extended Oil Fill and Dipsticks are shown in Figs. 6, 7, 8 and 9.

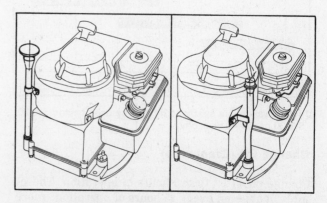

Fig. 6 — Model Series 92000, 100000, 110000, 130000

8

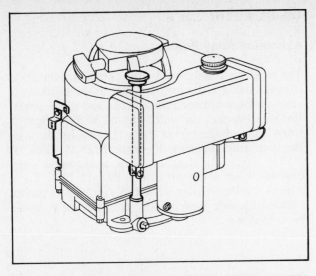

Fig. 7 — Model Series 146700, 170700, 190700, 251000

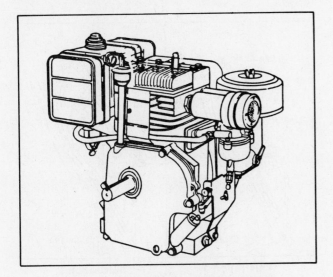

Fig. 8 — Model Series 170400, 190400

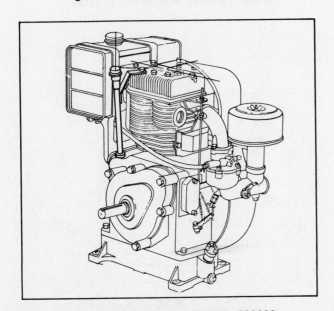

Fig. 9 — Model Series 300000, 320000

It is the breather's function to maintain a vacuum in the crankcase. The breather has a fibre disc valve, which limits the direction of air flow caused by the piston moving back and forth. Air can flow out of the crankcase, but the one way valve blocks the return flow, thus maintaining a vacuum in the crankcase.

A partial vacuum must be maintained in the crankcase to prevent oil from being forced out of engine, at the piston rings, oil seals, breaker plunger and gaskets.

Checking Breathers

If the fiber disc valve is stuck or binding, the breather cannot function properly and must be replaced. A .045" (1.1 mm) wire gauge should not enter the space between the fiber disc valve and body. (A spark plug wire gauge may be used.) Check as shown in Fig. 10. NOTE: The fiber disc valve is held in place by an internal bracket which will be distorted if pressure is applied to the fiber disc valve. Therefore, do not apply force when checking with wire gauge.

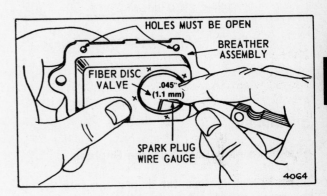

Fig. 10 — Checking Breather

If breather is removed for inspection, or valve repair, a new gasket should be used when replacing breather. Tighten screws securely to prevent oil leakage.

Most breathers are now vented through the air cleaner, to prevent dirt from entering the crankcase. Check to be sure venting elbows or tube are not damaged and seal properly.

Various breather assemblies are illustrated in Fig. 11.

8

LUBRICATION
Oil Dipper and Slinger

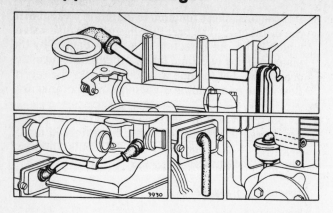

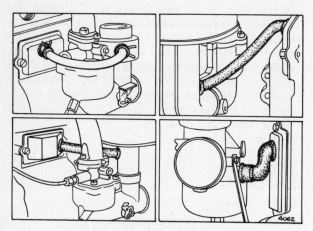

Fig. 11 — Breather Assemblies

OIL DIPPER

Aluminum Alloy and Cast Iron Engines

In the splash system, the dipper dips into the oil reservoir in base of engine. It has no pump or moving parts. Install connecting rod and dipper per engine model as shown in Fig. 12.

OIL SLINGER

Aluminum Alloy Engines

The oil slinger is driven by the cam gear. Old style slingers using a die cast bracket assembly have a steel bushing between the slinger and the bracket. Replace bracket on which the oil slinger rides if worn to a diameter of .49″ (12.4 mm) or less. Replace steel bushing if worn. Fig. 13. Illus. 1. Newer style oil slingers have a stamped steel bracket. Unit is one assembly. Fig. 13. Illus. 2 and Fig. 14. Spring washer is used only on Models 100900-130900. Inspect gear teeth, old and new style; replace if worn.

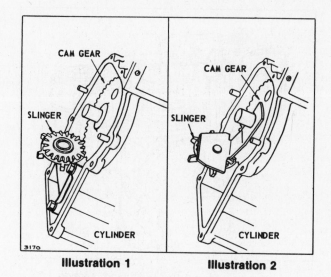

Illustration 1	Illustration 2

Fig. 13 — Oil Slinger and Bracket

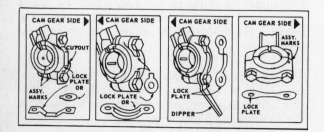

**Fig. 12 — Connecting Rod Installation
Horizontal Crankshaft Engines**

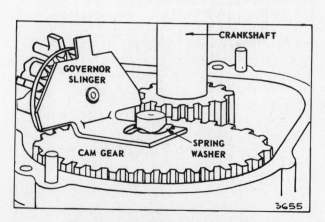

**Fig. 14 — Oil Slinger and Bracket
Vertical Crankshaft Engines**

Section 9
PISTONS — RINGS — RODS

Remove Piston and Connecting Rod

To remove the piston and connecting rod from the engine, bend down connecting rod lock. Fig. 1. Remove the connecting rod cap. Remove any carbon or ridge at the top of the cylinder bore; this will prevent breaking of the rings. Push the piston and rod out through the top of the cylinder.

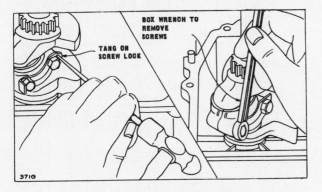

Fig. 1 — Bending Rod Lock

Pistons used in sleeve bore aluminum alloy engines are marked with an "L" on top of the piston. Fig. 2. Illus. 1. These pistons are tin plated. This piston assembly is NOT INTERCHANGEABLE with the piston used in aluminum bore (KOOL BORE) engines.

Pistons used in aluminum bore (KOOL BORE) engines are NOT marked on top of the piston.

Fig. 2. Illus. 2. The piston is chrome plated and is not to be used in a sleeve bore engine.

Fig. 2 — Piston Variations

Remove Connecting Rod

To remove connecting rod from piston, remove piston pin lock with thin nose pliers. One end of the pin is drilled to facilitate removal of the lock. Fig. 3.

Remove rings one at a time as shown in Fig. 4, slipping them over the ring lands. Use a ring expander to prevent damage to rings and piston.

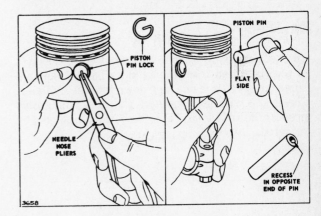

Fig. 3 — Removing Rod

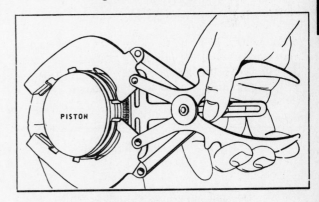

Fig. 4 — Removing Rings

Check Piston

If the cylinder is to be resized, there is no reason to check the piston, since a new oversized piston assembly will be used.

If, however, the cylinder is not to be resized, and the piston shows no signs of wear or scoring, the piston should be checked.

PISTONS — RINGS — RODS
Checking

To do so, clean carbon from top ring groove. Place a NEW ring on the groove, check the remaining space in the groove with a feeler gauge. Fig. 5. If a .007" (0.18 mm) feeler gauge can be inserted (all models), the piston is worn and should be replaced.

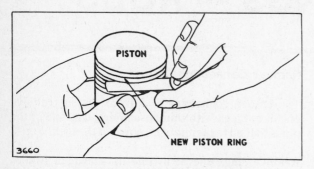

Fig. 5 — Checking Ring Grooves

Check Rings

To check rings, first clean all carbon from the ends of the rings and from the cylinder bore. Insert old rings one at a time one inch down into the cylinder. Check gap with feeler gauge. Fig. 6. If ring gap is greater than shown in Table No. 1, the ring should be rejected.

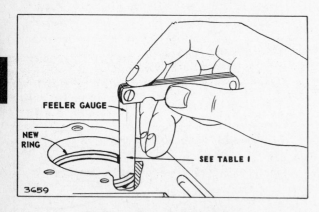

Fig. 6 — Checking Ring Gap

NOTE: Do not deglaze cylinder walls when installing piston rings in aluminum cylinder engines.

Chrome Rings

NOTE: Chrome ring sets are available for all current aluminum and cast iron cylinder models, no honing or deglazing is required. The cylinder bore can be a maximum of .005" (0.13 mm) oversize when using chrome rings. See Service Bulletin 479 or Engine Parts List.

TABLE NO. 1
RING GAP REJECTION SIZE

BASIC MODEL SERIES	COMP. RING		OIL RING	
ALUMINUM CYLINDER	Inches	Milli-meter	Inches	Milli-meter
6B, 60000, 8B, 80000				
82000, 92000, 110000, 111000				
100000, 130000	.035	0.80	.045	1.14
140000, 170000, 190000, 250000				
CAST IRON CYLINDER	Inches	Milli-meter	Inches	Milli-meter
5, 6, 8, N, 9				
14, 19, 190000				
200000, 23	.030	0.75	.035	0.90
230000, 240000				
300000, 320000				

TABLE NO. 2
CONNECTING ROD REJECT SIZES

BASIC MODEL SERIES	CRANK PIN BEARING		PISTON PIN BEARING	
ALUMINUM CYLINDER	Inches	Milli-meter	Inches	Milli-meter
6B, 60000	.876	22.25	.492	12.50
8B, 80000	1.001	25.43	.492	12.50
82000, 92000, 110000	1.001	25.43	.492	12.50
100000	1.001	25.43	.555	14.10
130000	1.001	25.43	.492	12.50
140000, 170000	1.095	27.81	.674	17.12
190000	1.127	28.63	.674	17.12
220000, 250000	1.252	31.80	.802	20.37
CAST IRON CYLINDER	Inches	Milli-meter	Inches	Milli-meter
5	.752	19.10	.492	12.50
6, 8, N	.751	19.08	.492	12.50
9	.876	22.25	.563	14.30
14, 19, 190000	1.001	25.43	.674	17.12
200000	1.127	28.63	.674	17.12
23, 230000	1.189	30.20	.736	18.69
240000	1.314	33.38	.674	17.12
300000, 320000	1.314	33.38	.802	20.37

Check Connecting Rod

If the crankpin bearing in the rod is scored, the rod must be replaced. Rejection sizes of crankpin bearing hole and piston pin bearing hole are shown in table No. 2. Pistons pins .005" (0.13 mm) oversize are available in case the connecting rod and piston are worn at the piston pin bearing. If, however, the crankpin bearing in the connecting rod is worn, the rod should be replaced. Do not attempt to "file" or "fit" the rod.

Check Piston Pin

If the piston pin is worn .0005" (.01 mm) out of round or below the rejection sizes listed below, it should be replaced. Table No. 3.

9

TABLE NO. 3
PISTON PIN REJECTION SIZE

BASIC MODEL SERIES	PISTON PIN		PIN BORE	
ALUMINUM CYLINDER	Inches	Milli-meter	Inches	Milli-meter
6B, 60000	.489	12.42	.491	12.47
8B, 80000	.489	12.42	.491	12.47
82000, 92000, 110000	.489	12.42	.491	12.47
100000	.552	14.02	.554	14.07
130000	.489	12.42	.491	12.47
140000, 170000, 190000	.671	17.04	.673	17.09
220000, 250000	.799	20.29	.801	20.35
CAST IRON CYLINDER	Inches	Milli-meter	Inches	Milli-meter
5, 6, 8, N	.489	12.42	.491	12.47
9	.561	14.25	.563	14.30
14, 19, 190000	.671	17.04	.673	17.09
200000	.671	17.04	.673	17.09
23, 230000	.734	8.64	.736	18.69
240000	.671	17.04	.673	17.09
300000, 320000	.799	20.29	.801	20.35

Assemble Piston and Connecting Rod

The piston pin is a push fit in both piston and connecting rod. On models using a solid piston pin, one end is flat, the other end is recessed. Other models use a hollow pin.

Place a pin lock in the groove at one side of the piston. From the opposite side of the piston, insert the piston pin, flat end first with solid pin, either end with hollow pins, until it stops against the pin lock. Fig. 3. Use a thin nose pliers to assemble the pin lock in the recessed end of the piston. Be sure the locks are firmly set in the grooves.

Assemble Rings to Piston

In Fig. 7, are shown the various rings and the proper position of each. Note especially the center compression ring. The scraper groove should always be down toward the piston skirt. Be sure the oil return holes are clean and carbon is removed from all grooves. NOTE: Install expander under oil ring, when required.

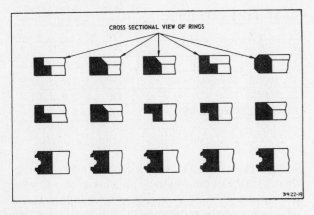

Fig. 7 — Position of Rings

Oil the rings and piston skirt, then compress rings with ring compressor (part 19070 or 19230). On all cast iron models, use ring compressor (19070) as illustrated in Fig. 8. Illustration 1.

On all aluminum engines, use compressor (19070) as illustrated in Fig. 8. Illustration 2.

NOTE: When using 19230 (2 band) ring compressor, use as shown in Fig. 8, Illus. 1 on all engines.

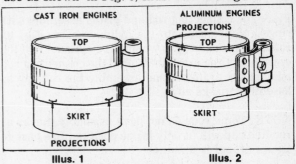

Fig. 8 — Compression Rings

Turn the piston and compressor upside down on the bench and push downward, so the piston head and edge of compressor band are even while tightening the compressor. Draw the compressor up tight to fully compress the rings, then loosen the compressor very slightly.

Do not attempt to install piston and ring assembly without ring compressor.

NOTE: The pistons used in the 220000 and 250000 engines have a notch as shown in Fig. 9. The notch must face the flywheel side of the cylinder when installed.

Installing Piston and Connecting Rod
Models 300000 and 320000

The piston has an identification mark "F" located next to piston pin bore. When assembling piston to the connected rod, the letter "F" on the piston must appear on the same side as the assembly mark on the connecting rod. Assembly mark on rod is also used to identify rod and cap alignment. Install piston rings as illustrated in Fig. 9.

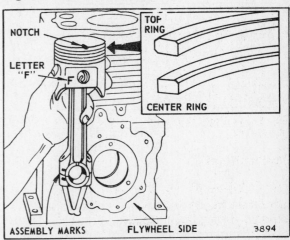

Fig. 9 — Assemble Piston to Rod

9

PISTONS — RINGS — RODS
Assembly

Install piston, connecting rod, and dipper. Piston identification mark "F" and notch at top of piston must be toward flywheel side. Torque connecting rod screw per Table No. 4. Move connecting rod back and forth on crankpin to be sure it is free.

Install Piston and Rod Assembly
All Models Except 300000 and 320000

Place the connecting rod and piston assembly with rings compressed into the cylinder bore, Fig. 10. Push piston and rod down into the cylinder. Oil the crankpin of the crankshaft. Pull the connecting rod against the crankpin and assemble the rod cap so assembly marks align. Fig. 11.

NOTE: Some rods do not have assembly marks as rod and cap will fit only in one position. Use care to insure proper installation.

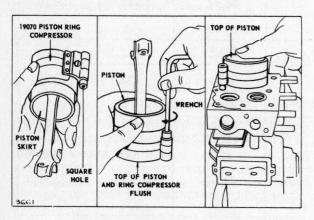

Fig. 10 — Install Piston Assembly

NOTE: Some rods may have flat washers under cap screws; remove and discard prior to installing rod.

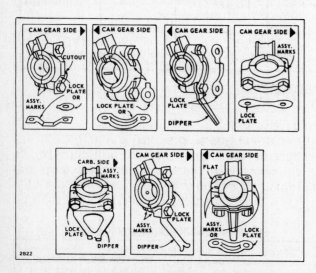

Fig. 11 — Connecting Rod Installation

Assemble the cap screws and screw locks with oil dipper (if used). Tighten cap screws to torque shown in Table No. 4. Fig. 12. Rotate the crankshaft two revolutions to be sure rod is correctly installed. If rod strikes, connecting rod has been installed wrong or cam gear is out of time. If crankshaft operates freely bend screw locks against screw heads. Fig. 12.

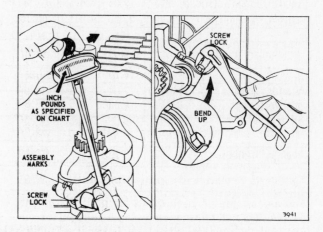

Fig. 12 — Bending Screw Locks

TABLE NO. 4
CONNECTING ROD CAP SCREW TORQUE

BASIC MODEL SERIES	AVERAGE TORQUE		
ALUMINUM CYLINDER	Inch Pounds	Kilogram Meter	Newton Meter
6B, 60000	100	1.2	11.3
8B, 80000	100	1.2	11.3
82000, 92000, 110000, 111000	100	1.2	11.3
100000, 130000	100	1.2	11.3
140000, 170000, 190000	165	1.9	18.7
250000	185	2.1	21.0
CAST IRON CYLINDER	Inch Pounds	Kilogram Meter	Newton Meter
5, 6, N, 8	100	1.2	11.3
9	140	1.6	15.8
14	190	2.2	21.5
19, 190000, 200000	190	2.2	21.5
23, 230000	190	2.2	21.5
240000, 300000, 320000	190	2.2	21.5

NOTE: Tighten rod screws securely. After tightening rod screws, rod should be able to move sideways on crankpin of shaft. A torque wrench must be used to prevent loose or overtight cap screws which results in breakage and/or scoring of rod. Fig. 12.

9

Section 10
CRANKSHAFTS & CAM GEARS

REMOVAL

Aluminum Cylinder Engines

To remove the crankshaft from aluminum alloy engines, remove rust or burrs from the power take-off end of the crankshaft. Remove crankcase cover or sump. If sump or cover sticks, tap lightly with soft hammer on alternate sides near dowel. Turn crankshaft to align the crankshaft and cam gear timing marks, lift out the cam gear, then remove the crankshaft. On ball bearing models, the crankshaft and cam gear must be removed together. Fig. 1.

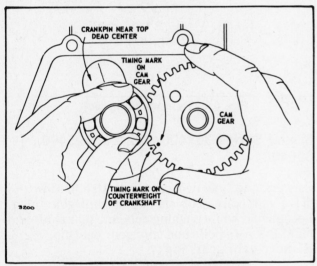

Fig. 1 — Ball Bearing Engines

Cast Iron Cylinder Engines

Model Series 5, 6, 8, N
Plain Bearings

Remove magneto. Remove burrs and rust from P.T.O. end of crankshaft. Remove crankshaft, Fig. 2.

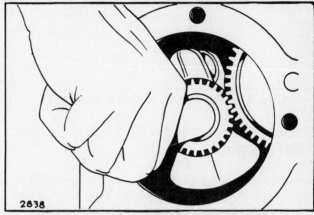

Fig. 2 — Remove or Install Crankshaft

Model Series 6FB, 6FBC, 6SFB, 8FB, 8FBC, 8FBP — Ball Bearings

Remove magneto. Drive out cam gear shaft while holding cam gear to prevent dropping, Fig. 3. Push cam gear into recess, Fig. 4. Pull crankshaft out from magneto side.

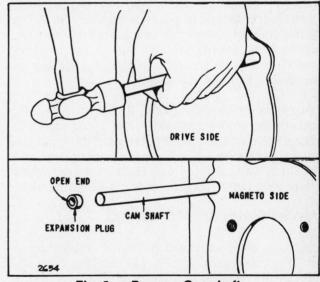

Fig. 3 — Remove Camshaft

10

OCTOBER, 1981

CRANKSHAFTS & CAM GEARS
Removal

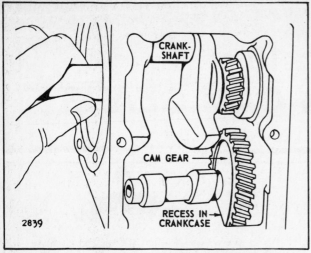

Fig. 4 — Remove or Install Crankshaft

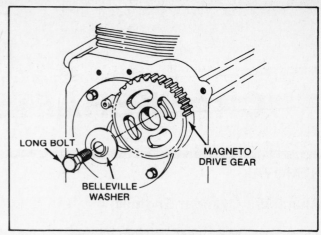

Fig. 5 — Remove Short Bolt

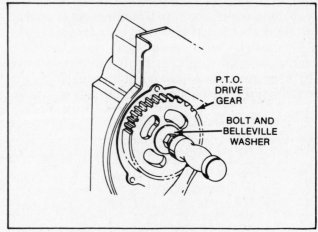

Fig. 6 — Remove Long Bolt

Model Series 9, 14, 19, 23, 200000, 230000 Plain Bearings

Remove crankshaft cover. Rotate crankshaft to approximate position shown in Fig. 2. Pull out crankshaft from P.T.O. side, twisting slightly, if necessary, to clear cam gear.

Model Series 9, 14, 19, 23, 190000, 200000, 230000, 240000, 300000, 320000 Ball Bearings

NOTE: On 240000, 300000, 320000, piston and rod must be removed from engine.

Remove crankcase cover and bearing support. Rotate crankshaft to position shown, Fig. 2. On some models, it may be necessary to position crankshaft approximately 180° from position shown in Fig. 2. Pull crankshaft out, turning as needed to remove crankshaft.

To remove cam gear from all cast iron models, except the 300000 and 320000, use a long punch to drive the cam gear shaft out toward the magneto side. (Save plug.) Fig. 3. Do not burr or peen end of shaft while driving out. Hold cam gear while removing punch so gear does not drop and nick.

Model Series 300400, 320400

Remove short bolt and Belleville washer from P.T.O. drive gear, Fig. 5. Loosen long bolt and Belleville washer two (2) turns on magneto side and tap head of bolt with hammer to loosen cam gear shaft. Turn bolt out while pushing out cam gear shaft. Remove bolts from cam gear bearing, Fig. 6. While holding cam gear, remove cam gear bearing and remove cam gear, Fig. 7.

Model Series 301400, 302400, 325400, 326400

Loosen long bolt two (2) turns. Use hammer to drive out cam gear shaft and cam gear plug. Loosen bolt while pushing out cam gear shaft and plug. Remove bolts and cam gear bearing, Fig. 6. Remove cam gear, Fig. 7.

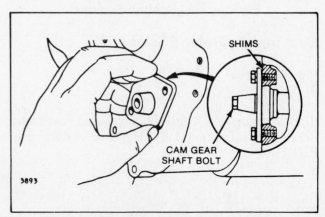

Fig. 7 — Removing Cam Gear Bearing

10

CHECKING CRANKSHAFT

All Engines

Table No. 1 shows the rejection sizes of the various wear points of the crankshaft. Discard crankshaft if worn smaller than the size shown. Keyways should be checked to be sure they are not worn or spread. Remove burrs from keyway edges to prevent scratching the bearing. Fig. 8 shows the various points to be checked on the crankshaft.

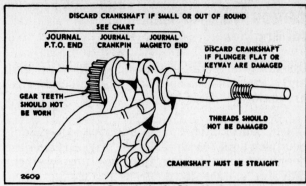

Fig. 8 — Crankshaft Check Points

NOTE: .020″ undersize connecting rods may be obtained for use on reground crankpin bearings. Complete instructions are inclued with the undersize rod. (See Service Bulletin #480 or Illustrated Parts List to find appropriate undersize rod.)

TABLE NO. 1
CRANKSHAFT REJECT SIZES

MODEL SERIES	P.T.O. JOURNAL		MAGNETO JOURNAL		CRANKPIN JOURNAL	
ALUMINUM CYLINDER	Inches	Millimeter	Inches	Millimeter	Inches	Millimeter
6B, 60000	.873	22.17	.873	22.17	.870	22.10
8B, 80000*	.873	22.17	.873	22.17	.996	25.30
82000, 92000*, 94000, 110900*, 111200, 111900*	.873	22.17	.873	22.17	.996	25.30
100000, 130000	.998	25.35	.873	22.17	.996	25.30
140000, 170000	1.179	29.95	.997#	25.32#	1.090	27.69
190000	1.179	29.95	.997#	25.32#	1.122	28.50
220000, 250000	1.376	34.95	1.376	34.95	1.247	31.67
CAST IRON CYLINDER	Inches	Millimeter	Inches	Millimeter	Inches	Millimeter
5, 6, 8, N	.873	22.17	.873	22.17	.743	18.87
9	.983	24.97	.983	24.97	.873	22.17
14, 19, 190000	1.179	29.95	1.179	29.95	.996	25.30
200000	1.197	29.95	1.179	29.95	1.122	28.50
23, 230000†	1.376	34.95	1.376	34.95	1.184	30.07
240000	Ball	Ball	Ball	Ball	1.309	33.25
300000, 320000	Ball	Ball	Ball	Ball	1.309	33.25

*Auxiliary drive models P.T.O. Bearing Reject Size — 1.003 in. (25.48 mm).
#Synchro-Balance Magneto Bearing Reject Size — 1.179 in. (29.95 mm)
†Gear Reduction P.T.O. — 1.179 in. (29.95 mm)

10

CRANKSHAFTS & CAM GEARS
Checking

CHECKING CAM GEAR
All Engines

Inspect gear teeth for wear and nicks. Cam shaft and cam gear journals and lobe rejection sizes are shown in Table No. 2.

Check automatic spark advance on models equipped with "Magna-Matic." Fig. 9. Place cam gear in normal operating position with the movable weight down. Press the weight down. Release. The spring should lift the weight. If not, the spring is stretched or the weight is binding. Repair or replace.

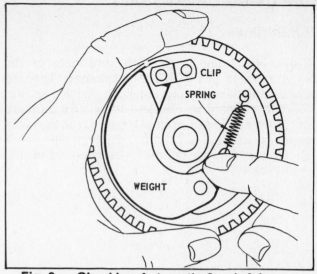

Fig. 9 — Checking Automatic Spark Advance

TABLE NO. 2
CAM GEAR REJECT SIZES

MODEL SERIES	CAM GEAR OR SHAFT JOURNAL		CAM LOBE	
ALUMINUM CYLINDER	**Inches**	**Millimeter**	**Inches**	**Millimeter**
6B, 60000	.498	12.65	.883	22.43
8B, 80000*	.498	12.65	.883	22.43
82000, 92000, 94000	.498	12.65	.883	22.43
110900, 111200, 111900	.436 Mag. .498 PTO	11.07 Mag. 12.65 PTO	.870	22.10
100000, 130000	.498	12.65	.950	24.13
140000, 170000, 190000	.498	12.65	.977	24.82
220000, 250000	.498	12.65	1.184	30.07
CAST IRON CYLINDER	**Inches**	**Millimeter**	**Inches**	**Millimeter**
5, 6, 8, N	.372	9.45	.875	22.23
9	.372	9.45	1.124	28.55
14, 19, 190000	.497	12.62	1.115	28.32
200000	.497	12.62	1.115	28.32
23, 230000	.497	12.62	1.184	30.07
240000	.497	12.62	1.184	30.07
300000	#	#	1.184	30.07
320000	#	#	1.215	30.86

*Auxiliary Drive Models P.T.O. — .751 in. (19.08 mm)
#Magneto Side — .8105 in. (20.59 mm)
 P.T.O. — .6145 in. (15.61 mm)

10

Checking Compression Release Cam

Model Series 111200, 111900

This cam gear has Easy-Spin® plus a compression release on the exhaust cam. In the starting position, the actuator cam moves the rocker cam so it will open the exhaust valve at the same time as the Easy-Spin® lobe. When the engine starts, the actuator cam moves out and lets the rocker cam move down and the exhaust valve operates normally.

To check, move actuator cam to the running position, Fig. 10. Push rocker cam against the actuator cam. Release the actuator cam. Actuator cam spring should pull actuator cam against the shoulder pin causing rocker cam to raise up to starting position. Fig. 11. There should be no binding. Replace if binding exists.

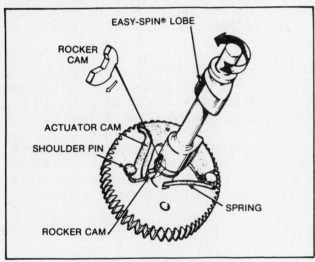

Fig. 10 — Running Position

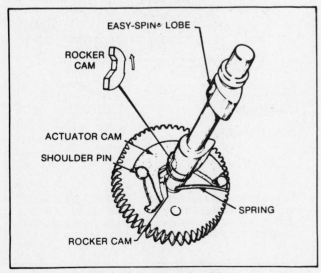

Fig. 11 — Start Position

BALL BEARINGS

Remove

The ball bearing is a press fit on the crankshaft. If either bearing or crankshaft is to be removed, use an arbor press, as shown in Fig. 12.

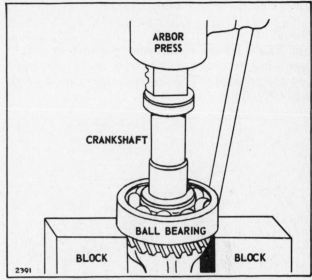

Fig. 12 — Removing Ball Bearing

Install

Heat bearing in hot oil [250° F max. (120° C)]; bearing must not rest on the bottom of the pan in which it is heated. Place crankshaft in vise with bearing side up. When bearing is quite hot it will become a slip fit on the bearing journal. Grasp bearing with the shield down and thrust it down on the crankshaft, Fig. 13. The bearing will tighten on the shaft while cooling. DO NOT QUENCH.

NOTE: Bearing shield faces crankshaft crankpin.

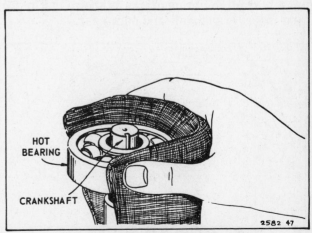

Fig. 13 — Installing Ball Bearing

10

CRANKSHAFTS & CAM GEARS
Installing
INSTALL CRANKSHAFT AND CAM GEAR

Aluminum Alloy Engines — Plain Bearing

In aluminum alloy models the tappets are inserted first, the crankshaft next, and then the cam gear. When inserting the cam gear, turn the crankshaft and cam gear so that the timing marks on the gears align. Fig. 14.

NOTE: Model series 94000, 171700, 191700, 251700, and 252700 have a removable timing gear. When installing timing gear, have inner chamfer toward crankpin. This assures that timing mark will be visible.

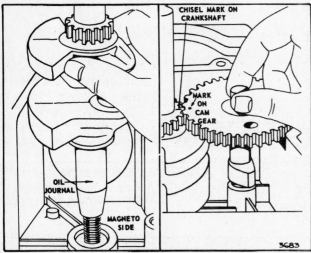

Fig. 14 — Aligning Timing Marks

Aluminum Alloy Engines — Ball Bearing

On crankshafts with ball bearings, the gear teeth are not visible for alignment of the timing marks, therefore, the timing mark is on the counterweight. Fig. 15. On ball bearing equipped models the tappets are installed first. The crankshaft and cam gear must be inserted together; align timing marks as shown in Fig. 15, and insert crankshaft and cam gear.

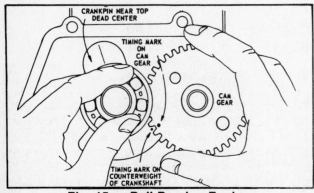

Fig. 15 — Ball Bearing Engines

CRANKCASE COVER and CRANKSHAFT END PLAY

All Models

The crankshaft end play on all models, plain and ball bearing, should be .002″ (.05 mm) to .008″ (.20 mm). The method of obtaining the correct end play varies, however, between cast iron, aluminum, plain and ball bearing models. New gasket sets include three crankcase cover or bearing support gaskets — .005″ (.13 mm), .009″ (.23 mm) and .015″ (.38 mm).

Aluminum Engines — Plain Bearing

The end play should be .002″ (.05 mm) to .008″ (.20 mm) with one .015″ (.38 mm) gasket in place. If the end play is less than .002″ (.05 mm), which would be the case if a new crankcase or sump cover is used, additional gaskets of .005″ (.13 mm) .009″ (.23 mm) or .015″ (.38 mm) may be added in various combinations to attain the proper end play.

If the end play is more than .008″ (.20 mm) with one .015″ (.38 mm) gasket in place, a thrust washer is available and to be placed on the crankshaft power take-off end, between the gear and crankcase cover or sump. Additional gaskets .005″ (.13 mm) or .009″ (.23 mm) will then have to be added to the .015″ (.38 mm) gasket for proper end play. NOTE: On aluminum models never use less than .015″ (.38 mm) gasket. Fig. 16.

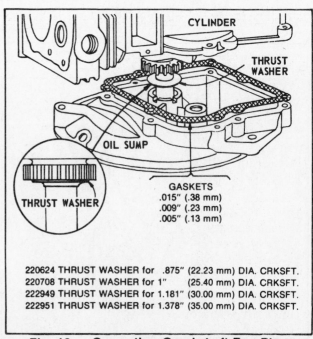

220624 THRUST WASHER for .875″ (22.23 mm) DIA. CRKSFT.
220708 THRUST WASHER for 1″ (25.40 mm) DIA. CRKSFT.
222949 THRUST WASHER for 1.181″ (30.00 mm) DIA. CRKSFT.
222951 THRUST WASHER for 1.378″ (35.00 mm) DIA. CRKSFT.

Fig. 16 — Correcting Crankshaft End Play

10

Aluminum Engines — Ball Bearing

Proceed as in aluminum plain bearings, except the thrust washer is added to the magneto end of the crankshaft instead of the power take-off end. Thrust washer cannot be used on engines with two (2) ball bearings.

Sump Installation

Model 100900 and 130900 Series

On these models use spring washer on cam gear as shown in Fig. 17.

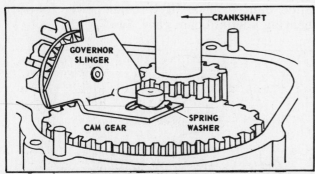

**Fig. 17 — Sump Installation —
Model Series 100900 and 130900**

To protect the oil seal while assembling the crankcase cover, put oil or grease on the sealing edge of the oil seal. Wrap a piece of thin cardboard around the crankshaft so the seal will slide easily over the shoulder of crankshaft. If the sharp edge of the oil seal is cut or bent under, the seal may leak.

Checking End Play

The end play may be checked by assembling a dial indicator on the crankshaft with the pointer against the crankcase. Move the crankshaft in and out. The indicator will show the end play. Fig. 18. The other method is to assemble a pulley to the crankshaft and measure the end play with a feeler gauge. Fig. 18. End play should be .002-.008″ (.05-.20 mm).

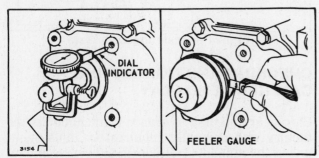

Fig. 18 — Checking Crankshaft End Play

INSTALL CRANKSHAFT AND CAM GEAR

Cast Iron Engines — Plain Bearing

Assemble the tappets to the cylinder, then insert the cam gear. Push the camshaft into the camshaft hole in the cylinder from the flywheel side through the cam gear. Wtih a blunt punch, press or hammer the camshaft until the end is flush with the outside of the cylinder on the power take-off side. Place a small amount of sealer on the camshaft plug, then press or hammer it into the camshaft hole in the cylinder at the flywheel side. Install crankshaft so timing marks on teeth and cam gear align.

All Cast Iron Engines — Ball Bearing

Except Models 300000 and 320000

Assemble the tappets, then insert cam gear into the cylinder, pushing the cam gear forward into the recess in front of the cylinder. Insert crankshaft into cylinder. Turn camshaft and crankshaft until timing marks align, then push cam gear back until it engages the gear on the crankshaft with timing marks together. Insert camshaft. Fig. 19. Place a small amount of sealer on the camshaft plug, then press or hammer it into the camshaft hole in the cylinder at the flywheel side.

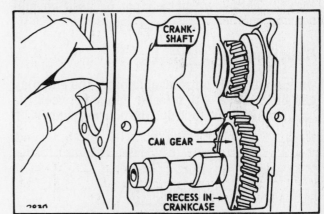

Fig. 19 — Install Crankshaft

Cast Iron Engines — End Play
Plain Bearing and Ball Bearing

The crankshaft end play should be .002″ (.05 mm) to .008″ (.20 mm) with one .015″ (.38 mm) gasket in place. If the end play is less than .002″ (.05 mm), additional gaskets of .005″ (.13 mm) or .009″ (.23 mm) may be added to the .015″ (.38 mm) gasket in various combinations to attain proper end play. If the end play is more than .008″ (.20 mm) with one .015″ (.38 mm) gasket in place, a .009″ (.23 mm) or .005″ (.13 mm) gasket may be used. Fig. 20.

10

CRANKSHAFTS & CAM GEARS
End Play

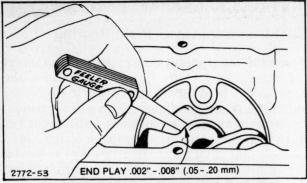

END PLAY .002" – .008" (.05 – .20 mm)
2772-53

Fig. 20 — Checking Crankshaft End Play

If the end play is more than .008" (.20 mm) with one .015" (.38 mm) gasket in place, a .009" (.23 mm) or .005" (.13 mm) gasket may be used. Fig. 20.

If the end play is more than .008" (.20 mm) with one .005" (.13 mm) gasket in place, a thrust washer is available and is placed on the crankshaft power take-off end. Fig. 20.

222949 Thrust Washer for 1.181" (30 mm) diameter crankshaft.

222951 Thrust Washer for 1.378" (35 mm) diameter crankshaft.

NOTE: Thrust washer cannot be used on ball bearing engines.

Checking End Play

On models with a removable base, the end play can be checked with a feeler gauge between the crankshaft thrust face and the bearing support on plain bearing engines. Fig. 20.

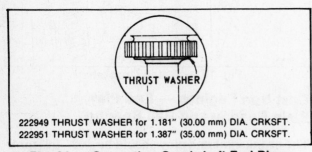

THRUST WASHER

222949 THRUST WASHER for 1.181" (30.00 mm) DIA. CRKSFT.
222951 THRUST WASHER for 1.387" (35.00 mm) DIA. CRKSFT.

Fig. 21 — Correcting Crankshaft End Play

SERVICE PROCEDURE FOR ENGINE MODEL SERIES 300400 and 320400

Install breaker plunger and tappets, then insert cam gear from power take-off side of cylinder. See Fig. 22.

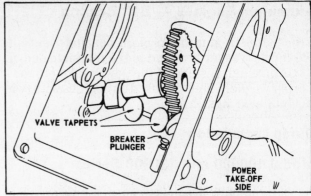

VALVE TAPPETS
BREAKER PLUNGER
POWER TAKE-OFF SIDE

Fig. 22 — Inserting Cam Gear

Slide cam gear shaft through power take-off bearing and into cam gear. See Fig. 23.

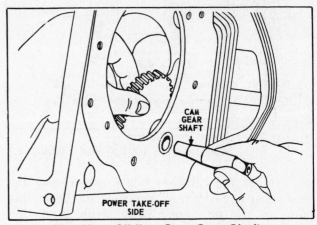

CAM GEAR SHAFT
POWER TAKE-OFF SIDE

Fig. 23 — Sliding Cam Gear Shaft

Insert magneto side cam gear bearing on cylinder. Torque cam gear bearing screws to 85 inch pounds (1.0 mkp, 9.6 Nm). Install long cam gear shaft bolt (5½") (14 cm) to prevent loss of shaft. See Fig. 24.

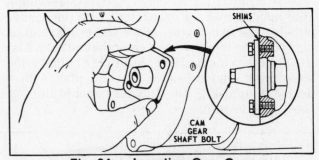

SHIMS
CAM GEAR SHAFT BOLT

Fig. 24 — Inserting Cam Gear

CHECKING AND CORRECTING CAM GEAR END PLAY

Cam gear end play tolerance is machined at the factory and normally requires no adjustment, unless the magneto side cam gear bearing or cam gear is replaced.

10

Cam gear end play is checked in the same manner as crankshaft end play.

Cam shaft end play must be .002" (.05 mm) to .008" (.20 mm). If end play is less than .002" (.05 mm), add service shims (#270516 – .009" (.23 mm); #270517 – .007" (.18 mm); or #270518 – .005" (.13 mm) to obtain proper end play. If end play is more than .008" (.20 mm), use service bearing assembly kit #299706, which includes above shims to obtain proper end play.

Use chalk or crayon to mark the top of crankshaft gear tooth, whose inner end is directly in line with the notch of the timing mark. See Fig. 25.

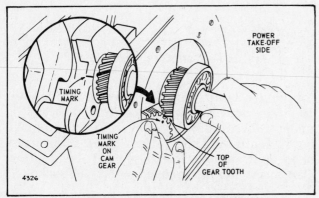

Fig. 25 — Aligning Timing Marks

Align timing marks on crankshaft and cam gear, and install crankshaft. Install crankshaft carefully so crankpin is not damaged.

Install power take-off and magneto side bearing supports. Torque power take-off support screws to 185 inch-pounds (2.2 mkp, 20.9 Nm). Torque magneto side support screw to 85 inch-pounds (1.0 mkp, 9.6 Nm). See Fig. 26.

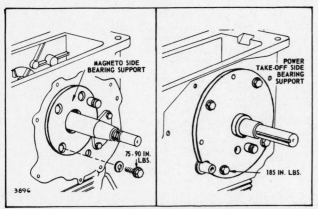

Fig. 26 — Installing Bearing Supports

See Section 12 for timing of synchro-balance timing gears.

CHECKING AND CORRECTING CRANKSHAFT END PLAY

Crankshaft end play tolerance is machined at the factory and normally requires no adjustment, unless the bearing supports or crankshaft is replaced.

Crankshaft end play must be .002" (.05 mm) to .008" (.20 mm). If end play is less than .002" (.05 mm), add service shims (#270513 – .015" (.38 mm); #270514 – .010" (.25 mm); or #270515 – .005" (.13 mm) to obtain proper end play. If end play is more than .008" (.20 mm), use service bearing support assembly kit #299705, which includes the above shims, to obtain proper end play.

Auxiliary P.T.O. — Model Series 92580, 92980, 94580, 94980, 110980, 111980

This auxiliary power take-off shaft is perpendicular to the crankshaft. It rotates at the rate of one revolution for every 8½ revolutions of the crankshaft. On these models, the cam gear, worm gear and oil slinger are a Factory assembly and are not available as separate pieces. See Fig. 27.

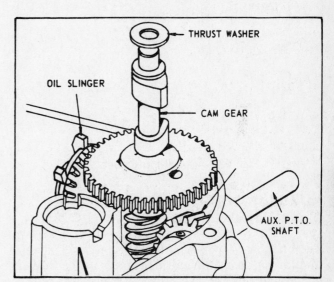

Fig. 27 — Remove and Install Sump Screw

NOTE: If rotation is counterclockwise, the thrust washer is placed next to the worm gear on camshaft.

To remove the sump: One of the six sump mounting screws is located under the auxiliary drive cover. Remove the cover. Lift out shaft stop. See Fig. 28. Slide gear and shaft sideways to expose head of sump mounting screw. Use 7/16" socket to remove screw.

10

CRANKSHAFTS & CAM GEARS
Auxiliary Drive with Clutch

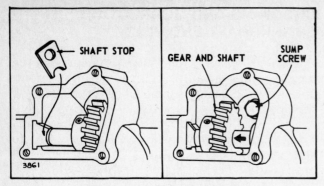

Fig. 28 — Auxiliary P.T.O.

When installing cover, Fig. 29, put non-hardening sealant on cover screws.

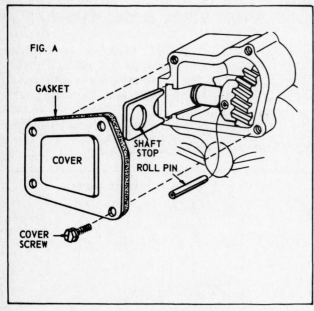

Fig. 29 — Installing Cover

AUXILIARY P.T.O. — With Clutch — Model Series 110980

This auxiliary power take-off shaft is perpendicular to the crankshaft. It rotates at the rate of one revolution for every 8-1/2 revolutions of the crankshaft. Rotation of the shaft is controlled by a clutch on the cam gear. The clutch is engaged or disengaged by a control lever mounted on the oil sump.

Early production cam gears, Fig. 30, are serviced as an assembly consisting of cam gear oil slinger, clutch hub, clutch spring and clutch sleeve assembly. Later production cam gears are serviced as individual parts except for the cam gear which consists of cam gear, oil slinger and clutch hub.

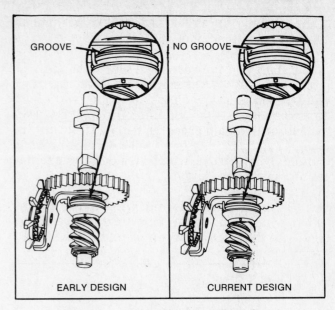

Fig. 30 — Cam Gear and Clutch

To remove sump: Sump is held on by six screws. Five screws are exposed. The sixth screw is under the auxiliary drive cover, Fig. 28. Remove cover and lift out shaft stop, Fig. 28. Slide driveshaft and gear over to expose head of cap screw. Cap screw can be removed with 7/16″ socket.

INSPECT CLUTCH OPERATION

Push on spring tang, "A," Fig. 31, turning spring and clutch sleeve in a counterclockwise direction. Spring and sleeve should rotate approximately 1/8″ turn. Worm gear should not rotate in the same direction. With clutch released, worm gear should rotate freely in both directions.

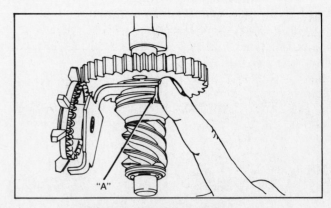

Fig. 31 — Inspect Clutch

CHECK CAM GEAR

Check worm gear end play using feeler gauges at point "A," Fig. 32. End play should not be less than .004″, (.10 mm) or more than .017″ (.43 mm).

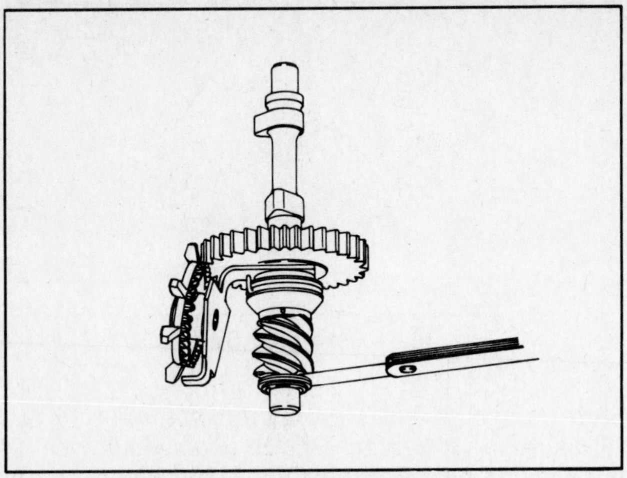

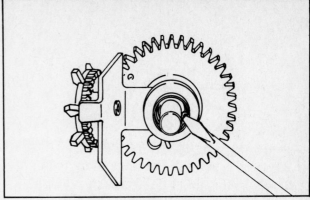

Fig. 33 — Remove Clutch Sleeve

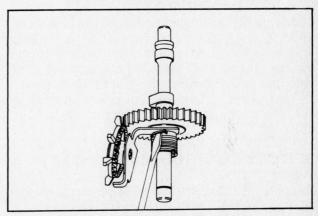

Fig. 34 — Remove Clutch Spring

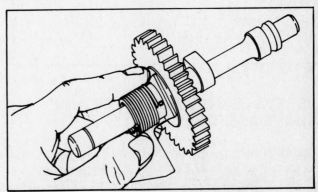

Fig. 32 — Check Cam Gear

CAM GEAR DISASSEMBLY — EARLY DESIGN

Remove "E" ring retainer. Slide off copper washer, thick thrust washer, worm and thin thrust washer. Cam gear, oil slinger, clutch sleeve and springs are serviced with a current production assembly.

INSPECT PARTS

Inspect for worn, burred or broken parts and replace as required.

ASSEMBLE CAM GEAR — EARLY DESIGN

Slide worm gear with thin thrust washer on cam gear. Slide on thick thrust washer. Slide on copper colored washer with gray coated side toward thick thrust washer. Install "E" ring retainer and check worm end play as described in "Check Cam Gear" section above. Inspect cam gear assembly as outlined in in "Inspect Clutch Operation" section above.

DISASSEMBLY CAM GEAR — CURRENT DESIGN

Remove "E" ring. Slide off thrust washers and worm gear. Use thin blade screwdriver or similar tool to pry lower clutch spring tab out of hole in clutch sleeve, Fig. 33. Remove clutch sleeve. Slide clutch spring down, Fig. 34 and lift out upper spring tab to remove spring. Cam gear, oil slinger and clutch drive hub are serviced as an assembly.

INSPECT PARTS

Inspect for worn, broken or burred parts. Replace as required.

ASSEMBLE CAM GEAR — CURRENT DESIGN

Assemble clutch spring as shown in Fig. 35. Align hole in clutch sleeve with tab or spring and slide on. Depress spring tab, if required. When clutch sleeve is in place, spring tab should be in sleeve hole, Fig. 36.

Fig. 35 — Assemble Clutch Spring

10

CRANKSHAFTS & CAM GEARS
Auxiliary Drive with Clutch

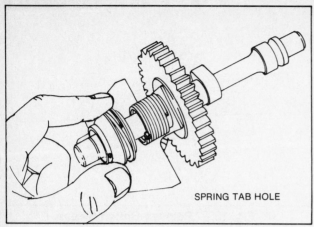

SPRING TAB HOLE

Fig. 36 — Install Clutch Sleeve

Slide thin thrust washer and worm on cam gear. Slide in thick thrust washer. Slide on copper washer with gray coated side toward thrust washer. Install "E" ring and check worm gear end play as described in "Check Cam Gear" section, page 10. Inspect cam gear assembly as outlined in "Inspect Clutch Operation" section, page 10.

REMOVE CONTROL LEVER SHAFT

Remove "E" ring, Fig. 37. Slide control lever and shaft out slowly until lever clears boss on sump. Slowly release spring tension and then remove shaft, spring and "O" ring seal.

Inspect shaft assembly for loose lever, worn or broken parts. Replace as needed.

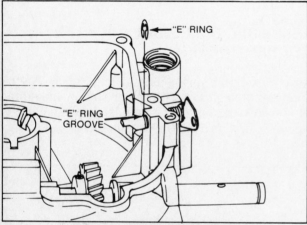

"E" RING

"E" RING GROOVE

Fig. 37 — Remove "E" Ring

ASSEMBLE CONTROL LEVER AND SHAFT ASSEMBLY

Install return spring on shaft and lever assembly as shown in Fig. 38. Then install "O" ring seal on shaft. Lubricate "O" ring and shaft lightly with engine oil.

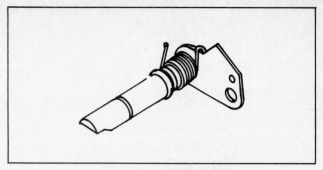

Fig. 38 — Assemble Spring

Slide control lever assembly into shaft bore, Fig. 39, as far as it will go. Rotate lever clockwise to put tension on return spring. When lever clears stop boss, push lever and spring in until lever stops. Install "E" ring. Leg of spring may need to be pushed against sump, Fig. 40.

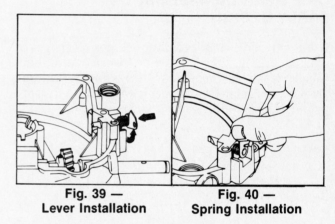

**Fig. 39 —
Lever Installation**

**Fig. 40 —
Spring Installation**

CYLINDER CLIP WASHER

Should clip washer in cylinder require replacing, be sure flat on clip washer is in line with flat on cam bearing boss and spring tabs are on both sides of cam bearing web, Fig. 41.

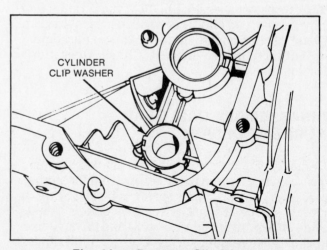

CYLINDER CLIP WASHER

Fig. 41 — Cylinder Clip Washer

10

Section 11
CYLINDERS & BEARINGS

INSPECTION

All Models

Always inspect the cylinder after the engine has been disassembled. Visual inspection will show if there are any cracks, stripped bolt holes, broken fins or if the cylinder wall is damaged. Use a telescoping gauge and dial indicator or inside micrometer to determine the size of the cylinder bore. Measure at right angles. See Fig. 1. Table No. 1 lists the standard cylinder bore sizes.

If the cylinder bore is more than .003″ (.08 mm) oversize, or .0015″ (.04 mm) out of round on cast iron cylinders, or .0025″ (.06 mm) out of round on lightweight cylinders, it must be resized.

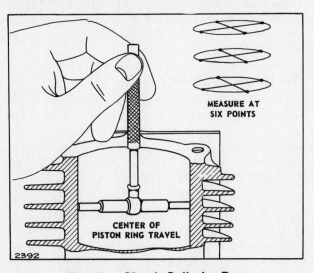

MEASURE AT
SIX POINTS

CENTER OF
PISTON RING TRAVEL

2392

Fig. 1 — Check Cylinder Bore

NOTE: Do not deglaze cylinder walls when installing piston rings in aluminum cylinder engines.

NOTE: Chrome ring sets are available for most models. See Bulletin #479 or Illustrated Parts List. They are used to control oil consumption in bores worn to .005″ (.13 mm) over standard and do not require honing or glaze breaking the bore to seat.

RESIZING

Resize Cylinder Bore to Next Oversize

All Models

ALWAYS RESIZE TO EXACTLY .010″ (.25 mm) or .020″ (.51 mm), or .030″ (.76 mm) OVER STANDARD SIZE AS SHOWN IN TABLE NO. 1. IF THIS IS DONE ACCURATELY, THE STOCK OVERSIZE RINGS AND PISTONS WILL FIT PERFECTLY AND PROPER CLEARANCES WILL BE MAINTAINED. Cylinders, either cast iron or aluminum, can be quickly resized with a good hone such as Briggs & Stratton part #19205 for aluminum cylinders or part #19211 for cast iron cylinders. Contact your Briggs & Stratton source of supply. Use the stones and lubrication recommended by the hone manufacturers for the various engine models, to produce the correct cylinder wall finish.

TABLE NO. 1

BASIC ENGINE MODEL OR SERIES	STANDARD BORE SIZE DIAMETER			
	MAX.		MIN.	
ALUMINUM CYLINDER	Inches	Milli-meters	Inches	Milli-meters
6B, 60000 before Ser. #5810060	2.3125	58.74	2.3115	58.71
60000 after Ser. #5810030	2.3750	60.33	2.3740	60.30
8B, 80000, 82000	2.3750	60.33	2.3740	60.30
92000, 93000, 94000	2.5625	65.09	2.5615	65.06
100000	2.5000	63.50	2.4990	63.47
110000	2.7812	70.64	2.7802	70.62
130000	2.5625	65.09	2.5615	65.06
140000	2.7500	69.85	2.7490	69.82
170000, 190000	3.0000	76.20	2.9990	76.17
220000, 250000	3.4375	87.31	3.4365	87.29

(Table No. 1 — Cast Iron Cylinders continued on page 2.)

CYLINDERS
Resizing Bore

BASIC ENGINE MODEL OR SERIES	STANDARD BORE SIZE DIAMETER			
	MAX.		MIN.	
CAST IRON CYLINDER	Inches	Milli-meters	Inches	Milli-meters
5, 5S, 6, N	2.0000	50.80	1.9990	50.77
8	2.2500	57.15	2.2490	57.12
9	2.2500	57.15	2.2490	57.12
14	2.6250	66.68	2.6240	66.65
19, 23, 190000, 200000	3.0000	76.20	2.9990	76.17
230000	3.0000	76.20	2.9990	76.17
240000	3.0625	77.79	3.0615	77.76
300000	3.4375	87.31	3.4365	87.29
320000	3.5625	90.49	3.5615	90.46

If a boring bar is used, a hone must be used after the boring operation to produce the proper cylinder wall finish.

Honing can be done with a portable electric drill, but it is easier to use a drill press.

To Set Up For Honing

Clean cylinder at top and bottom to remove burrs and pieces of base and head gaskets.

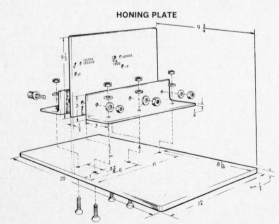

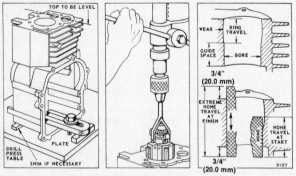

HONING PLATE

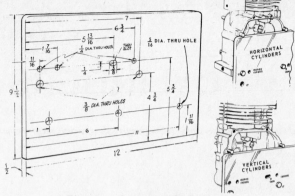

Fig. 2 — Honing Cylinder
(See page 8 for enlarged drawing.)

Fasten cylinder to a heavy iron bracket or use honing plate. Fig. 2. Some cylinders require shims. Use a level to align drill press spindle with bore.

Oil surface of drill press table liberally. Set plate and cylinder on drill press table. (Do not anchor to drill press table.) If using portable drill, set plate and cylinder on floor. Place hone drive shaft in chuck of drill or portable drill.

Slip hone into cylinder; Fig. 2, Illus. 2. Connect drive shaft to hone and set stop on drill press so hone can only extend 3/4" (20.0 mm) to 1" (25.0 mm) from top or bottom of cylinder. If using a portable drill, cut a wood block to place inside of cylinder as a stop for home.

To Hone Cylinder

Place hone in middle of cylinder bore. Tighten adjusting knob with finger or small screwdriver until stones fit snugly against cylinder wall. DO NOT FORCE. Hone should operate at 300 to 700 RPM. Lubricate hone as recommended by manufacturer.

Connect drive shaft to hone. Be sure that cylinder and hone are centered and aligned with drive shaft and drill spindle. Start drill and, as hone spins, move it up and down at lower end of cylinder. Fig. 2, Illus. 3. The cylinder is not worn at the bottom but is round so it will guide the hone to straighten cylinder bore. As the bottom of the cylinder increases diameter, gradually increase strokes until hole travels full length of bore. Do not extend hone more than 3/4" (20.0 mm) to 1" (25.0 mm) at either end of cylinder bore.

As cutting tension decreases, stop hone and tighten adjusting knob. Check cylinder bore frequently with an accurate micrometer. Hone about .0005" (.01 mm) large to allow for shrinkage when cylinder cools.

On cast iron cylinders, change from rough stone to finishing stone when within .0015" (.04 mm) of desired size, then use finishing stones. ALWAYS HONE .010" (.25 mm) or .020" (.51 mm), or .030" (.76 mm) ABOVE THE STANDARD DIMENSIONS GIVEN IN TABLE NO. 1.

CYLINDER FINISH AND CLEANING

The finish resized cylinder should have a cross-hatch appearance, Fig. 3. Proper stones, lubrication and spindle speed along with rapid movement of hone within the cylinder during the last few strokes, will produce this finish. Cross-hatching will allow proper lubrication and ring break-in.

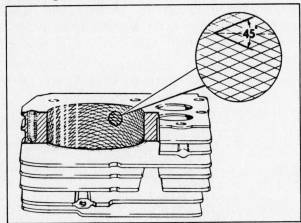

Fig. 3 — Cross Hatch

IT IS MOST IMPORTANT THAT THE ENTIRE CYLINDER BE THOROUGHLY CLEANED AFTER HONING. WASH THE CYLINDER CAREFULLY IN A SOLVENT SUCH AS KEROSENE OR COMMERCIAL SOLVENT. THE CYLINDER BORE SHOULD THEN BE CLEANED WITH A BRUSH, SOAP AND HOT WATER.

BEARINGS

BALL BEARING

To check a ball bearing, rotate the bearing slowly by hand; if any roughness is noted, bearing should be replaced.

Wash bearing in a clean solvent. Re-oil with engine oil during assembly.

Ball bearings are a press fit on the crankshaft. If bearing is to be replaced, it should be removed in an arbor press. Fig. 4. (bearing should not be reused if removed from crankshaft.)

NOTE: Bearing shield faces crankshaft crankpin.

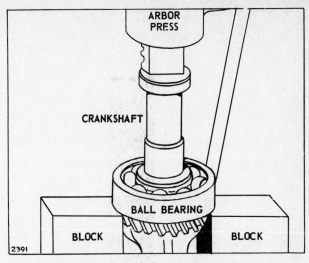

Fig. 4 — Removing Ball Bearings

To install, heat bearing in hot (250° F Max.) (120° C Max.) oil. Place crankshaft in a vise with bearing side up. When bearing is hot it will be a slip fit on crankshaft journal. Grasp bearing with the shield down and slide it on the crankshaft. Fig. 5. The bearing will tighten while cooling. Do not quench.

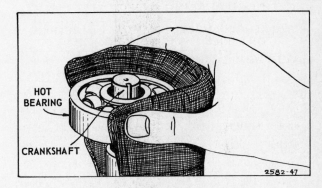

Fig. 5 — Install Ball Bearings

PLAIN BEARINGS

Checking

Bearings should be replaced if scored or if plug gauge will enter. Try gauge at several locations in bearing. Fig. 6. See gauge listing in Table No. 3.

11

CYLINDERS
Plain Bearing

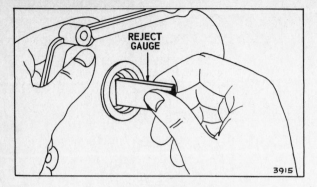

Fig. 6 — Checking Bearing

REPLACING PLAIN BEARINGS

Models 9, 14, 19, 20 and 23 Series

The crankcase cover or bearing support should be replaced if the bearing is worn or scored. Select the correct assembly part number by referring to the Parts List covering the engine. Refer to Table No. 3 for main bearing gauges.

TABLE NO. 2
CYLINDER BEARING REJECT SIZE CHART

BASIC ENGINE MODEL OR SERIES	PTO BEARING		BEARING MAGNETO	
ALUMINUM CYLINDER	Inches	Milli-meter	Inches	Milli-meter
6B, 8B*	.878	22.30	.878	22.30
60000, 80000*	.878	22.30	.878	22.30
82000, 92000*, 94000*	.878	22.30	.878	22.30
110900*, 111900*	.878	22.30	.878	22.30
100000, 130000	1.003	25.48	.878	22.30
140000, 170000	1.185	30.10	1.004#	25.50#
190000	1.185	30.10	1.004#	25.50#
220000 Horiz.	Ball	Ball	Ball	Ball
220000 Vert., 250000	1.383	35.13	1.383	35.13
CAST IRON CYLINDER	Inches	Milli-meter	Inches	Milli-meter
5, 6, 8, N	.878	22.30	.878	22.30
9	.988	25.09	.988	25.09
14	1.185	30.10	1.185	30.10
19, 190000, 200000	1.185	30.10	1.185	30.10
23, 230000†	1.382	35.10	1.382	35.10
240000, 300000	Ball	Ball	Ball	Ball
320000	Ball	Ball	Ball	Ball

†Gear Reduction PTO — 1.185" (30.10 mm)

*Auxiliary drive models PTO Bearing Reject size 1.003" (25.48 mm)

#Synchro-Balanced Magneto Bearing Reject size 1.185" (30.10 mm)

REPLACING MAGNETO BEARING

Aluminum Cylinder Engines Except 171700, 191700

There is no removable bearing in these models; the cylinder must be reamed out so a replacement bushing can be installed.

Place pilot guide bushing in the sump bearing, with flange of pilot guide bushing toward inside of sump.

Assemble sump on cylinder. Be careful that pilot guide bushing does not fall out of place. Place reamer guide bushing into the oil seal recess in the cylinder. The reamer guide bushing, along with the pilot guide bushing, will center the counterbore reamer with the opposite bearing even though old bearing might be badly worn.

Place counterbore reamer on pilot and insert into cylinder until the tip of the pilot enters the pilot guide bushing in the sump. Fig. 7.

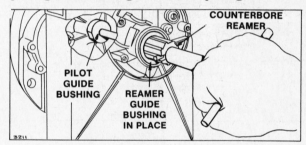

Fig. 7 — Counterbore Reaming

Turn reamer clockwise with a steady even pressure until it is completely through the bearing. Lubricate reamer with kerosene or Stoddard Solvent.

NOTE: Counterbore reaming may be undertaken without any lubricant. However, as aluminum material builds up on reamer flutes, eventual damage to the reamer and oversize counterbores will be experienced.

Remove sump and pull reamer out without backing it through the bearing. Clean out reaming chips. Remove reamer guide bushing from oil seal recess.

Hold new bushing, with notch toward cylinder and in line with notch on inside of cylinder, (Fig. 8, insert), against reamed out bearing. Note position of split in bushing. At a point opposite to the split in the bushing, using a chisel or screwdriver and hammer, make a notch in the reamed out cylinder bearing at a 45° angle. Fig. 8.

TABLE NO. 3
MAIN BEARING TOOL CHART

BASIC ENGINE MODEL SERIES	CYLINDER SUPPORT	PILOT	COUNTER-BORE REAMER	REAMER GUIDE BUSHING MAG.	REAMER GUIDE BUSHING PTO	BUSHING DRIVER	PILOT GUIDE BUSHING MAG.	PILOT GUIDE BUSHING PTO	FINISH REAMER	PLUG GAUGE
5, N, 6, 8	19123	19096	—	—	—	19124	19094	19094	19095	19166
6B, 60000, 8B, 80000, 82000, 92000, 94000, 110900, 111200, 111900	19123	19096	19099	19101	19100	19124	19094	19094	19095	19166
8BHA* 80590* 81590* 92590* 80790* 81790* 92990* 110990* 111990*	19123	19096	19099	19101	†	19124	19094	†	19095	19166
100000 130000	19123	19096	19099 MAG 19172 PTO	19101	19186V 19170H	19124	19094	19168	19095 MAG 19173 PTO	19166 19178
140000 170000, 190000	19123	19096	19172 MAG 19174 PTO	19170	19171	19179	19168	19169	19173 MAG 19175 PTO	19178
171700 191700	19123	19096	19174 MAG 19174 PTO	19201	19171	19179	19169	19169	19175 PTO 19175 MAG	19178
9, 14, 19, 20, 23, 191400, 193400, 200400, 230000	Replace support and cover.									19117

†Use sump or cover with 7/8″ diameter bearing and 19094 guide.
*Replace sump if PTO bearing is worn.

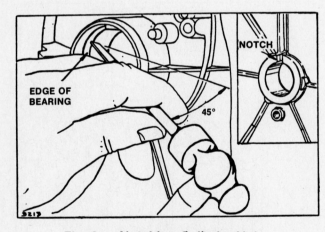

Fig. 8 — Notching Cylinder Hub

Press in the new bushing, being careful to align the oil notches, with driver and support until the outer end of the bushing is flush with the end of the reamed out cylinder hub. Fig. 9. If oil notches do not line up, bushing can be pressed through into recess in cylinder support and then reinstalled.

With a blunt chisel or screwdriver, drive a portion of the bushing into the notch previously made in the cylinder. See Fig. 8. This is called staking and is done to prevent the bushing from turning.

Reassemble sump to cylinder with pilot guide bushing in the sump bearing.

Place finish reamer on pilot and insert the pilot into the cylinder bearing until the tip of the pilot enters the pilot guide bushings in the sump bearing. Fig. 10.

Lubricate the reamer with kerosene, fuel oil or Stoddard Solvent, then ream the bushing turning the reamer clockwise with a steady even pressure until reamer is completely through the bearing. Improper lubricants will produce a rough bearing surface. Remove sump and pull reamer out without backing it through the bearing. Remove pilot guide bushing; clean out all reaming chips.

On most cylinders, the breaker point plunger hole enters the reamed out main bearing and a burr is formed by the counterbore reaming operation. Burr can be removed using 19058 finish reamer. Clean out dirt and reaming chips.

CYLINDERS
Plain Bearing

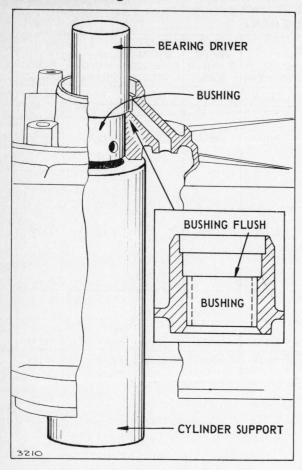

Fig. 9 — Pressing in New Bushing

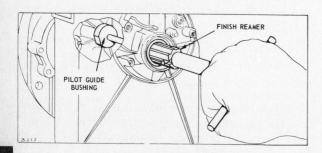

Fig. 10 — Shell Reaming

MAGNETO BEARING
Model Series 171700, 191700

Counterbore ream worn bearing using tools per Table No. 3 and procedure for standard magneto bushing. Then place new bushing against reamed out bearing on inside of cylinder, with bushing notch against cylinder and in line with oil hole, Fig. 11. Note position of split in bearing. At a point opposite the split in bushing, use a chisel or screwdriver and hammer to make a notch in the reamed out bearing at a 45° angle.

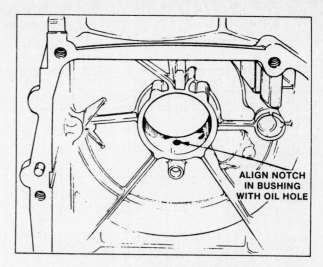

Fig. 11 — Location of Oil Hole

Press in new bushing from outside cylinder, Fig. 12, using care to keep notch in line with oil hole, Fig. 11, with bushing driver and cylinder support until bushing is flush with inside edge of cylinder, Fig. 12. If bushing notch and bushing oil hole are not aligned, press bushing through and reinstall.

With a chisel or screwdriver, drive a portion of the bushing into the notch previously made in cylinder. See Fig. 11. This is called staking and is done to prevent the bushing from turning.

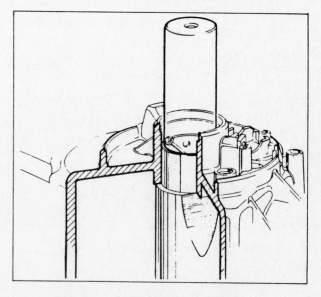

Fig. 12 — Pressing in New Bushing

Finish ream bushing using same procedure for standard magneto bushing. Clean out breaker point plunger hole with 19058 finish reamer. Clean out dirt and chips.

11

REPLACING PTO BEARING

Aluminum Cylinder Engines

The sump or crankcase cover bearing can be repaired in the same manner as the magneto bearing. However, one bearing should be completely repaired before starting the other bearing. After the bearings are finished, press in the new oil seals.

> NOTE: Model 8B-HA, 80590, 81590, 82590, 80790, 81790, 82990, 92590, 92990, 110990, 111990.
>
> The magneto bearing can be replaced as above; if the sump bearing is worn, the sump must be replaced. No tools are available for replacing the sump bearing.

REPLACING OIL SEAL

The oil seal is assembled with the sharp edge of the leather or rubber toward the inside of the engine. Lubricate inside diameter of oil seals with "Lubriplate," or equivalent, before assembling engines.

Most oil seals are pressed in, flush with the hub. However, models 60000, 80000, 100000 and 130000 using a ball bearing with mounting flange have the seal pressed 3/16" below crankcase mounting flange. Fig. 13.

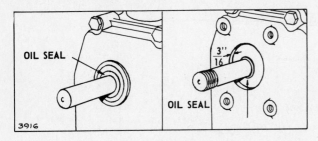

Fig. 13 — Replacing Oil Seal

CHECKING CAM GEAR BEARINGS

Check cam gear bushing using 19164 plug gauge as shown, Fig. 14. If 1/4" or more of gauge enters bearing bore, bearing is worn beyond reject and the cylinder, sump or crankcase cover must be replaced.

NOTE: On Model Series 111200, 111900, plug gauge 19164 is used on the sump or crankcase cover cam gear bearing bore. Reject size of the cylinder cam bearing is .443 or larger.

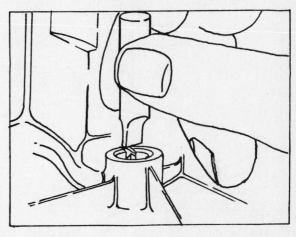

Fig. 14 — Checking Cam Gear Bearing

CYLINDERS

9 3/4
247.65 mm

241.30mm 9 1/2

130902
130202

130202
9 &
1300

17
9
130202
17

76.20 mm

3

12.70 mm

6.35mm 1/4

1/2

3
76.20 mm

98.43 mm

152.40mm
11
279.40 mm

25.40 mm

3 7/8 6

8 1/16
204.79 mm

20
508.0 mm

1

12
304.80 mm

12.70mm 1/2

Honing Fixture

177.8 mm 7

171.45 6 3/4
mm

147.64 mm 5 13/16

1 7/16 36.51 mm 1/4 DIA. THRU HOLES
6.35 mm

THRU
SLOT

17.46
mm

11/16

6.35mm 1/4

3/8 9.53mm

9 1/2
241.3 mm

9.53 mm 3/8 DIA. THRU HOLES

4 3/4
120.65 mm

5 3/4
146.05 mm

5/16 DIA. THRU HOLE
(3) 7.94 mm

1 24.5 mm

6
152.4 mm

11
120.65 mm

1 11/16
42.86 mm

12
304.8 mm

1/2
12.7 mm

11

Section 12
SYNCHRO-BALANCE

Briggs & Stratton uses two methods of Synchro-Balancing engines.

One system uses counterweights that are geared to rotate in a direction opposite from the crankshaft counterweights. The other system uses a counterweight that oscillates opposite to the direction of the piston. Each system performs the same function of substantially reducing engine vibration, thereby giving exceptionally smooth engine performance.

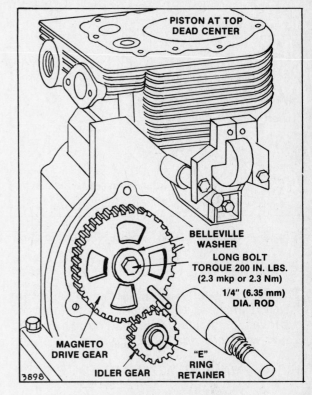

Fig. 2 — Installing and Timing Magneto Drive Gear

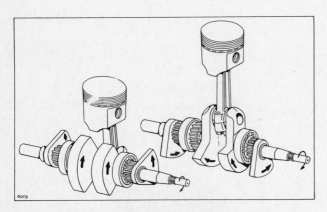

Fig. 1 — Cast Iron Engines, Rotating Counterbalance

ASSEMBLING AND TIMING ROTATING SYNCHRO-BALANCERS, CAST IRON ENGINES

Remove all traces of oil or dirt from tapered surfaces of drive gears and cam shaft before assembling gears to camshaft. Turn crankshaft until piston is at top dead center.

Remove long 5-1/2″ (139.7 mm) cam gear shaft bolt, place magneto drive gear on cam gear taper. Install bolt with Belleville washer, finger tight. See Fig. 2.

On MODEL SERIES 300400 and 320400 only, place PTO drive gear on the other end of camshaft. Install short cam gear bolt with Belleville washer, finger tight. See Fig. 3.

To time drive gears, insert short pieces of 1/4″ (6.35 mm) rod through 1/4″ (6.35 mm) holes in drive gears, and into locating holes in crankshaft bearing support plates. Fig. 2. For MODEL SERIES 300400 and 320400 also see Fig. 3. With piston at exactly TOP DEAD CENTER, torque cam gear bolt(s) [with 1/4″ (6.35 mm) rods in place] to 200 inch pounds (2.3 mkp or 22.6 Nm). Be certain piston does not move. Remove the 1/4″ (6.35 mm) rods.

Install idler gear(s). Install snap-in "E" rings to retain gears. No timing is necessary. Figs. 2 and 3.

SYNCHRO-BALANCE
Rotating & Oscillating Counterbalance

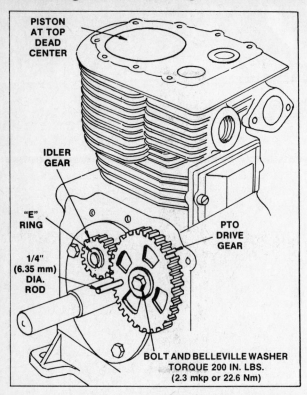

Fig. 3 — Installing and Timing PTO Drive Gear

The counterweights and ball bearings are an integral part of the covers, and cannot be removed. Lubricate the ball bearings and gears with a few drops of engine oil.

PISTON MUST BE AT TOP DEAD CENTER.

Remove the timing hole screw from cover assembly. Fig. 4. Insert a short piece of 1/8″ (3.18 mm) rod through timing hole in cover and into maching hole in counterweight. Fig. 4. The rod holds the counterweight in the proper position while cover is installed on engine.

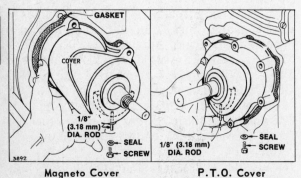

Fig. 4 — Removing Timing Hole Screw

Install cover assembly and gasket, using care to avoid damage to oil seal and making sure that bolt holes line up with tapped holes in cylinder. To minimize gear backlash, push magneto side cover toward idler gear and torque bolts to 120 inch pounds (1.4 mkp or 13.5 Nm). For MODEL SERIES 300400 and 320400 repeat above for PTO cover, torquing bolts to 200 inch pounds (2.3 mkp or 22.6 Nm).

Remove timing rods. Coat threads of timing hole screw with a non-hardening sealant, then install screw and fibre sealing washer.

MODEL SERIES 251400, 252400 & 253400

These Model Series utilize two gear driven counterweights in constant mesh with the crankshaft gear.

The cut-away view illustrates these gears, mounted in the crankcase cover, and how the Synchro-Balance counterweights rotate in opposite direction to crankshaft rotation, Fig. 5.

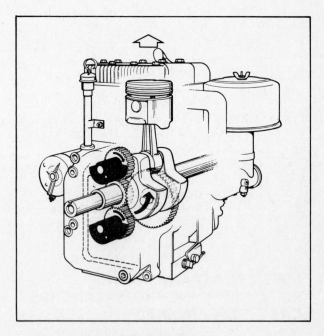

**Fig. 5 — Aluminum Engines
Rotating Counterbalance System**

SERVICE PROCEDURES FOR MODEL SERIES 251400, 252400 & 253400

The gear driven counterweights must be properly aligned when cover is installed.

To do so remove two small screws from cover and insert 1/8″ (3.18 mm) diameter locating pins through screw hole and into timing hole provided in counterweights, Fig. 6.

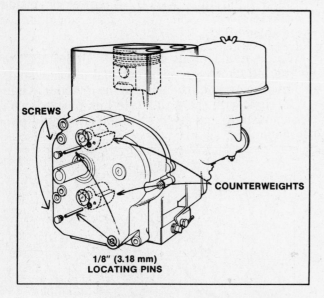

Fig. 6 — Timing Counterbalance Gears

With the piston at TOP DEAD CENTER, install the crankcase cover assembly and cover gasket. Remove the locating pins. Coat threads of timing hole screws with a non-hardening sealant, then install screws and fibre sealing washers.

If counterweights are removed from crankcase cover, exercise care in handling or cleaning to prevent losing needle bearings.

ASSEMBLY OF COUNTERWEIGHTS

Install counterweights on shafts in crankcase cover. Install counterweight retainers and torque screws to 50 inch pounds (.57 mkp or 5.6 Nm).

SERVICE PROCEDURES FOR MODEL SERIES 171700, 191700, 251700 & 252700 OSCILLATING COUNTERBALANCE SYSTEM

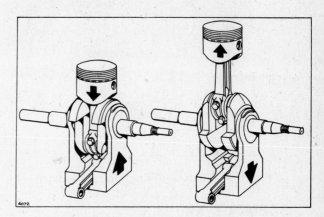

Fig. 7 — Oscillating Counterbalance

Disassembling Oscillating Counterbalance

Use a screwdriver and hammer to open the connecting rod cap screw locks — remove connecting rod screws — remove connecting rod and piston assembly. Remove crankshaft and counterweight assembly. Remove crankshaft gear — in the event it should fit tight, it can be pried off with two screwdrivers, being careful not to damage the gear. Fig. 8. Save the key on MODEL SERIES 171700 only. Key is staked in on MODEL SERIES 191700, 251700 and 252700.

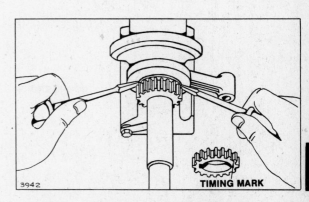

Fig. 8 — Removing Crankshaft Gear

Disassemble the counterweight. Open the locks and remove one or two screws holding the halves of the counterweight together. Separate and remove the dowel pin, link and spacer. Fig. 9.

12

3

SYNCHRO-BALANCE
Oscillating Counterbalance

Remove counterweight from the shaft.

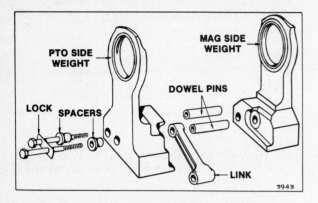

Fig. 9 — Disassembling Counterweight

ASSEMBLY

Assemble magneto side of counterweight to the magneto side of the crankshaft. Hold the crankshaft and counterweight in an upright position in a vise. Install both dowel pins. Slip link over dowel pin with rounded edge of free end up. Fig. 10.

NOTE: New style counterweight assemblies use only one (1) dowel pin, one (1) spacer, and one (1) bolt. No lock is required. Torque to 115 in/lbs. (1.32 mkp or 13.0 Nm).

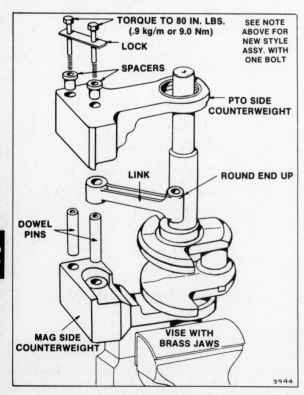

Fig. 10 — Assembling Counterweight to Crankshaft

Slip PTO counterweight in place, aligning counterweight bearing to the eccentric of crankshaft and against magneto half of counterweight. Install spacers and torque bolts to 80 inch-pounds (.9 mkp or 9.0 Nm). Bend up bolt locks and install crankshaft gear (and key on MODEL SERIES 171700). Gear is a slip fit — if tight, it may be heated to expand by laying it on a light bulb. NOTE: Chamfer on inside diameter of gear must face shoulder of crankshaft.

Lay cylinder on its side with cylinder head to the left. Start magneto journal of crankshaft into the magneto bearing in the cylinder. Align the link with the crankcase link pin and push crankshaft and counterweight assembly into place. Fig. 11.

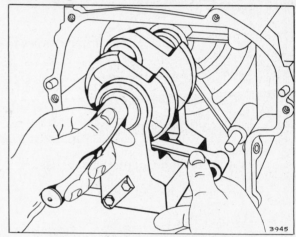

Fig. 11 — Installing Crankshaft and Counterweight Assembly

Install connecting rod and piston with lubrication hole in rod toward magneto side. This will expose rod assembly marks to view.

Assemble the cap screws and screw locks with dipper toward cam gear side. Torque screws and bend up locks. Proceed to install tappets, cam gear, etc., in usual manner.

Table No. 1

Crankshaft Eccentric Reject Sizes		
Basic Model Series	**Eccentric**	
	Inch	Millimeter
171700 & 191700	1.870	47.50
251700 & 252700	2.120	53.85

Counterweight Bearing Reject Sizes		
Basic Model Series	**Counterweight Bearing**	
	Inch	Millimeter
171700 & 191700	1.881	47.78
251700 & 252700	2.131	54.13

12

Section 13
TOOLS

It is assumed that Authorized Briggs & Stratton Service Centers have all common tools needed to repair engines.

Specialized tools in addition to the Briggs & Stratton #291661 Tool Kit, are required to analyze, repair and restore engines to proper operating condition.

The following tachometers have been found to work well on Briggs & Stratton engines:

TYPE	NAME	RPM RANGE	SOURCE
Vibration	Trysit Sirometer	800-25000	Order from your Briggs & Stratton Source of Supply — Part No. 19200.
Vibration	Frahm #2516	1000-4000	James G. Biddle Company Plymouth Meeting, PA 19462
Electronic	Merc-O-Tronic Model 67 – 100T	1000-5000 1000-10000	Merc-O-Tronic Instruments Corp. 215 Branch Street Almont, MI 48003

Note: Product brand names are given in some instances. However, any tool or test instrument of equivalent accuracy is acceptable in the following list.

DESCRIPTION	RANGE OR TYPE	SOURCE
Torque Wrench	0-200 in. lbs. — Part No. 19197	Briggs & Stratton Source
Valve Guide Tool Guide	Part No. #19191	Briggs & Stratton Source
Valve Seat Refacer	Part No. #19237	Briggs & Stratton Source
Valve Lapper	Woods Powr-Grip	Woods Powr-Grip Manufacturer 233 Cascade Wolf Point, MT 59201
Dial Caliper	0-4 in. — Part No. 19199	Briggs & Stratton Source
Telescope Gauge	2-1/8 – 3-9/16″ — Part No. 19198	Briggs & Stratton Source
VOA Meter	Part No. 19236 Volts Scale — Reads 0 to 400 AC or DC volts. Ohms Scale — Reads 0 to 500,000 ohms. Amps Scale — Reads 0 to 40 and 400 DC amps amps with shunt. Reads 0 to 16 AC amps.	Briggs & Stratton Source
Ignition Timing Light or Continuity Tester	Merc-O-Tronic Model 701FCT	Briggs & Stratton Source

13

BRIGGS & STRATTON REPAIR TOOLS
See Price List MS-6636 in Section One of the Master Parts Manual

Tools are listed by description and by kits. Kit 291661 is a requirement of the Authorized Registered Service Dealer. An Authorized Service Distributor is required to have the 291661 Kit and the 19158 Kit. Other additional tools should be obtained, as required to provide efficient service. Order through your Briggs & Stratton source of supply.

NOTE: 291661 Tool Kit is recommended for Public Schools conducting air-cooled engine courses.

291661 TOOL KIT

PART NO.	DESCRIPTION
19051	Spark Tester
19055	Breaker Plunger Gauge
19056	Plunger Bushing Counterbore Reamer
19057	Plunger Bushing Driver
19058	Plunger Bushing Finish Reamer
19061	Screwdriver, Carburetor
19062	Screwdriver, Carburetor
19063	Valve Spring Compressor
19064	Valve Guide Bushing Counterbore Reamer
19065	Valve Guide Bushing Driver
19066	Valve Guide Bushing Finish Reamer
19069	Flywheel Puller
19114	Starter Clutch Wrench
19122	Valve Guide Reject Gauge
19151	Valve Guide Reject Gauge
19165	Flywheel Puller
19167	Flywheel Holder
19191	Reamer Guide Bushing
19203	Flywheel Puller
19230	Ring Compressor

19232 VALVE GUIDE PULLER KIT*

PART NO.	DESCRIPTION
19204	Bushing Driver
19231	Piloted Reamer
19233	Finish Reamer
19234	Guide Bushing
19238	Bushing Puller
19239	Nut
19240	Washer

*Model Series: 140000, 170000, 190000, 220000, 233000, 243000, 250000, 300000, 326000.

BRIGGS & STRATTON REPAIR TOOLS (Continued)

19158 TOOL KIT

MAIN BEARING TOOL KIT

Model Series 6, 8, 6B, 8B, N, 60000, 80000, 82000, 92000, 94000, 100000, 110000, 130000.

PART NO.	DESCRIPTION
19094	Pilot Guide Bushing
19095	Finish Reamer
19096*	Pilot
19097	Pilot Guide Bushing, Ball Bearing Cover
19099	Counterbore Reamer
19100	Reamer Guide Bushing
19101	Reamer Guide Bushing
19123	Support Jack
19124	Bushing Driver
19166	Plug Gauge

*Included in Tool Kit 19184.

NOTE: For Model Series 100000, 130000 Vertical Crankshaft use 19186 Reamer Guide Bushing (not part of 19158 Tool Kit) for PTO Sump Bearing.

For Model Series 100000, 130000 Horizontal Crankshaft use 19170 Reamer Guide Bushing (part of 19184 Tool Kit) for PTO Sump Bearing.

19184 MAIN BEARING TOOL KIT

Model Series 140000, 170000, 171000, 190000, 191000

PART NO.	DESCRIPTION
19096*	Pilot
19168	Pilot Guide Bushing
19169	Pilot Guide Bushing
19170	Reamer Guide Bushing
19171	Reamer Guide Bushing
19172	Counterbore Step Reamer
19173	Finish Reamer
19174	Counterbore Step Ramer
19175	Finish Reamer
19178	Plug Gauge
19179	Bushing Driver
19201	Reamer Guide Bushing

*Included in Tool Kit 19158.

13

3

TOOLS

BRIGGS & STRATTON REPAIR TOOLS (Continued)

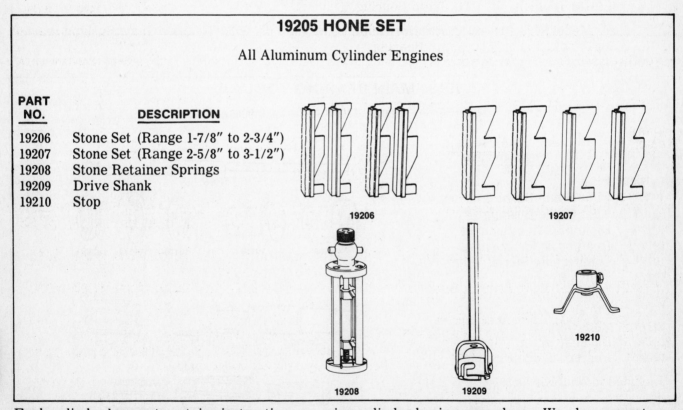

VALVE SEAT REPAIR TOOLS

PART NO.	DESCRIPTION
19126	Pilot, Valve Seat Counterbore
19127	Pilot, Valve Seat Counterbore
19129	Driver Shank, Counterbore Cutter
19130	T Handle, Driver Shank
19131	Counterbore Cutter, Valve Seats
19132	Counterbore Cutter, Valve Seats
19133	Counterbore Cutter, Valve Seats
19135	Knockout Pin, Remove Driver Shank from Counterbore Cutter
19136	Insert Driver, Install Valve Seats
19137	T Handle for Pilots
19138	Insert Puller, To Pull Valve Seats
19139	Puller Nut, Remove Valve Seats
19140	Puller Nut, Remove Valve Seats
19141	Puller Nut, Remove Valve Seats

19126 19131 19135
19127
19129 19132 19136
19130 19133 19137

19138 VALVE SEAT PULLER KIT

19140   19141   19182   19139

19205 HONE SET

All Aluminum Cylinder Engines

PART NO.	DESCRIPTION
19206	Stone Set (Range 1-7/8″ to 2-3/4″)
19207	Stone Set (Range 2-5/8″ to 3-1/2″)
19208	Stone Retainer Springs
19209	Drive Shank
19210	Stop

19206   19207
19208   19209   19210

Each cylinder hone set contains instructions covering cylinder honing procedures. We also suggest you review your Briggs & Stratton Repair Instructions IV for all standard cylinder bore sizes. Contact your source of supply for pricing information.

13

BRIGGS & STRATTON REPAIR TOOLS (Continued)
19211 HONE SET
All Cast Iron Cylinder Engines

PART NO.	DESCRIPTION
19212	Stone Set (60 Grit)
19213	Stone Set (220 Grit)
19214	Stone Carrier (Range 2-1/2″ to 3-5/16″)
19215	Stone Carrier (Range 3-5/16″ to 4-1/8″)
19216	Stone Retainer Springs
19217	Drive Shank
19218	Extension

PART NO.	DESCRIPTION	MODELS OR SERIES USED ON
		DRIVERS
*19057	Install Plunger Bushing	5, 6, 6B, 8, 8B, N, 23C, 60000, 80000, 82000, 92000, 94000, 100000, 110000, 130000, 140000, 170000, 190000, 220000, 250000
*19065	Install Valve Guide Bushing	5, 6, 6B, 8, 8B, N, 60000, 80000, 82000, 92000, 94000, 100000, 110000, 130000
**19124	Install Main Bearing Bushings	5, 6, 8B, 8, 8B, N, 60000, 80000, 82000, 92000, 94000, 100000, 110000, 130000
19136	Install Valve Seat Inserts	All Models and Series
†19179	Install Main Bearing Bushings	140000, 170000, 171000, 190000, 191000
††††19204	Install Valve Guide Bushing	140000, 170000, 190000, 200000, 220000, 230400, 233000, 240000, 243000, 250000, 300000

*Included in No. 291661 Tool Kit
**Included in No. 19158 Tool Kit

†Included in No. 19184 Tool Kit
††††Included in No. 19232 Kit

13

BRIGGS & STRATTON REPAIR TOOLS (Continued)

PART NO.	DESCRIPTION	MODELS OR SERIES USED ON

REAMERS

PART NO.	DESCRIPTION	MODELS OR SERIES USED ON
*19056	Breaker Plunger Bushing Reamer	5, 6, 6B, 8, 8B, N, 23C, 60000, 80000, 82000, 92000, 94000, 100000, 110000, 130000, 140000, 170000, 190000, 220000, 250000
*19058	Finish Reamer, Breaker Plunger Bushing	5, 6, 6B, 8, 8B, N, 23C, 60000, 80000, 82000, 92000, 94000, 100000, 110000, 130000, 140000, 170000, 190000, 220000, 250000
*19064	Valve Guide Bushing Counterbore Reamer	5, 6, 6B, 8, 8B, 60000, 80000, 82000, 92000, 94000, 100000, 110000, 130000
*19066	Finish Reamer, Valve Guide Bushing	5, 6, 6B, 8, 8B, 60000, 80000, 82000, 92000, 94000, 100000, 110000, 130000
**19095	Finish Reamer, Main Bearing	5, 6, 6B, 8, 8B, N, 60000, 80000, 82000, 92000, 940000, 100000, 110000, 130000
**19099	Counterbore Reamer, Main Bearings	6B, 8B, 60000, 80000, 82000, 92000, 940000, 100000, 110000, 130000
†19172	Counterbore Reamer, Main Bearings	100000, 130000, 140000, 170000, 190000
†19173	Finish Reamer, Main Bearings	100000, 130000, 140000, 170000, 190000
†19174	Counterbore Reamer, Main Bearings	140000, 170000, 171000, 190000, 191000
†19175	Finish Reamer, Main Bearings	140000, 170000, 171000, 190000, 191000
††††19231	Bushing Reamer, Valve Guides	9, 14, 19, 23, 140000, 170000, 190000, 200000, 220000, 230000, 240000, 250000, 300000, 320000
††††19233	Finish Reamer	9, 14, 19, 23, 140000, 170000, 190000, 200000, 220000, 230000, 240000, 250000, 300000, 320000

PILOTS

PART NO.	DESCRIPTION	MODELS OR SERIES USED ON
†**19096	Main Bearing Reamer Pilot	5, 6, 6B, 8, 8B, N, 60000, 80000, 82000, 90000, 92000, 94000, 100000, 110000, 130000, 140000, 170000, 171000, 190000, 191000
19126	Expansion Pilot for Valve Seat Counterbore Cutter	5, 6, 6B, 8, 8B, N, 60000, 80000, 82000, 90000, 92000, 94000, 100000, 110000, 130000
19127	Expansion Pilot for Valve Seat Counterbore Cutter	9, 14, 19, 23, 140000, 170000, 190000, 200000, 220000, 230000, 240000, 300000, 320000
19137	"T" Handle for Pilots	9, 14, 19, 23, 140000, 170000, 190000, 200000, 220000, 230000, 240000, 300000, 320000

REAMER GUIDE BUSHINGS

PART NO.	DESCRIPTION	MODELS OR SERIES USED ON
**19100	Reamer Guide Bushing, Main Bearing Reaming	6B, 8B, 60000, 80000, 82000, 92000, 94000, 110000
**19101	Reamer Guide Bushing, Main Bearing Reaming	6B, 8B, 60000, 80000, 82000, 92000, 94000, 100000, 110000, 130000
†19170	Reamer Guide Bushing, Main Bearing Reaming	100000, 130000, 140000, 170000, 190000

13

*Included in No. 291661 Tool Kit
**Included in No. 19158 Tool Kit

Included in No. 19184 Tool Kit
††††Included in No. 19232 Kit

BRIGGS & STRATTON REPAIR TOOLS (Continued)

PART NO.	DESCRIPTION	MODELS OR SERIES USED ON

REAMER GUIDE BUSHINGS (Continued)

19186	Reamer Guide Bushing, Main Bearing Reaming	100000, 130000
*19191	Reamer Guide Bushing, Valve Guide Reaming	5, 6B, 8B, 60000, 80000, 82000, 92000, 94000, 100000, 110000, 130000
††††19234	Reamer Guide Bushing, Valve Guide Reaming	9, 14, 19, 23, 140000, 170000, 190000, 200000, 220000, 230000, 240000, 250000, 300000, 320000
†19201	Reamer Guide Bushing, Main Bearing Reaming	171000, 191000

PLUG GAUGES

*19055	Check Breaker Plunger Hole	5, 6, 6B, 8, 8B, N, 23C, 60000, 80000, 82000, 92000, 940000, 100000, 110000, 130000, 140000, 170000, 190000, 220000, 250000
*19122	Check Valve Guide	5, 6, 6B, 8, 8B, 60000, 80000, 82000, 92000, 940000, 100000, 110000, 130000
*19151	Check Valve Guides	9, 14, 19, 23, 140000, 170000, 190000, 200000, 220000, 230000, 240000, 250000, 300000, 320000,
19164	Check Camshaft Bearings	6B, 8B, 60000, 80000, 92000, 100000, 110000, 130000, 140000, 170000, 190000, 220000, 250000
**19166	Check Main Bearings	5, 6, 6B, 8, 8B, 60000, 80000, 82000, 92000, 94000, 100000, 110000, 130000
†19178	Check Main Bearings	100000, 130000, 140000, 170000, 171000, 190000, 191000

PILOT GUIDE BUSHINGS

**19094	Pilot Guide Bushing, Main Bearing Reaming	5, 6, 6B, 8, 8B, 60000, 80000, 82000, 92000, 94000, 100000, 110000, 130000
**19097	Pilot Guide Bushing, Main Bearing Reaming, Ball Bearing Covers	6, 6B, 8B, N, 60000, 80000, 100000, 111200, 130000
†19168	Pilot Guide Bushing, Main Bearing Reaming	100000, 130000, 140000, 170000, 190000
†19169	Pilot Guide Bushing, Main Bearing Reaming	140000, 170000, 190000

COUNTERBORE CUTTERS

19115	Counterbore Valve Guide Hole	5, 6, 6B, 8, 8B, N, 60000, 80000, 82000, 92000, 100000, 130000
19131	Counterbore Valve Seat Insert	14, 19, 23, 190000, 200000, 230000, 243000
19132	Counterbore Valve Seat Insert	8, 9
19133	Counterbore Valve Seat Insert	5, 6, 8, N

13

*Included in No. 291661 Tool Kit
**Included in No. 19158 Tool Kit

†Included in No. 19184 Tool Kit
††††Included in No. 19232 Kit

BRIGGS & STRATTON REPAIR TOOLS (Continued)

PART NO.	DESCRIPTION	MODELS OR SERIES USED ON

CRANKCASE SUPPORT JACK

**19123	To Support Crankcase to Remove and Install Main Bearings	5, 6, 6B, 8, 8B, N, 60000, 80000, 82000, 92000, 94000, 100000, 110000, 130000, 140000, 170000, 190000

FLYWHEEL PULLERS

*19069	Removal of Flywheel	6, 6B, 8, 8B, 60000, 80000, 82000, 92000, 94000,
*19165	Removal of Flywheel	100000, 110000, 140000, 170000, 190000, 250000
*19203	Removal of Flywheel	9, 14, 19, 23, 190000, 200000, 220000, 230000, 240000, 250000, 300000, 320000
93029	Self-Threading Screw for Flywheel Pullers	6B, 8B, 60000, 80000, 82000, 92000, 100000, 140000, 170000, 190000, 250000

STARTER CLUTCH WRENCH

*19114	For Removal and Installation of Starter Clutch	All Models with Rewind Starters
19161	For Removal and Installation of Starter Clutch (To be used with ½″ drive socket or torque wrench)	All Models with Rewind Starters

VALVE SPRING COMPRESSOR

*19063	To Compress Valve Springs	All Models and Series

PISTON RING COMPRESSOR

19230	To Compress Rings on Piston	9, 14, 23, 60000, 80000, 82000, 92000, 94000, 100000, 110000, 130000, 140000, 170000, 190000, 220000, 230000, 240000, 250000, 300000, 320000

SPARK TESTER

*19051	For Testing Ignition Spark	All Models and Series

FLYWHEEL HOLDER

*19167	To hold Flywheel while loosening or tightening nut	*6B, 8B, 60000, 80000, 82000, 92000, 100000

TANG BENDING TOOL

19229	Governor Tang Bending Tool	140000, 170000, 190000, 200000, 220000, 250000, 401000

13

*Included in No. 291661 Tool Kit
**Included in No. 19158 Tool Kit

13

Section 14
THEORIES OF OPERATION

COMPRESSION

The general subject of compression is a familiar one to most mechanics. It has been discussed in detail by valve manufacturers, ring manufacturers, piston manufacturers, and by makers of valve grinding equipment. The home mechanic, or handy-man, thinks nothing of getting out his grinding compound, lapping in the valves and putting a new set of rings on the piston — all without knowledge of proper fit or tolerance. Whether he does the job right or not, he thinks it is easy. And, it is easy. There is nothing difficult or mysterious about compression, and the nice part is that a good job that will create lasting customer satisfaction is about as easy to do as a poor job.

We must keep in mind, however, that the Briggs & Stratton engine is an air-cooled, single cylinder engine. The rules that hold true on liquid-cooled, multi-cylinder engines do not always apply to Briggs & Stratton engines. For example:

The operating temperature of a liquid-cooled engine is quite constant. The operating temperature of an air-cooled engine, however, may vary greatly with changes in air temperature, the load, and the speed. This necessitates differences in tolerances and clearances of parts like pistons, which must be fitted to Briggs & Stratton's established clearances. These can differ from those used in most automotive engines.

The advantages of an air-cooled engine are many. There is no need for a complicated cooling system. The engine is lighter in weight and occupies less space than its liquid-cooled counterpart, and is comparatively easy to repair.

Before we get into the mechanics of the subject, let us clarify some of the terms in common use.

On single cylinder engines we think of good compression, not in terms of pounds of pressure per square inch, but in terms of horsepower output. If the engine produces the power for which it was designed, we believe the compression must be good. It is extremely difficult to make an accurate compression test on a small, one cylinder engine without expensive machinery. The reasons for this are the lack of a starter to crank the engine at a constant speed and the small displacement of the cylinder. Therefore, we do not publish any compression pressure figures. As a simple compression test, give the flywheel a quick spin. If the flywheel rebounds on the compression stroke, the compression is at least good enough to start the engine.

We talk about "compression" stroke and "power stroke". What are they? The Briggs & Stratton engine is a four stroke cycle engine, or as it is commonly called, a four cycle engine. It operates on the same principle as an automobile engine. The crankshaft makes two complete revolutions to each power stroke of the piston.

14

1

FOUR STROKE CYCLE

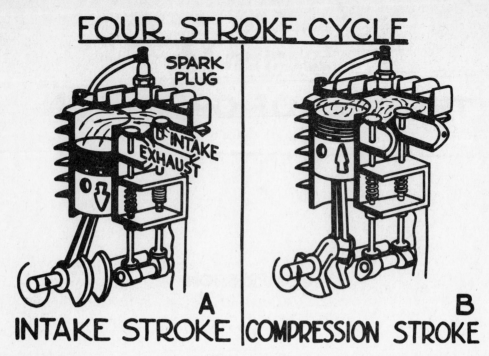

Figure 1

First is the intake stroke. With the exhaust valve closed and the intake valve open, the piston moves downward and the air-fuel mixture is drawn into the cylinder. (A – Fig. 1)

Then, the intake valve closes, and the piston moves upward on the compression stroke. The air-fuel mixture becomes greatly compressed in the small space between the top of the piston and the cylinder head. (B – Fig. 1)

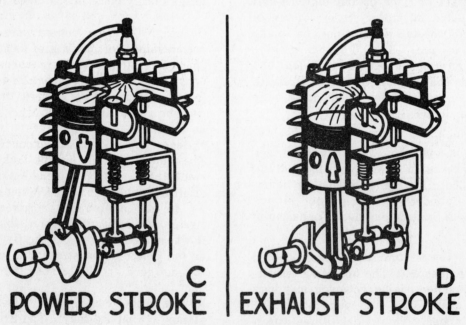

Figure 2

The spark occurs, igniting the mixture, and the force of the expanding gases push the piston down. This is the power stroke. (C – Fig. 2)

The exhaust valve opens, and the upward movement of the piston on the exhaust stroke forces

the burnt gases out of the cylinder. (D – Fig. 2) Then the exhaust valve closes, the intake valve opens, and the engine is ready to repeat the cycle just described. Thus four strokes complete the cycle.

14

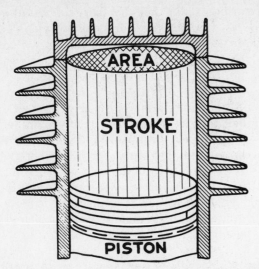

PISTON DISPLACEMENT

Figure 3

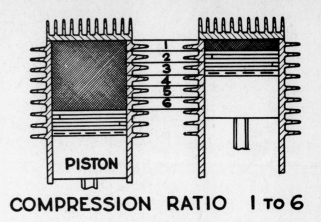

COMPRESSION RATIO 1 TO 6

Figure 4

What is "piston displacement"? It is the space displaced by the piston in its up and down movement or the volume shown above the piston in Figure 3. The bigger the bore and the longer the stroke, the greater the piston displacement. Displacement is computed by the following formula:

$$Displacement = \frac{(Bore)^2}{4} \times \pi \times Stroke$$

Let us compute the displacement of a Model 6 engine which has a 2" bore and a 2" stroke. Using the above formula:

$$Displacement = \frac{2 \times 2}{4} \times 3.1416 \times 2$$

Displacement = 6.2832 cubic inches

Our specification sheets show 6.28 cubic inches as the displacement for the Model 6 engine.

The model numbers of the current engines indicate the approximate piston displacement. Model 60000 has 6.65 cubic inches; Model 14 has 14.21 cubic inches, etc.

Piston displacement indicates the relative size of the engine, and usually horsepower is in direct proportion to size.

What do we mean when we say an engine has a 6 to 1 compression ratio? We mean that the space in the cylinder when the piston is at the top of the stroke is only one-sixth as great as when the piston is at the bottom of the stroke.

Compression ratios do not tell us the horsepower of an engine. They do have a meaning as regards the efficiency of an engine.

Generally, the higher the compression ratio, the greater the efficiency. However, as compression ratios are increased, the loads and stresses upon engine parts become more severe. Premium fuels may be required with high compression ratios. Experience has proven that compression ratios in the range of 5-1 to 6-1, currently used in Briggs & Stratton engines, are the best for the work and the conditions under which these engines must operate. Therefore premium fuel is not needed and "regular" is recommended.

It is generally conceded that the valves are the most important factor in good compression. They operate under more severe conditions than any other parts of the engine. This is particularly true of the exhaust valve.

TIMING

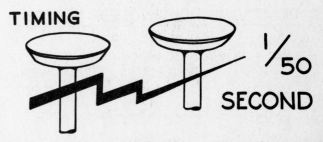

Figure 5

The valves open and close in a little less than one revolution. When the engine is operating at 3000 RPM, each valve opens and closes in about 1/50 of a second.

14

3

HEAT

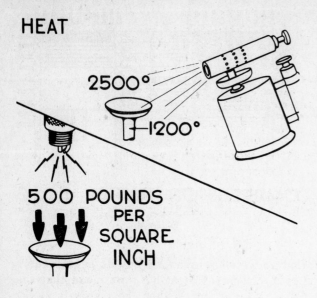

Figure 6

Valves have to seal well enough to stand pressures up to 500 pounds per square inch. Under full load, the exhaust valve is exposed to temperatures high enough to cause it to operate at a red heat. The temperature of the valve under these conditions may be 1200° F. or more. The intake valve is cooled by the incoming mixture. The exhaust valve is subjected to high temperature exhaust gases passing over it on their way out of the cylinder. It is, therefore, very difficult to cool the head of the exhaust valve. The cylinder head, the cylinder, and the top of the piston are exposed to this same heat, but these parts are cooled by air from the flywheel fan and oil from the crankcase. Very special steel is required in the exhaust valve to enable it to withstand the corrosive action of the high temperature exhaust gases.

RELATIVE IMPORTANCE OF VALVES

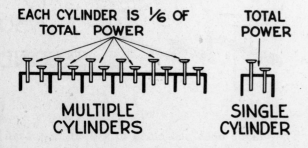

Figure 7

Remember again that the Briggs & Stratton engine is a single cylinder engine with two (2) valves as compared to the customary 12 or 16 valves in an automotive engine. The fewer the valves, the more important they become.

In a 1 cylinder engine one bad valve can cause a great drop in horsepower or cause the engine to stop entirely. In a multicylinder engine, one valve may fail and only 1/6th or 1/8th of the power is affected as the bad cylinder may be motorized by the other good cylinders. Hence, good valve condition is even more important in 1 cylinder engines than it is in multicylinder engines.

Now if the valves and seats are so important, how do we do a good valve job on a Briggs & Stratton engine?

The first requirement is good equipment. A valve refacer and valve seat grinders are necessary. If you do not have them, arrangement should be made with your local Briggs & Stratton dealer.

After the valves are removed, they should be thoroughly cleaned on a wire brush wheel to remove all carbon deposits. You will find sometimes it is easier to polish carbon than to remove it, but it must come off. Also, remove carbon from valve guides. When the valves are clean, they should be visually inspected.

VALVE FAILURES

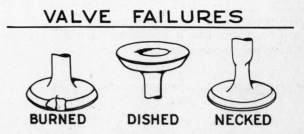

Figure 8

As mentioned above, when a valve becomes defective in a multicylinder engine, the bad cylinder is motorized by the other cylinders. This may cause serious damage to the valve and seat. Briggs & Stratton engine valves are seldom subjected to the extremes of abuse that automotive valves are. While valves may burn to some extent, it is very seldom that a valve seat or face is very badly burned. Dished or necked valves are almost never found.

14

Valve seat burning is usually caused by an accumulation of carbon or fuel lead either on the valve stem or on the valve face, or from insufficient tappet clearance. These deposits on the valve stem or on the face will hold the valve open, allowing the hot flames of the burning fuel to eat away the valve face and seat. A dished valve is one that has a sunken head. This is caused by operating at too high a temperature with too strong a spring, or the head can be eroded away by highly leaded fuels. A necked valve is one that has the stem directly beneath the head eaten away badly by heat or where the stem has been stretched.

Valve sticking is caused by fuel lead, gum or varnish forming on the valve stem and in the valve guide. We believe that most of the deposits formed are caused by carbon, fuel lead, or gum. Since the amount of lead in different fuels varies, the rate of deposit build-up naturally will vary. When an exhaust valve no longer closes properly, due to excess deposits, the hot gases escaping from the combustion chamber heat up the valve stem and guide excessively. This causes the oil on the valve stem to oxidize into varnish which holds the valve partially open and causes burning. Intake valve sticking may be caused by the use of fuels having an excessively high gum content. Fuels that are stored for too long a period of time may contain high amounts of gum.

If burning occurs in a rather limited area on the valve face, it indicates that something may have caused the valve to tip. This could be due to a bent valve stem or a deposit on one side of the valve seat or stem.

Such a condition would leave an opening for the passage of hot exhaust gases which could burn the valve so badly that it could not be refaced. These valves must be discarded.

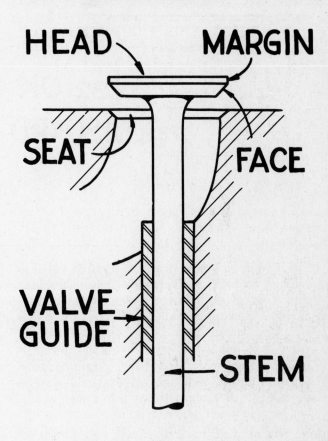

VALVE PART NAMES

HEAD MARGIN

SEAT FACE

VALVE GUIDE STEM

Figure 9

The important parts of a valve are the head, the margin, face, and stem. They make contact with the seat and the valve guide in the cylinder. The margin is the edge of the valve head. As a general rule, the valve should be discarded when the margin becomes less than one-half of the original thickness.

14

MARGIN DIMENSIONS

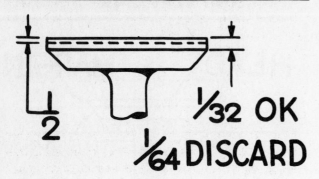

1/32 OK
1/64 DISCARD

Figure 10

VALVE SEAT DIMENSIONS

3/64" TO 1/16"

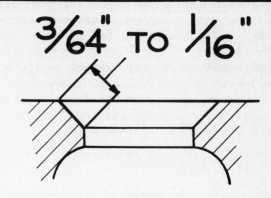

Figure 11

The margin on a new Briggs & Stratton valve is 1/32 of an inch, so that when it becomes less than 1/64 of an inch the valve should be discarded. Remember, this is after all pit marks and burn marks have been removed from the valve face. If the valve is bent, the face will be ground unevenly, and if the margin becomes too thin on one side the valve should also be discarded. A valve with too thin a margin will not be able to withstand the heat and will quickly crack and burn. After facing the valves and the valve seats to a 45° angle, place a little fine grinding compound on the valve face, and very lightly lap the valve to the seat. Use of fine grinding compound removes any grinding marks and gives a clear picture of the valve seat width. Be sure to remove all grinding compound from seat and valve.

The valve seat width is usable up to 5/64 of an inch, but a new seat should be between 3/64 and 1/16 of an inch, and it should be in the center of the valve face. After the valve seat and faces are ground, the valve should be installed in the guide, the cam gear turned to the proper position, and the tappet clearance checked. Refer to Repair Instructions for tappet clearance. Usually the clearance will be too small, and the end of the valve stem will have to be ground off to obtain the proper clearance. Care should be taken not to overheat the end of the valve stem while this grinding is taking place; be sure the end is square with the stem. It is recommended that the valve springs and retainers be assembled immediately after setting the tappet clearance to prevent chances of dirt getting under the valve seat.

14

CARBURETION

The basic purpose of a carburetor is to produce a mixture of fuel and air on which an engine will operate; to do so is relatively easy. However, producing economical fuel consumption and smooth engine operation over a wide range of speeds creates the need for a more complicated mechanism than a mere mixing valve. There is an additional problem in that the price of such a carburetor must be held in proportion to the price of the engine. The price of a Briggs & Stratton engine is not much greater than the price of the carburetor on an automobile.

Atmospheric Pressure

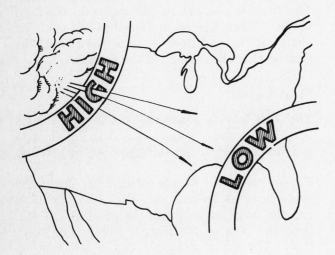

Figure 12

Keeping this in mind, we must utilize the force of atmospheric pressure and the principles of the venturi and the airfoil.

Atmospheric pressure, while it may vary slightly due to altitude or temperature, is a constant potent force which tends to equalize itself in any given area. It is the weight of the air in the atmosphere pushing down and outward in all directions and is commonly figured as between 13 and 15 pounds per square inch. We know that air moves from a high pressure area to a low pressure area.

To use this force of atmospheric pressure in a carburetor, we artificially create low pressure areas and thus obtain movement either of air or of intervening fuel. We will show you how a little later.

The greater the difference in pressure between the two areas the greater the velocity or the greater the distance we can raise the fuel.

In the interest of brevity we often use the terms vacuum or suction when we actually mean the difference in pressures.

Venturi

What is a venturi? Have you ever noticed that the wind blowing through a narrow space between two buildings always seems to be much stronger than in the open? In other words, the velocity is greater. The same thing can be seen in a river. The current is always faster in a narrow, shallow place than in the deep wide pools.

In a fashion, these narrow places are venturi's. The great bulk of air or water suddenly forced through a constricted space has to accelerate in order to maintain the volume of flow.

This is the way a venturi is placed in a carburetor. Fig. 13. The shape is carefully designed to produce certain air flow patterns.

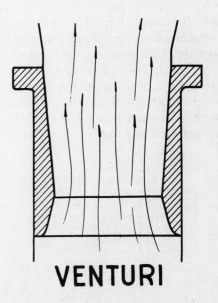

VENTURI

Figure 13

14

THEORIES OF OPERATION
Carburetion

Airfoil

Now, what is an airfoil? Here is a picture of a tube in an air stream. When still, the pressure is equal on all sides. Under movement, an air pattern is formed, Fig. 14, so that we have a high pressure area and a very low pressure area.

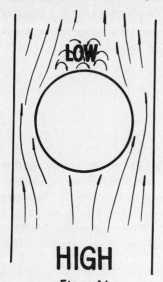

Figure 14

Now how does all this apply to Briggs & Stratton engines that employ three types of carburetors, the Flo-jet (gravity feed or float type), the Vacu-jet (suction feed) and the newer Pulsa-jet (fuel pump) type?

FLOW-JET CARBURETORS OR GRAVITY FEED

First, let us consider the gravity feed system. The tank is above the carburetor and fuel flows by gravity. Notice an air vent hole in the tank cap so that air can flow in as fuel flows out and a vent hole in the carburetor bowl so that air can flow out as fuel flows in. If one or both of these holes were plugged, the flow of fuel would cease and stop the engine. See Fig. 15 and 16.

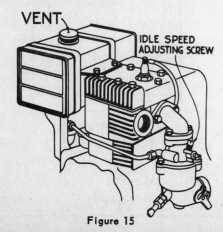

Figure 15

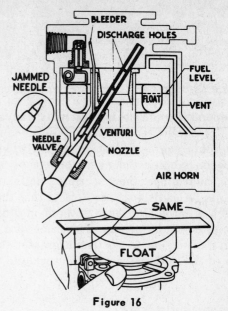

Figure 16

As the fuel enters the bowl, it raises the float. The float in turn raises the needle in the float valve. When the needle touches the seat, it shuts off the fuel flow, and the position of the float at this time is called the float level.

Float Level

The float level in general should be high enough to afford an ample supply of fuel at full throttle and low enough to prevent flooding or leaking.

To set the level on the carburetor, invert the upper body as shown. See Fig. 16. The float and the body cover should be parallel. If not, bend the tang on the float to obtain this position. The actual distance on the small carburetors is 5/16 of an inch between the float and the gasket. On the larger models it is 3/16 of an inch. It is seldom necessary to measure this distance. The float level is not as critical as on some carburetors. Remember, however, that there should be one gasket between the float valve seat and the carburetor. No gasket or two gaskets will change the float level.

Now, the fuel is down into the bowl but how does it get into the cylinder?

Here is shown the position of the nozzle and the fuel level. See Fig. 16. The fuel in the bowl seeks its own level, which is well below the discharge holes. Notice that the discharge holes are in the venturi, the place of greatest air velocity. As the piston in the cylinder moves down with the intake valve open, it creates a low pressure area that extends down into the carburetor throat and venturi. Two things start to happen.

14

The air pressure above the fuel in the bowl pushes the fuel down in the bowl and up in the nozzle to the discharge holes. At the same time the air rushes into the carburetor air horn and through the venturi where its velocity is greatly increased.

The nozzle extending through this air stream acts as an air foil, creating a still lower pressure area on the upper side. This allows the fuel to stream out of the nozzle through the discharge holes into the venturi where it mixes with the air and becomes a combustible mixture ready for firing in the cylinder.

A small amount of air is allowed to enter the nozzle through the bleeder. This air compensates for the difference in engine speed and prevents too rich a mixture at high speed.

The story of carburetion could end right here if the engine were to run at only one speed and under ideal conditions. However, since smooth economical operation is desired at varying speeds, some additions must be made to the carburetor.

The ideal combustion mixture is about 14 or 15 pounds of air, in weight, to one (1) pound of gasoline. Remember that an engine operating under heavy load requires a richer mixture than under light load. In order to regulate the mixture, we place in the carburetor a threaded needle valve with a tapered point which projects into the end of the nozzle. See Fig. 16.

To adjust the carburetor for maximum power, run the engine at the desired operating speed, then turn in the needle valve until the engine slows down, which indicates a lean mixture. Note the position of the needle valve, then turn the needle valve out until the engine speeds up and then slows down, which indicates a rich mixture, Note the position of the needle valve, then turn the needle valve to midway between the lean and rich position. Adjust the mixture to the requirement for each engine. Remember that too lean a mixture is not economical. It causes overheating, detonation, and short valve life. Also, since there is no accelerator pump, the mixture must be rich enough so that the engine will not stop when the throttle is suddenly opened. Engines which run at constant speeds can be slightly leaner than those whose use requires changes in speed.

The inset of Fig. 16 shows what happens when the needle valve is turned too far. A square shoulder is produced on the taper. It is possible, of course, to adjust the carburetor with the needle valve in this condition, but it is quite difficult, because a small movement of the needle makes a big difference in the amount of fuel that can enter the nozzle. And, if you do get it adjusted, the vibration can soon throw it off.

Throttle

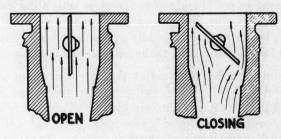

Figure 17

To allow for different speeds, a flat disc called a butterfly, mounted on a shaft, is placed in the carburetor throat above the venturi. This is called the throttle. See Fig. 17.

The throttle in the wide open position does not affect the air flow to any extent. However, as the throttle starts to close, it restricts the flow of air to the cylinder and this decreases the power and speed of the engine. At the same time it allows the pressure in the area below the butterfly to increase. This means that the difference between the air pressure in the carburetor bowl and the air pressure in the venturi is decreased, the movement of the fuel through the nozzle is slowed down; thus the proportion of fuel and air remain approximately the same. As the engine speed slows down to idle, this situation changes. See Fig. 18.

At idle speed the throttle is practically closed, very little air is passing through the venturi and the pressure in the venturi and in the float bowl are about the same. The fuel is not forced through the discharge holes, and the mixture tends to become too lean.

Idle Valve

To supply fuel for the idle, the nozzle is extended up into the idle valve chamber. It fits snugly in the upper body to prevent leaks. Because of this tight fit, the nozzle must be removed before upper and lower bodies are separated, or the nozzle will be bent.

14

THEORIES OF OPERATION
Carburetion

The idle valve chamber leads into the carburetor throat above the throttle. Here the pressure is low, and the fuel rises in the nozzle past the idle valve and into the carburetor throat through the discharge slot. The amount of fuel is metered by turning the idle valve in or out until the proper mixture is obtained. Here again we see what happens if the needle is screwed in too far. A damaged idle valve can result.

Adjustment of the idle valve is similar to that of the needle valve but should be made <u>after</u> the needle valve has been adjusted. The idle speed is not the slowest speed at which the engine will run. On small engines it is 1750 RPM. On larger engines the idle speed may be as low as 1200 RPM. Use a tachometer to set the speed.

Turn the idle speed adjusting screw (located on throttle shaft) until the desired idle speed is obtained and hold throttle closed. Turn the idle valve in until speed decreases, then out until speed increases and again decreases. Then turn the idle valve to a point midway between these two settings. Usually the idle speed adjusting screw will have to be reset to the desired idle speed.

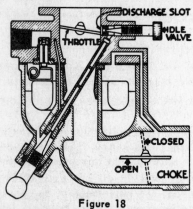

Figure 18

The next problem is starting the engine in different temperatures and with different fuels. A butterfly, mounted on a shaft, is placed in the air horn. With this choke we can close, or almost close, the air horn and get a low pressure area in the venturi and throat. See Fig. 18.

Thus, a rush of fuel is obtained from the nozzle with a relatively small amount of air. Even with low vaporization this extra rich mixture will give easy starting. Only a portion of the fuel will be consumed while choking, and a large portion will remain in the cylinder. This raw gasoline will dilute the crankcase oil and may even cause scuffing due to washing away of the oil film from between the piston rings and the cylinder wall. For this reason, prolonged choking should be avoided.

This now is our complete carburetor.

VACU-JET CARBURETORS OR SUCTION FEED

Now let us take a look at the Vacu-jet or suction feed system. Here the fuel tank is below the carburetor, so obviously the fuel will not flow by means of gravity. Therefore, the force of atmospheric pressure must be employed.

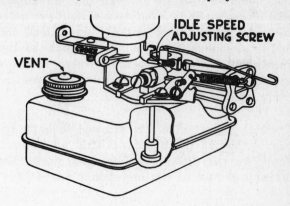

Figure 19

Again we have a vent hole in the fuel tank cap to allow the pressure in the tank to remain constant. Now here is something important. Before adjusting the carburetor pour in enough fuel to HALF fill the tank. The distance the fuel has to be lifted will affect the adjustment. At half full we have an average operating condition, and the adjustment will be satisfactory if the engine is run with the tank full or nearly empty.

As the piston goes down in the cylinder with both the intake valve and the throttle open, a low pressure area is created in the carburetor throat. A slight restriction is placed between the air horn and the carburetor throat at the choke. This helps to maintain the low pressure.

The difference in pressure between the tank and the carburetor throat forces the fuel up the fuel pipe, past the needle valve, through the two discharge holes. The throttle is relatively thick, so we have, in effect, a venturi at this point, thus aiding vaporization. A spiral is placed in the throat to help acceleration and also to help keep the engine from dying when the throttle is opened suddenly.

The amount of fuel at operating speed is metered by the needle valve and seat. Turning the needle valve in or out changes the setting until the proper mixture is obtained. This adjustment must always be done while the engine is running at operating speed, not at idle speed. While the needle valve may look like an idle valve due to its position, it is a true high speed mixture adjusting valve.

14

Since no accelerator pump is used on this carburetor and since many of these engines are used on lawn mowers where rapid acceleration is needed, the mixture should be rich. Turn the needle valve in until the engine begins to lose speed, indicating a lean mixture. Then, open the needle valve past the point of smooth operation until the engine just begins to run unevenly. Since this setting is made without load, the mixture should operate the engine satisfactorily under load.

These carburetors do not have an idle valve, but the mixture at idle speed is controlled in a different way. As the throttle closes to idle, the leading edge takes a position between the two discharge holes. The larger of the discharge holes is now in the high pressure area, and the flow of fuel through it will cease. The small hole will continue to discharge fuel but the amount will be metered by the hole size and will be in proportion to the reduced air flow. For this reason it is important that the small discharge hole be of the proper size. The needle valve will allow much more fuel to pass than should go through the small discharge hole. A number 68 drill can be used as a plug gauge to check the small hole. A number 56 drill can be used to check the larger hole. This can be done with the needle valve and seat removed. See Fig. 20.

You will notice a small section is milled out of the throttle where it meets the discharge hole. This concentrates the flow of air past the hole and assures good vaporization.

The idle speed adjusting screw should be set to obtain an idle speed of 1750 RPM. This may seem fast to people accustomed to auto engines, but it is necessary in order to have fast acceleration. It also helps cooling and lubrication. A slight unevenness may be noticed at idle speed, but this is normal and no readjustments of the needle valve should be made.

The choke is the sliding plate mounted at the outer end of the carburetor. Fig. 20 and 21. The choke is pushed in to close the air intake for starting but should be pulled out as soon as the engine starts. The use of this choke should be understood clearly. Many complaints of engine trouble, upon investigation prove to be nothing more than failure to properly use the choke, especially where the choke is operated by a remote control. The choke must close fully.

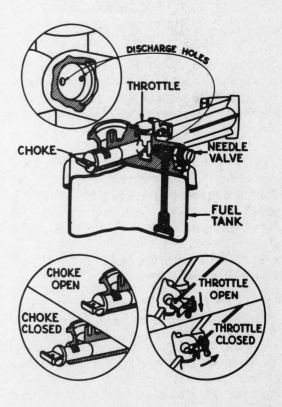

Figure 21

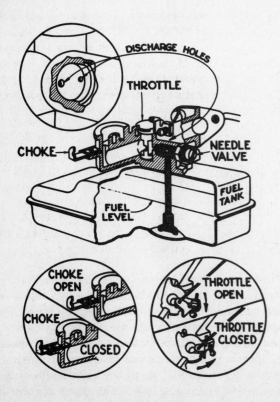

Figure 20

The latest engines with Vacu-Jet carburetors incorporate a ball check in the fuel pipe which assures a steady flow of fuel to the needle valve and discharge holes.

14

PULSA-JET CARBURETORS

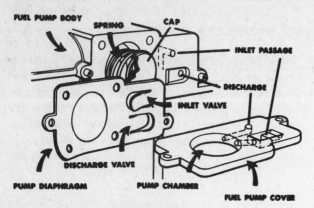

Figure 22

The Pulsa-Jet is a full carburetor incorporating a diaphragm type fuel pump and a constant level fuel chamber.

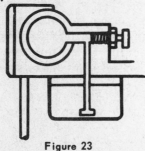

Figure 23

The fuel tank, the fuel pump and the constant level fuel chamber serve the same functions as the gravity feed tank, the float and the float chamber of conventional "float type" carburetors.

This new design makes it possible to obtain just as much horsepower from the Pulsa-Jet carburetor as is obtained from more complex "float type" carburetors. This is due to the fact that the Pulsa-Jet provides a constant fuel level directly below the venturi as illustrated in Fig. 23. With this design, very little fuel "lift" is required to draw gasoline into the venturi. The venturi can be made larger, permitting a greater volume of fuel-air mixture to flow into the engine with a consequent increase in horsepower.

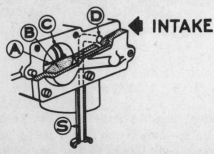

Figure 23A

Vacuum created in the carburetor elbow by the intake stroke of the piston pulls cap A and pump diaphragm B inward and compresses spring C.

The vacuum thus created on the "cover side" of the diaphragm pulls gasoline up suction pipe S and under intake valve D into the pocket created by the diaphragm moving inward.

DISCHARGE

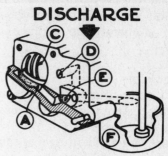

Figure 23B

When engine intake stroke is completed, spring C pushes plunger A outward. This causes gasoline in the pocket above the diaphragm to close inlet valve D and open discharge valve E. The fuel is then pumped into fuel cup F.

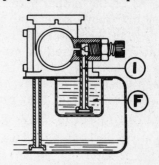

Figure 23C

On the next intake stroke the cycle is repeated and this pulsation of the diaphragm keeps the fuel cup full. Excess fuel flows back into the tank.

The venturi of the carburetor is connected to intake pipe I which draws gasoline from the fuel cup F.

Since a constant level is maintained in the fuel cup, the engine gets a constant air-fuel ratio no matter what fuel level exists in the main tank.

From this point on the carburetor operates and is adjusted in the same manner as is the Vacu-Jet carburetor except that the fuel tank does not have to be half full as in the Vacu-Jet. It can be full or almost empty and the adjustment will be the same since the fuel level in the small cup is always the same. There are no valve checks in the fuel pipes. The flaps on the diaphragm serve as valves.

Gas and Oil

We recommend the use of fresh, clean, "REGU-LAR" gasoline. Do not use store gas, naptha or other such low-test fuels that have a rating below 80 octane. Neither is it necessary to use highly leaded premium fuels.

It is recommended also that fuel be purchased in amounts that will be used up within a short time. Stale gasoline can cause gum or varnish in the fuel tank, carburetor, and combustion chamber. If the engine is not to be used for a period of 30 days or more, drain the fuel tank and carburetor to avoid gum deposits.

The recommended oils are those identified as being "suitable for service MS". For summer (over 40° F) use SAE 30. If not available, use 10W-30 oil. For winter (under 40° F) use SAE 5W-20. If not available, use 10W oil and dilute with 10% kerosene.

The air entering the engine is important in engine performance and engine life. Power will decrease 3½% for every 1,000 feet above sea level.

Power will also decrease 1% for every 10 degrees Fahrenheit above the standard temperature of 60 degrees Fahrenheit. In addition the ambient temperature is important in the cooling of the engine. (Ambient temperature is the temperature of the air immediately surrounding the engine.)

One of the reasons for engine wear is dirt that gets into the engine. When you consider that one of these 3 HP engines operating at 3600 RPM uses about 390 cubic feet of air an hour entering at the rate of about 24 miles an hour and that many such engines operate in very dusty conditions you can visualize the amount of dust and dirt that can enter an engine if it does not have an air cleaner or if the air cleaner is not functioning properly. If dirt gets past the air cleaner it enters the combustion chamber. Some may be blown out through the muffler but some may adhere to the cylinder where it creates ring wear or it may work down the walls into the crankcase where it causes wear on all the moving parts.

While speaking of the air cleaner we should remember to stress regular and proper maintenance of this important device. Occasionally,

we have reports of operators adding oil to the exact center of the air cleaner body. Of course, this fills the air cleaner elbow and carburetor with oil, causing starting trouble and excess smoking. The operator should add oil to the air cleaner body only — and not to fill above the oil level mark.

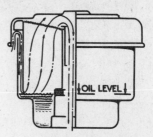

Figure 24

Dirt that enters the engine through the breather also can wear out any engine. It is very important to see that the breather is vented on all engines used in dusty surroundings.

Oil Foam No Spill Air Cleaners

For many years the oil bath air cleaner, see Fig. 24, was considered the best, but recently Briggs & Stratton developed the Oil Foam "No Spill" Air Cleaner. See Fig. 25. This cleaner employs a polyurethane element. The important patented feature is that it is sealed. Other cleaners are made with a polyurethane element but some are merely blocks of material with no seals of any kind thus allowing the air and dirt to by-pass the element. The Briggs & Stratton cleaner uses the edges of the element as gaskets so that the air must pass through the element.

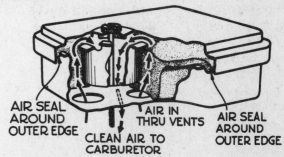

AIR SEAL AROUND OUTER EDGE   AIR IN THRU VENTS   AIR SEAL AROUND OUTER EDGE   CLEAN AIR TO CARBURETOR

Figure 25

There are two other important features of the "No Spill" cleaner. Oil will not spill if the engine is tilted. If the element becomes loaded with dirt the air supply will be shut off so the engine will lose power or stop entirely. Then the element can be cleaned, reoiled and reinstalled as good as new. The element _must_ be re-oiled after cleaning.

IGNITION

A magneto in a sense consists of two simple circuits, one called a primary circuit and the other the secondary circuit. Both circuits have windings which surround the same iron core and the magnets in the flywheel or rotor act on both circuits. Current can be induced in each by changing the magnetism in or around the coils of the circuit.

The primary circuit has relatively few turns of heavy wire and the circuit includes a set of breaker points and a condenser.

The secondary circuit has a coil with many turns of lighter wire which are wound around the out-side of the primary winding, and includes a spark plug. There are about 60 turns in the secondary to each turn in the primary.

A permanent magnet is mounted in the flywheel or rotor. As the flywheel rotates, the magnet is brought into proximity with the coil and core.

The Briggs & Stratton new ignition magneto system differs from ordinary magnetos in that the voltage produced is tailored to the needs of the engine. See Fig. 26. The magnet used in this new type is a ceramic which develops a very high magnetic strength in a very short distance. The length of this magnet is 3/8" as compared with the Alnico magnet length of 7/8".

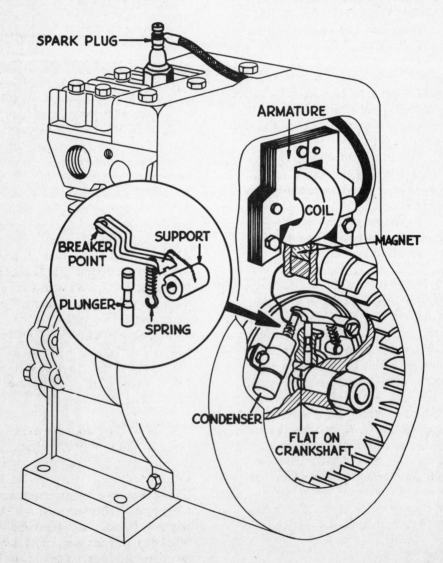

Figure 26

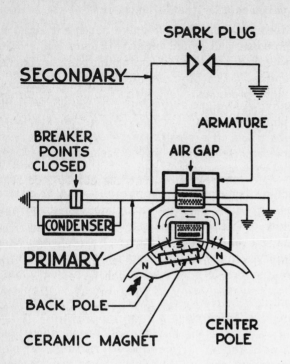

Figure 27

Fig. 27 shows the flow of magnetism through the iron core of the coil as the magnet in the flywheel approaches the armature. The arrows indicate the direction of flow of the magnetic field. You will notice that there is no (or very little) magnetism flowing through the upper part of the core. This is because of the air gap at the top which causes a resistance. In this position our breaker points close.

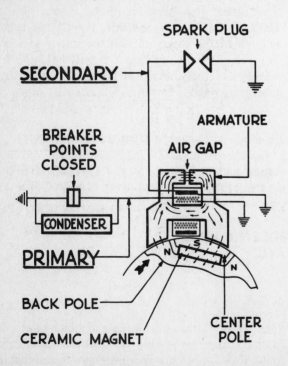

Figure 28

The flywheel continues to rotate to the position shown in Fig. 28. The magnetism continues to flow in the same direction and magnitude through the center of the core because of primary current. However, the magnetism flows in an opposite direction through the outer portion of the core and through the top air gap because of the change of flywheel position. Since the shunt air gap provides a path for the flux from the armature legs and the core, the required current flow through the primary circuit is low, assuring long breaker point life.

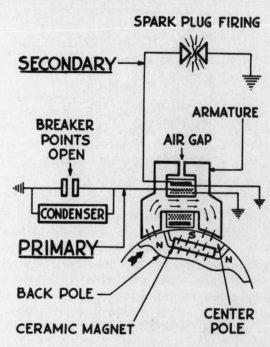

Figure 29

At this position our breaker points open, the current stops flowing in the primary circuit and therefore the electromagnetic effect ceases. The magnetism instantaneously changes from the flow shown in Fig. 28 to that shown in Fig. 29. Note the opposite direction of the arrows indicating a complete reversal of magnetism which has happened so fast that the flywheel magnet has not had a chance to move any noticeable amount.

The rapid change in magnetism produces 170 volts in the primary winding. A voltage is also induced in the secondary but it is in proportion to the turns ratio, i.e., 60 to 1 or 10,000 volts. This voltage is more than ample to fire across the spark plug electrodes. This rapid magnetism change is very short and therefore the flow of current across the spark plug gap is as long as necessary, but short enough to afford long electrode life. Thus we achieve our aims of full power plus long life and dependability.

14

Now, we haven't said much about one thing, the condenser. The condenser is a sort of safety valve on the primary circuit. It is connected across the breaker points to prevent the circuit from jumping the breaker point gap, arcing, as it is called.

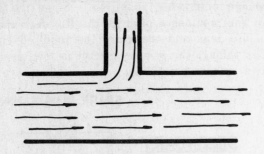

Figure 30A

Let us explain it this way. Suppose we had a large pipe through which we forced water at a high rate of speed, Figure 30A. This corresponds to our primary circuit. Coming out of the large pipe is a much smaller pipe. This is our secondary circuit. As long as the large pipe is unobstructed, the water is free to flow and very little will flow out through the small pipe.

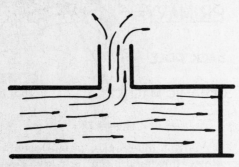

Figure 30B

Now suppose we could suddenly shut off the large pipe, Figure 30B. The water will stop flowing through the large pipe, but the inertia of the water back in the large pipe will force the water out through the small pipe at a tremendous velocity until the pressure is dissipated. This corresponds to the high voltage in our secondary circuit.

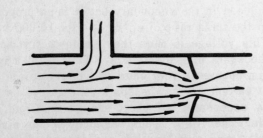

Figure 30C

However, suppose our valve could not stand the pressure and would break. (Figure 30C.) This would correspond to arcing across the breaker points. The flow would continue through the large pipe, and very little would flow through the small pipe.

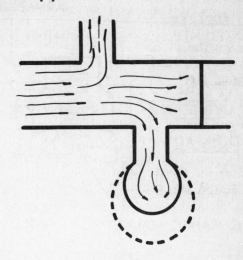

Figure 30D

If we put another small pipe near the valve, (Figure 30D) and over the end place a strong rubber bag, we have the equivalent to our condenser. Thus, when we close our valve, the pressure on the valve would be partially absorbed by the rubber bag, the valve would not break and water would stream out the small pipe where we want it to go.

The rubber bag must be of the proper size and strength. If it is too small, it will not take up enough of the pressure and the valve will break anyway. If it is too large, it will hold too much water, and there will not be enough pressure to force the water out through the small pipe.

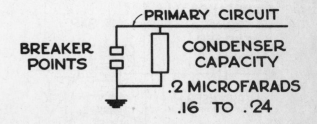

PRIMARY CIRCUIT

BREAKER POINTS

CONDENSER CAPACITY

.2 MICROFARADS
.16 TO .24

Figure 31

The same thing applies to the condenser. The proper capacity should be about .2 microfarads or .16 to .24. This is just right to prevent arcing at the points and still cause the primary current to stop flowing.

14

Spark plug cables are molded into the coil so that moisture cannot short out the spark as could happen on older coils that had an open connection between coil and spark plug cable.

We would like to point out that at one time some mechanics would try to judge the condition of the magneto system by the brightness and the noise or "snap" of the spark. This is not a good criterion as you can quickly demonstrate by using a resistor type spark plug and a regular type spark plug. Lay them on top of the cylinder head and connect the spark plug cable to first one and then the other. Spin the flywheel and notice the spark across the electrodes. You will see that the spark across the resistor plug will be much thinner and makes less noise and yet we know that engines run very well on these plugs.

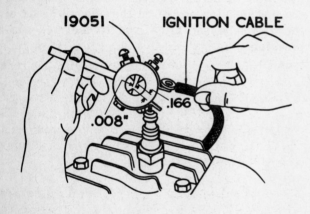

Figure 32

The magneto can be tested by placing the spark tester, #19051, between the ignition cable and the spark plug as shown in Fig. 32. Then spin the flywheel vigorously. The spark should jump the .166″ gap.

This test can also be performed with the engine running but the cable should be shifted quickly from spark plug to tester or from tester to spark plug. Damage to the coil can result if the engine spins more than just a few revolutions with the cable disconnected. This running test should not be performed on the Models 9, 14, 19, 23 with the Magnematic ignition system.

Through the years the magneto systems on the various Briggs & Stratton engines have differed somewhat in the design of the parts. However, the basic principle of a primary and a secondary circuit is used in all models.

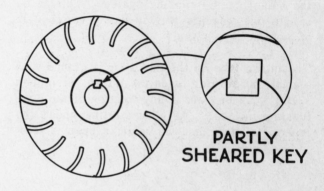

Figure 33

On small engines, be sure that the flywheel key is not partially sheared as this can cause the timing to be off enough to result in hard starting. Do not, however, use a steel key. The soft metal key is used so that if the flywheel should become loose the key will be sheared, allowing the flywheel to shift and stop the engine before any further damage occurs. Remember that the flywheel key is a locater and not a driver.

"EASY SPIN" STARTING

Good compression is necessary in order to obtain the full horsepower of the engine but at the same time this makes it more difficult to turn the engine over fast enough to start it. The resistance of compression is most noticeable during the first few revolutions after which the momentum of the flywheel and crankshaft help until firing starts in the cylinder.

In order to reduce this resistance during starting time, various types of compression releases have been used. However, none proved entirely satisfactory until Briggs & Stratton developed the "Easy Spin" starting system. This is so simple one wonders why it was never thought of before.

The intake lobe on the cam gear is ground with a small ramp which holds the intake valve open 1/100 of an inch for a tiny fraction of the compression stroke. At slow starting speed the interval of time that the valve is open is relatively long and therefore enough air escapes to noticeable reduce the compression. However, at operating speeds the interval of time is so short that there is practically no escape and therefore horsepower is unimpaired. Actually at 3600 RPM the valve is opened for a mere 1/200 of a second. In all other respects the valves operate as in any other four stroke cycle engine.

The force required to start an engine is reduced by 50% with "Easy Spin" and would be noticed most by a person who has difficulty starting the ordinary engine.

One thing we must remember. When testing the compression of "Easy Spin" engine one must spin the flywheel "backward", in the opposite direction to normal rotation. This will bring the compression stroke on the opposite side of the cam lobe and allow you to feel the compression.

14

GOVERNING

While some people think that a governor on an engine is to prevent overspeeding, the real purpose in the small engine field is to maintain a desired speed regardless of load. With a fixed throttle position, the engine could speed up if the load was lightened; if the load is increased the engine would slow down or even stop.

A governor on the other hand will close the throttle if the load is lightened or open the throttle to obtain more power if the load is increased.

Basically, governors consist of two types — the pneumatic or air vane type, Fig. 34, and the mechanical or flyball weight type, Fig. 35.

The pneumatic governor as illustrated in Fig. 34 is operated by the force of the air from the fly-wheel fins. When the engine is running the air from the fins pushes against the air vane. The air vane is connected to the carburetor throttle by means of a link. The force and movement of these parts tends to close the carburetor and thus slow down the engine speed.

Opposed to this is the governor spring which tends to pull the opposite way, opening the throttle. This spring is usually connected to an adjustable control of some kind so that the tension on the spring can be changed at the will of the operator. Increasing the tension of the spring will increase the engine speed. Decreasing the tension will lower the engine speed. The point at which the pull of the spring equals the force of the air vane is called the "governed speed"

ENGINE NOT RUNNING   ENGINE RUNNING

Figure 34

14

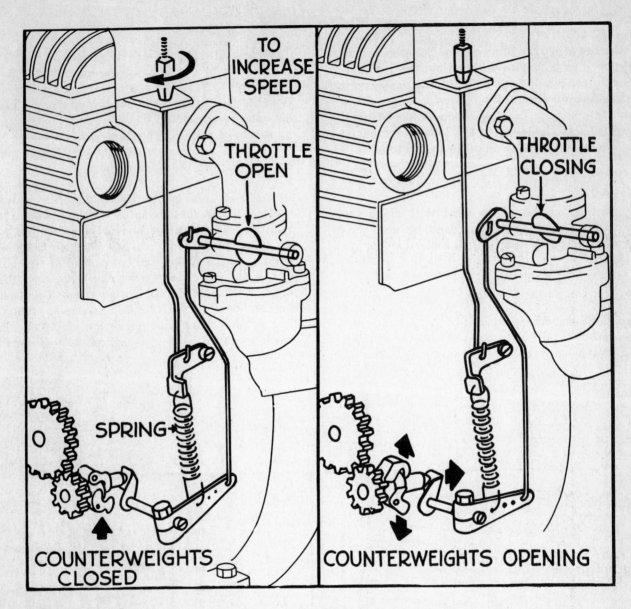

Figure 35

The mechanical governor, Fig. 35, works in a similar manner except that instead of the force of the air blowing against the vane, we have the centrifugal force of flyball weights opposing the governor spring.

In either case, operation is the same. As the load on the engine increases, the engine will start to slow down. As soon as this happens, the centrifugal force of the flyball weights lessens. This allows the governor spring to pull the throttle open wider increasing the horsepower to compensate for the increased load and thus maintain the desired governed speed.

If the load on the engine lessens, the engine starts to speed up. This will increase the pressure of the centrifugal force and the spring will be stretched a little farther thus closing the throttle and reducing the engine power. A properly functioning governor will maintain this desired governed speed within fairly close limits.

In general, an engine that has good compression, carburetion, and ignition will operate efficiently. However, dirt or neglect can ruin an engine quickly. It should be the duty, therefore, of every salesman or repair man to instruct the customer in the proper operation and care of the engine so that he will obtain the long service life that is built into the engine at the factory.

14